WINTER GAMES PITCHES

THE CONSTRUCTION AND MAINTENANCE OF NATURAL TURF PITCHES FOR TEAM GAMES

Edited by

R.D.C. EVANS BSc
Turfgrass Agronomist
The Sports Turf Research Institute

with contributions from the following members of the STRI staff:

S.W. Baker	BSc, PhD	Senior Research Officer
D.F. Boocock	NDA	Senior Agronomist
A.R. Cole	BSc	Turfgrass Agronomist
S.P. Isaac	BSc	Turfgrass Agronomist
D.M. Lawson	BSc, PhD	Soil Chemist
A.J. Newell	BSc, PhD	Cultivar Evaluation Officer
S.T. Pool	NDH, M I Hort	Drainage & Construction Specialist
N.R.W. Squires	BSc	Turfgrass Agronomist

Published by:

THE SPORTS TURF RESEARCH INSTITUTE
BINGLEY,   WEST YORKSHIRE,   BD16 1AU

Published by:

THE SPORTS TURF RESEARCH INSTITUTE, BINGLEY, WEST YORKSHIRE, BD16 1AU, ENGLAND

ISBN 1-873431-03-1

COPYRIGHT © STRI 1994

❋ ❋

NOTE 1: The fact that photographs of particular items of equipment or machinery appear in this text should not be taken to imply that the STRI endorses one firm's products over another. When purchasing equipment for a club it is always wise to obtain details of all rival products and to make a choice based on full on-site demonstrations and on the exact requirements of the particular club, bearing in mind the supply of spare parts, local servicing facilities etc.

NOTE 2: The application rates given in the following text for pesticides should be regarded as being for guidance only, although every effort has been made to ensure that quoted rates are appropriate. It should be understood that pesticide users are under an obligation to comply with legal requirements governing the usage of such materials and that the instructions included with each product are mandatory, including instructions regarding application rates. Users should be familiar with the Food and Environment Protection Act (1985), Part 3 : Control of Pesticides Regulations (1986).

This volume is one of a series produced by the STRI on various aspects of turfgrass management. Other titles currently available are:

Baker, S.W. (1990). *Sands for Sports Turf Construction and Maintenance*, 71 pp. ISBN 0-9503647-8-9.
Baldwin, N.A. (1990). *Turfgrass Pests and Diseases*, 72 pp. ISBN 0-9503647-9-7.
Evans, R.D.C. (1991). *Cricket Grounds : The Evolution, Maintenance and Construction of Natural Turf Cricket Tables and Outfields*, 279 pp. ISBN 1-873431-00-7.
Evans, R.D.C. (1992). *Bowling Greens : Their History, Construction and Maintenance, Revised 2nd Edition*, 211 pp. ISBN 1-873431-01-5.
Hayes, P., Evans, R.D.C. & Isaac, S.P. (1992) (Eds). *The Care of the Golf Course*, 269 pp. ISBN 1-873431-02-3.
Lawson, D.M. (1991). *Fertilisers for Turf*, 47 pp. ISBN 0-9518259-9.

ACKNOWLEDGEMENTS

The STRI's involvement in producing books on turf culture and all aspects of the management of grass swards for outdoor sports and games can be traced back to 1939 when our first Director, Mr R B Dawson, produced *Practical Lawn Craft*. Published by Crosby Lockwood in London, the book proved to be a highly popular manual for amateur gardeners, groundsmen and greenkeepers alike and went through seven editions - the final one being revised by R Hawthorn and published by William Clowes (London) in 1977. An ex-member of the Bingley staff, I G Lewis, also ventured into print - his book entitled *Turf: A Book About Golf Greens, Tennis Courts, Bowling Greens and Playing Pitches No Less Than Lawns; Their Making and Keeping According to Modern Practice* appeared via Faber & Faber Ltd. (London) in 1948. The STRI's second Director, Mr J R Escritt, followed with the *ABC of Turf Culture* (Kaye & Ward, London) in 1978. Aimed more at the amateur landowner, R B Dawson also wrote *Lawns*, (Amateur Gardening Handbook No. 11, Collingridge, London, 1954) and his successor, J R Escritt, a 'teach yourself' book *Lawns*, published by Hodder & Stoughton of Sevenoaks in 1979. *Sports Ground Construction Specifications* of 1965 was another success, written by R B Gooch (National Playing Fields Association & J R Escritt, published by the NPFA.

By 1959, the Institute itself became a publisher of books in its own right, as a supplement to its long-standing commitment towards publishing its own periodicals, the annual *Journal* and quarterly *Bulletin*. *Fungal Diseases of Turf Grasses* by J Drew Smith was published by the STRI in 1959 and became a standard reference work, before being reprinted in 1979 in a simplified format, rewritten by N A Baldwin in 1987 and expanded by the same author, under the title *Turfgrass Pests and Diseases* in 1990.

The debt owed to our predecessors in this field of activity must be acknowledged by all current members of the STRI staff.

In more recent years, the STRI has been even more committed to publishing, an aspect of its activities enthusiastically supported by the current Director, Dr Peter Hayes. My own *Bowling Greens* pioneered modern activity and I am personally most grateful to the STRI Board of Management and Director for their continuing support for this and subsequent publishing ventures.

With specific reference to this current volume, my thanks must first go to those seven of my colleagues who individually produced sections of the text, i.e. Steve Baker, David Boocock, Andy Cole, Steve Isaac, David Lawson, Andy Newell, Stuart Pool and Neil Squires - particularly to those who produced copy on time! James Westwood must be thanked for Plate 47 and the STRI Experiment Ground Superintendent, David Moore, for checking all machinery references - his practical knowledge of modern turf implements proved invaluable.

Another member of the STRI staff, Gareth Goddard, helped considerably by checking pitch layouts and dimensions. Information on this subject was received from Mrs Jenny Pearson of the Scottish Lacrosse Association, Maurice F Oldroyd of the British Amateur Rugby League Association, Pat Daly of Cumann Lúthchleas Gael, John Clark of the Rugby Football Union, David Barber of the Football Association, Joe Mendell of the British American Football Association, Brigadier A R Douglas-Nugent of Cowdray Park Polo Club and George Croft of the Hockey Rules Board.

Useful photographs to illustrate the section on mechanical equipment were supplied to Steve Isaac by a number of machinery manufacturers, namely Ransomes Sims & Jefferies Ltd. of Ipswich, Dennis of Derby, Lloyds & Co. Letchworth Ltd., Sisis Equipment (Macclesfield) Ltd., F W McConnel Ltd. of Ludlow, Twose of Tiverton Ltd., Fleet (Line Markers) Ltd. of Malvern, Kubota UK Ltd. of Thame, Amazone Ground Care of Saltash, Hoverdry Ltd. of London and Hardi Ltd. of Hinckley. Their co-operation is much appreciated.

My colleague, Andy Cole, now regionalised to Solihull, W. Midlands, has asked me to record that much assistance in preparing his section on pitch renovation was received from Mr David Pack, head groundsman of the Guards Polo Club, and that photographs were kindly supplied by Inturf of Pocklington and by the Warwickshire Gaelic Athletic Association (Pairc nah Eireann).

All credit for the cover artwork goes to John W Holroyd of Shipley. Finally, as has been the case with a whole series of recent publications, I must record my sincere thanks to Diane S Hill for sterling work with the STRI's desk top publishing system - her expertise has once again proved invaluable.

RDC EVANS
Editor
STRI, Bingley,

DEDICATION

This volume is respectfully dedicated to all members of the

INSTITUTE OF GROUNDSMANSHIP
1934–1994

with congratulations on their Diamond Jubilee

CONTENTS

SECTION 1
AN INTRODUCTION, THE GAMES INVOLVED AND SOME HISTORY
By R.D.C. Evans

In preparing this volume, the aim has been to provide a comprehensive and practical guide to the construction and subsequent maintenance of winter games pitches. Prevailing climatic conditions play a very significant role in determining the most appropriate procedures in both the initial construction and the seasonal maintenance of playing field areas. This text is written with the weather of the British Isles primarily in mind, although much of the information could well be relevant to recreation grounds in other parts of the world.

It is intended to concentrate exclusively on natural grass sports facilities - it is appreciated that the various forms of artificial or synthetic surface are now of considerable importance and increasingly popular, but they best considered a separate and specialised subject and will be regarded as outside the scope of this particular text-book. The use of the phrase "Winter Games Pitches" in the title is not one hundred per cent satisfactory, as most of the sports and games being catered for here are played in autumn and spring as well as winter (and polo is of course a summer sport, as is Irish hurling to a certain extent), but the meaning of the term is commonly understood and seems more appropriate than any possible alternative title. Some of the grass areas which will be dealt with in these pages may indeed see some secondary summer use - as cricket outfields, athletic fields etc. - but the need to cater adequately for team sports played through the winter season is regarded as being of primary importance when planning the construction and care of facilities of this kind.

Because, under British climatic conditions, the usage of such facilities tends to be concentrated through the wetter months of each year, the need to provide for good drainage tends to be of over-riding importance. The primary need to provide for rapid surface drainage tends to dominate the initial construction of sports fields and day to day maintenance must also be geared to preserving or improving drainage characteristics. It may be a slight exaggeration to say that a good pitch is a well-drained pitch, or that conversely a poorly drained pitch is automatically unsatisfactory, but this is probably a close approximation of the practical truth of the matter. Good drainage is by no means unimportant in the context of other types of recreational grass areas, such as golf courses, bowling greens, tennis courts, cricket tables etc., but its significance is more overwhelming when one is dealing with winter games pitches.

In the following pages we will be primarily dealing with what are often referred to as "coarse turf areas" rather than the fine turf swards required for golf greens, bowling greens or the best ornamental lawns. By and large, the requirement is for relatively coarse and vigorous swards, ideally dominated by perennial ryegrass (*Lolium perenne*), rather than the finer, more closely mown type of grass cover based on browntop bent grass (*Agrostis tenuis*) or Chewings fescue (*Festuca rubra*). In the winter games situation, other grass species must not be ignored entirely but perennial ryegrass is certainly the most appropriate and successful species in most situations and its particular requirements are important in determining maintenance procedures such as mowing heights, fertiliser regimes and other aspects of the groundsman's routine. There are some possible exceptions to this general reliance on perennial ryegrass as the most suitable grass species (fundamentally finer swards might, for example, be more appropriate for the best of grass hockey pitches) but it is certainly the most significant species in the majority of winter games swards.

THE GAMES OR SPORTS INVOLVED
Before considering pitch construction and maintenance in detail, it will be worth listing the games and sports which are being catered for. This provides an opportunity to introduce the important subject of pitch dimensions and markings - relevant of course to the initial choice of site for a proposed playing field development, in particular its overall size requirement and of basic significance to the day to day working life of the groundsman, in view of the need to set out and constantly renew the pattern of pitch markings appropriate to each particular game. Line marking equipment, materials and techniques will be discussed more comprehensively in a later chapter but pitch dimensions and markings can be appropriately introduced at this point.

The job specification of the average British groundsman will be dominated by the upkeep of Association Football (soccer) pitches, with Rugby football (Union and League) areas running a close second and hockey pitches in third place. A complete list of the games played on grass pitches in the British Isles is, however, far more extensive and it is hoped that the following alphabetical list will cover most of the games and pitch layouts which the sports ground constructor or groundsman may be required to provide.

AMERICAN (COLLEGE) FOOTBALL

The marking-out of an American football grid iron pitch is a far more complex task than the similar exercise for any other team game and presents a rather daunting challenge to the inexperienced British groundsman.

The basic width of lines should be 4" (100 mm), with some exceptions and the standard colour is white (although again with some exceptions).

The layout is based on a rectangle composed of two side lines 360' (109.73 m) long and two end lines 160' (48.77 m), extending the width of the pitch at each end. Around the outside of this rectangle runs a larger rectangle made up of a broken limit line and a continuous coaching line. Limit line and coaching line are 12' (3.66 m) outside the side lines and end lines, except where space does not permit. If the total field surface area does not permit the standard spacing, then limit line and coaching line should not be less than 6' (1.83 m) outside side lines and end lines. Limit lines should be 4" (100 mm) in width and may be yellow. The "dashes" of the broken limit line should be 12" (305 mm) long and 24" (610 mm) spacing.

The two sections of continuous coaching line extend from 25 yd line to 25 yd line of the finished pitch markings (see below) and are therefore 150' (45.7 m) long. It is desirable to fill in the whole area between coaching line and side line on either side of the pitch in solid white colour.

Team benches are positioned outside the two coaching lines 10 yd (9.14 m) back from the side lines.

Turning now to the pitch area inside the main rectangle; two end zones are formed inside the end lines by means of two goal lines 30' (9.14 m) from the end lines. Goal lines are of double width - 8" (200 mm) - and their entire width lies within the end zones. They may be painted in contrasting colours.

Between the two goal lines the pitch is marked at 15' (4.57 m) intervals with yard lines running across the pitch from side line to side line. These are 4" (100 mm) in width and should be extended outside the side lines to form a 4" (100 mm) long "dash" where they cross the coaching lines and side limit lines. It is recommended that every other yard line be marked with field numbers (10, 20, 30 etc., representing distance from the goal lines), the 50 marking the midfield stripe. Numbers should be 6' (1.83 m) in height and 4' (1.22 m) in width, the tops of the numbers being 9 yd (8.23 m) from the side lines on each edge of the pitch. Directional arrows next to field numbers (except the 50) indicate the direction of the opponents goal line. Arrows should be triangular, painted in white, with the top of the base 4" (100 mm) from the top of the number. The arrow has an 18" (457 mm) base and two 36" (914 mm) sides.

Hash marks are 2' (0.61 m) "dashes" set 3' (0.914 m) apart between each yard line, 6" (152 mm) inside the side lines and again 68' 9" (20.95 m) in from each side line. The two inner series of hash marks align with the goal posts. There is an 18' 6" (5.64 m) gap between the two inner series of hash marks. An additional hash mark (the three-yard line) is set centrally between the two side lines 9' (2.74 m) from each goal line.

Goals are set on end lines (not goal lines, although in the 1930's they were moved to the goal lines for American professional football). In the USA they are of 'Y' form, 23' 4" (7.1 m) between the uprights, at least 20' (6.1 m) high with crossbar 10' (3.05 m) above the ground. They are usually gold coloured with ribbons at the tops to aid kickers in judging wind speed. Normal Rugby posts have, however, been allowed in the UK (e.g. at Motspur Park), although they are strictly speaking narrower than the US standard. In addition, orange pylons may be placed at the junctions of goal lines and side lines, and sometimes at the corner junctions of end lines and side lines as well.

Even basic pitch marking is a full day's work for the average groundsman. The task may be further complicated by filling in the entire area of each end zone with multi-coloured team "logos" and sometimes by painting an additional logo in the centre of the pitch between the hash lines and bisected by the midfield stripe. American groundsmen use a water-soluble rubber-based paint which can be removed relatively easily. Scarification and vacuuming the pitch may be necessary to remove the paint, however, and grass is inevitably damaged. Constant reseeding during the playing season is therefore often required.

Since it was introduced to the UK sporting scene in 1982-83, American football has gained in popularity for both participants and spectators with astonishing rapidity. The complex pitch-marking exercise may therefore become an increasingly common task for British groundsmen in future.

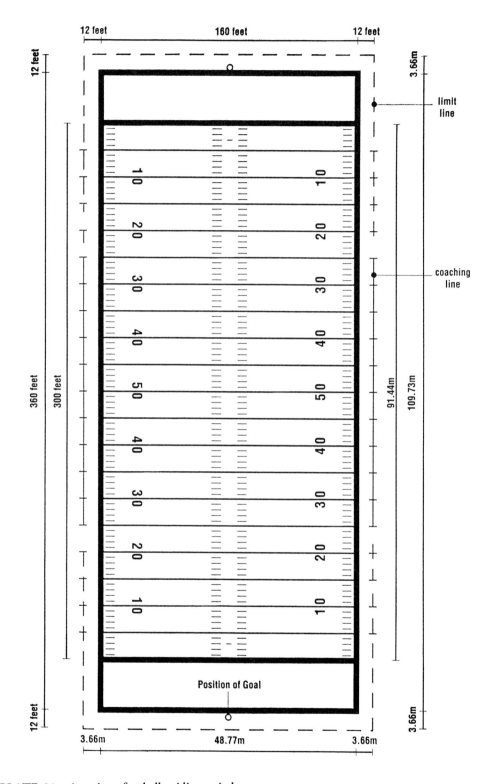

PLATE 01: American football gridiron pitch

ASSOCIATION FOOTBALL (SOCCER)

Colour of lines is not specifically referred to in Football Association rules, but is traditionally white. Lines should be a maximum of 5" (120 mm) wide, although the two goal lines should be the same width as the goal posts.

As far as overall pitch dimensions are concerned, considerable latitude is allowed but pitch length should always exceed pitch breadth. Pitch length should be maximum 130 yd (120 m) and minimum 100 yd (90 m). Pitch breadth should be maximum 100 yd (90 m) and minimum 50 yd (45 m).

For international matches, the size limits are more rigorous. Pitch length should be maximum 120 yd (110 m) and minimum 110 yd (100 m). Pitch breadth should be maximum 80 yd (75 m), minimum 70 yd (64 m).

The boundary lines which form the main pitch rectangle are within the playing area and should be inside the area which they mark - the theoretical pitch measurements are therefore the outside edge of the four lines.

The dimension of the centre circle is measured from the centre of the field. The centre of the penalty kick mark is measured 12 yd (11 m) from the outside edge of the goal line. The penalty area arc is measured 10 yd (9.15 m) from the centre of the penalty mark after the latter has been pinpointed.

The goal area and penalty area rectangles must be measured from the inside edge of the goal posts along the goal line.

The 4 quarter-circle arcs for corner kicks are arcs of a circle of 1 yd (1 m) radius.

The two goals each occupy an area 8 yd (7.32 m) by 8 ft (2.44 m) behind the goal line. Goal upright posts and cross bar should be the same width and not more than 5" (120 mm) wide. Uprights should be 8 yd (7.32 m) apart, this being the inside measurement. The crossbar is 8' (2.44 m) above ground level, measured to its lower edge. Goal posts and cross bar may be of square, rectangular, round, half-round or elliptical cross-section. (Square-section posts are traditionally preferred in Scotland.) They must be of wood or metal - steel or aluminium - or other material approved by the International FA Board. They should have a white finish. Nets should be attached to the two posts, the cross bar and the ground behind the goal and should be supported.

Four flags and flag-posts should be placed at the corners. Posts should not be less than 5' (1.5 m) high. If desired, optional flags may also be placed to mark the centre-line and should be at least 1 yd (1 m) outside the touch lines.

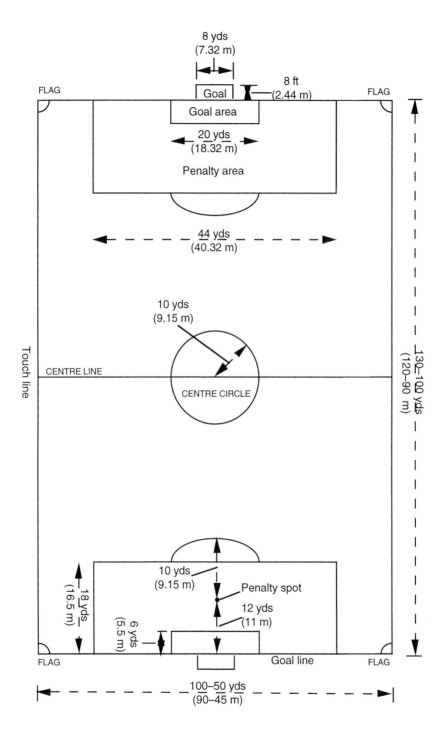

PLATE 02: Association football pitch.

CAMOGIE

Ireland's national game for women, Camogie is a modified form of hurling played by a 12-woman team. The game was formalised in 1904, the first competitive matches being played and the Dublin-based Camogie Association of Ireland being set up in that year. The Association was reorganised on a national basis in 1932.

Pitch marking presents few difficulties for the groundsman, the basic layout being a rectangle bisected by a half-way line. In addition, a 15 m and a 30 m line are marked at the appropriate distances in front of each goal line. The two goal areas are simple rectangles as shown in the diagram, 8.5 m wide and 4 m deep.

Camogie goal posts are a very distinctive feature, as there can be two crossbars. Vertical posts are 4.5 m apart, with the lower crossbar 2 m above the ground and the second higher crossbar 6 m above the ground. Alternatively, if the upper crossbar is omitted then the goals resemble Rugby posts with uprights 6 m high and the only crossbar again 2 m above the ground.

THE "CAXTON" LAWN TENNIS MARKER.

No. 15053.

No. 15952.

No. 15952A.

THE ROTARY TENNIS COURT MARKERS.

PLATE 03. Victorian line markers : from an 1883 catalogue.

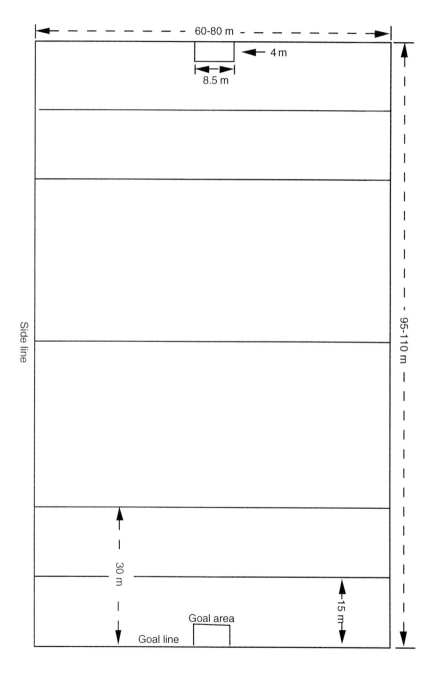

PLATE 04: Camogie pitch.

GAELIC FOOTBALL

Ireland's national 15-a-side football game was formalised in 1884 with the founding of the Gaelic Athletic Association. Today the game is played in England, Scotland and the USA, although it remains firmly rooted in Irish soil. Australian rules football is regarded as a related game, but played on a different pitch layout.

Pitch markings are a relatively straightforward arrangement of straight lines and rectangles, as shown in the diagram. Pitch dimensions include the width of the lines and lines should have a maximum width of 5" (125 mm). They are normally white, but any distinctive colour is permissible.

Goals are basically H-shaped (similar to Rugby posts), 21' (6.4 m) apart, 23' (7.0 m) minimum height and with the crossbar 8' (2.5 m) above the ground. For practically all matches, soccer-type goal nets are used.

In recent years, the Irish authorities have produced the modified pitch layout shown opposite, which conveniently can be used for both Gaelic football and hurling (for the latter game see later comments). Metric measurements are now normally used.

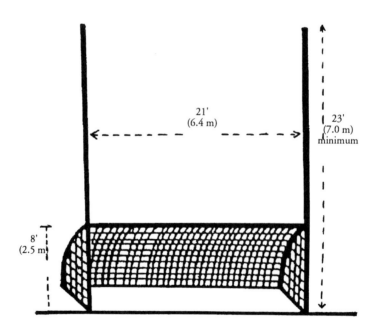

PLATE 05. Gaelic football goal.

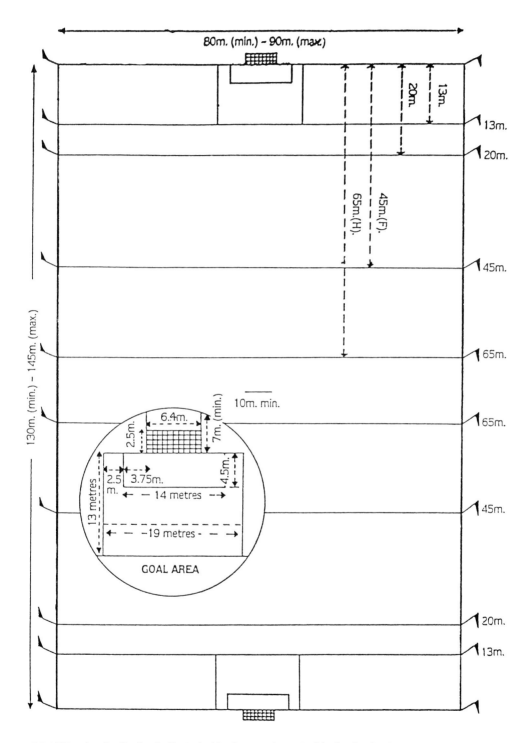

PLATE 06: Gaelic football pitch (dual use : also suitable for hurling).

HOCKEY

Lines should be 3" (75 mm) wide and are traditionally white, although no colour is officially stated and yellow lines are commonly encountered on synthetic pitches.

The pitch is a rectangle as shown, made up of side lines and back lines, the length of back line between the goal posts being the goal line.

A centre line and two 25 yd lines should be marked, the middle of these lines being 50 yd and 25 yd respectively from the outer edge of the back lines.

To aid control of the hit-in, across the centre line and each 25 yd line a mark should be made 2 yd (1.83 m) in length, positioned parallel to and 5 yd (4.55 m) inside the outer edge of each side line.

A mark 12" (0.3 m) in length should be marked inside the field of play on each side line parallel to the back line and 16 yd (14.63 m) from the inner edge of the back line.

To guide penalty corner hits, the pitch should be marked inside the field of play on the back lines on both sides of each goal at 5 yd (4.55 m) and 10 yd (0.10 m) from the outer edge of the nearer goal post, these distances being to the far edge of these lines. For corner hits, the pitch should be marked inside the field of play on the back lines 5 yd (4.55 m) in from the outer edge of the side lines. All the above short lines should be 12" (0.3 m) in length.

A penalty flick spot 6" (150 mm) in diameter should be marked in front of the centre of each goal 7 yd (6.40 m) in from the inner edge of the goal line. The two striking circles are made up of two quarter circle arcs of 16 yd (14.63 m) radius, measured from each goal post and joined by a straight section 4 yd (3.66 m) long, the latter being the width of the goals. Goal dimensions are shown in the diagram.

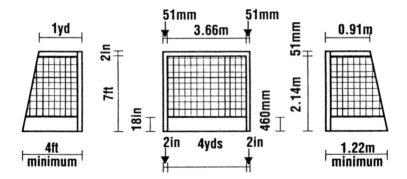

PLATE 07. Hockey goal design.

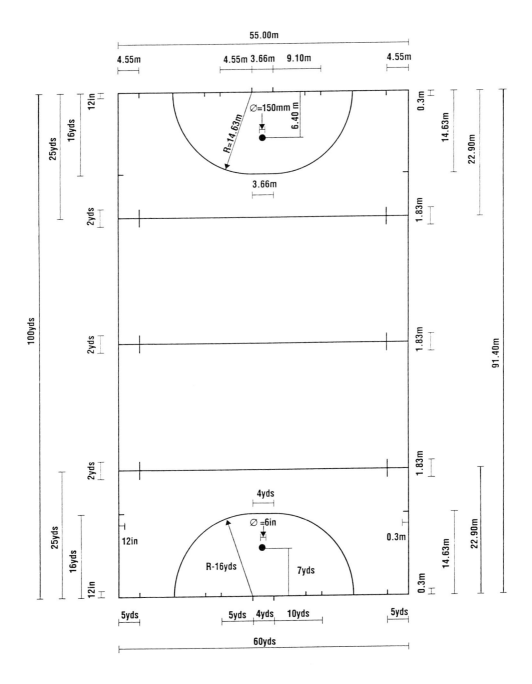

PLATE 08: Hockey pitch.

HURLING

Ireland's ancient stick and ball game is, like Gaelic football, controlled by the Gaelic Athletic Association and the modern game dates back to the formation of that organisation in 1884, although its roots are very ancient. The All-Ireland Championship dates back to 1887.

The pitch was traditionally a rectangle with mid-field, free-stroke, 21 yd and 14 yd lines drawn parallel to the end lines as shown in the diagram. Goal area parallelograms are of the dimension shown. However, the task of the groundsman has been simplified in recent years by the adoption of pitch markings which can be used for both hurling and Gaelic football - see under the latter game.

Goals are H-shaped with uprights 6.5 m apart and 7 m (min) tall. The crossbar is 2.5 m above the ground (i.e. identical to the currently approved specification for a Gaelic football goal. Lines are usually marked in white.

Ireland's hurling championships are played from May to September with the final at Croke Park in the latter month. The hurling league games are, however, played in the winter season.

PLATE 09. The Metropolitan Hurling Club at practice in the Phoenix Park, Dublin - spring 1884.

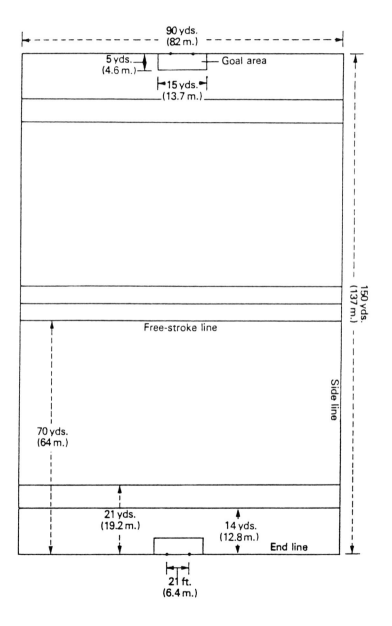

PLATE 10. Hurling pitch. The above is the traditional hurling pitch layout. For the current dual-use Gaelic football - hurling pitch markings - see previous section on Gaelic football.

LACROSSE : MEN'S & WOMEN'S

English Lacrosse Union (men's)

Play area should be 110 yd (100 m) long and 60 yd (55 m) wide and the main pitch rectangle should be marked out on the ground. Internal pitch lines consist of a centre line parallel to end lines, with a centre spot and restraining lines 20 yd (18 m) each side of the centre line and parallel to it. Wing restraining lines parallel to the side lines should be 20 yd (18 m) from the centre spot and should extend 10 yd (9 m) each side of the centre line.

Goal lines are 6' (1.83 m) long - from goal post to goal post - and of the same thickness as the goal posts. They are 15 yd (14 m) inside the end lines. Goal circles are drawn from the centre of the goal line and are of 3 yd (2.74 m) radius.

Goal posts and cross bars are 6' (1.8 m) apart and 6' (1.8 m) high, these being inside dimensions. They should be painted white and not more than 3" (76 mm) thick, round or square. Nets are of 1¹/₂" (38 mm) maximum mesh, attached to posts and cross bar. A bracket is fixed to the rear top of each upright to give a net roof between 9-12" (229-305 mm) deep and the net is fixed 6' (1.8 m) behind the goal. Flags should be placed at each corner and at the ends of the centre line. Flags also mark a 'players gate' 6' (2 m) either side of centre line, away from the pitch area.

All England Women's Lacrosse Association

The pitch has a recommended area of 120 yd (110 m) by 70 yd (60 m) but is most unusual in that the main rectangle need not be marked and is therefore shown as a broken line in the diagram. The centre circle of radius 10 yd (9 m) contains a line 10' (3 m) in length and parallel to goal lines. Goal circles are 8'6" (2.6 m) in radius from the centre of the goal lines. Goals are 100 yd (92 m) apart. Goals are of the same size as those for the men's game, but posts and cross bar must be 2" (5 cm) square or of the same diameter if circular sectioned. They should be white and of wood or metal. Net mesh should be 1¹/₂" (40 mm) or less and nets are as described for the men's game. Arcs should be drawn in front of goal circles as shown.

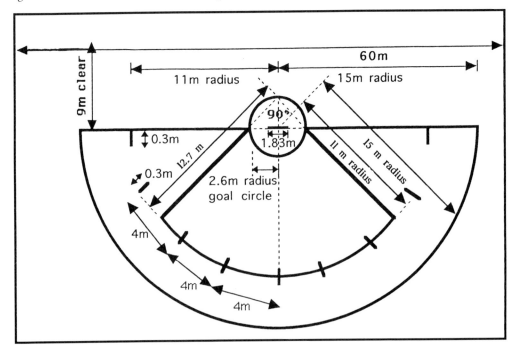

PLATE 11. Women's lacrosse - enlarged view of goal markings.

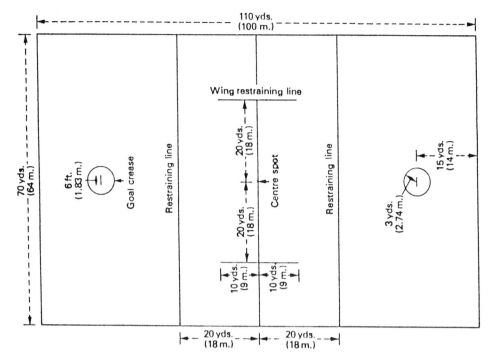

PLATE 12. Lacrosse pitch : men..

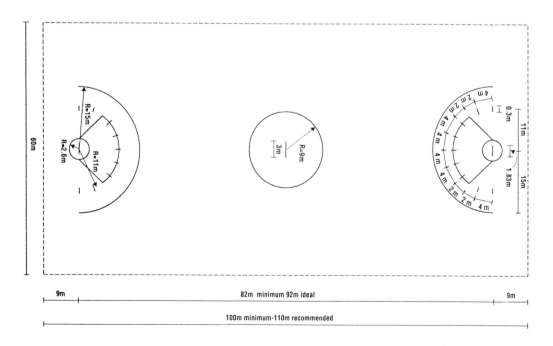

PLATE 13. Lacross pitch : women.

POLO

Even though there are only four players in a team, the fact that they are mounted on horseback means that polo players require a larger ground area than any of the other sportsmen, whose activities are covered in this text. The polo ground dimensions shown in the diagram are an ideal maximum, but if space is limited then a smaller area is acceptable for lower handicap polo. Width can, for example, be reduced to 160 yd if necessary, but in this case boards must be placed along the sides to keep the ball within the playing area. Such boards should be 10" high - obviously a total of 600 yd of such boarding are required to cover the full length of each touch line. Details of polo board design are shown below. Curved board runs are allowed at the four corners and should curve in from the 30 yd line to a point 15 yd in from the corner on the back line.

Marking out presents no problems for the groundsman, apart from the sheer length of straight lines required - a full sized ground can after all cover 6-8 hectares (15-20 acres), enough to accommodate five soccer pitches. In addition to the main rectangle, 30 and 60 yd lines are required, running across each end of the ground and three crosses or spots in the positions shown. Goal posts are 8 yd apart and are 10' high, no cross bar being fitted. A light, central pole of about 1¹/₂" diameter carrying club colours is often placed mid-way between the goal posts, all uprights being light and collapsible to avoid injury to horse or player if they are collided with. Sockets which allow goals to be widened to 16 yd should be provided.

Small paddock polo fields are acceptable for beginners and may be as small as 0.8-1.2 hectare (2-3 acres). Bicycle polo can be played on an area 60-80 yd by 90-110 yd and can therefore be easily accommodated within the area of a soccer or Rugby pitch. Metric measurements are not normally employed for marking out polo grounds.

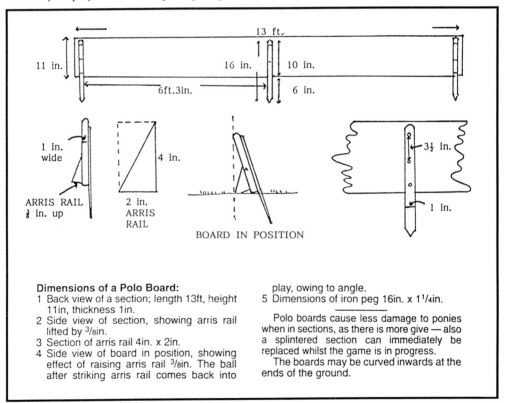

Dimensions of a Polo Board:
1 Back view of a section; length 13ft, height 11in, thickness 1in.
2 Side view of section, showing arris rail lifted by ³/₈in.
3 Section of arris rail 4in. x 2in.
4 Side view of board in position, showing effect of raising arris rail ³/₈in. The ball after striking arris rail comes back into play, owing to angle.
5 Dimensions of iron peg 16in. x 1¹/₄in.

Polo boards cause less damage to ponies when in sections, as there is more give — also a splintered section can immediately be replaced whilst the game is in progress.

The boards may be curved inwards at the ends of the ground.

PLATE 14. Approved design of polo boards for use on smaller grounds.

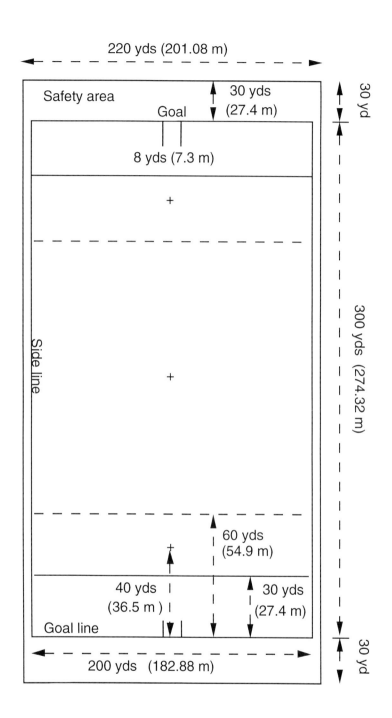

PLATE 15. Polo ground.

RUGBY LEAGUE FOOTBALL

Line colour is unspecified by the Rugby League, but white is usual. Lines are typically 3" (150 mm) wide.

External pitch dimensions exclude width of lines, whilst other measurements indicated in the diagram are distances between lines. Broken lines should consist of marks or dots on the ground not more than 2 m apart. It is considered advantageous for transverse broken lines to be drawn across the full width of the pitch but if restricted, then each should not be less than 15 m long.

Flags may be placed as indicated overleaf for Rugby Union - corner posts are in touch and in goal. Posts should be of non-rigid material and not less than 1.25 m high.

Goal posts are on the goal line and are 5.5 m (6 yd) apart, this being the internal spacing. The bottom 2 m (6') of each post may be padded. Height above ground to the LOWER side of the crossbar is 3 m and the height of the goal posts should be a minimum of 4 m.

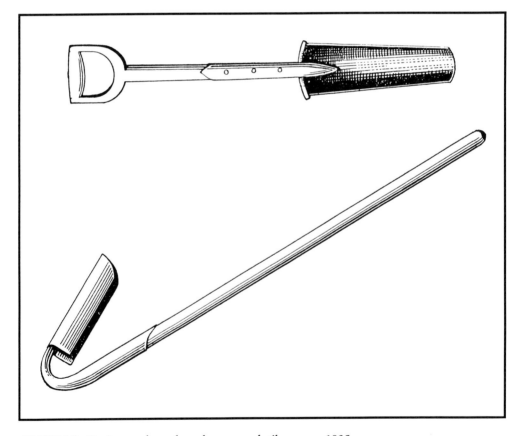

PLATE 16. Drain trench spade and goose-neck tile scoop : 1935.

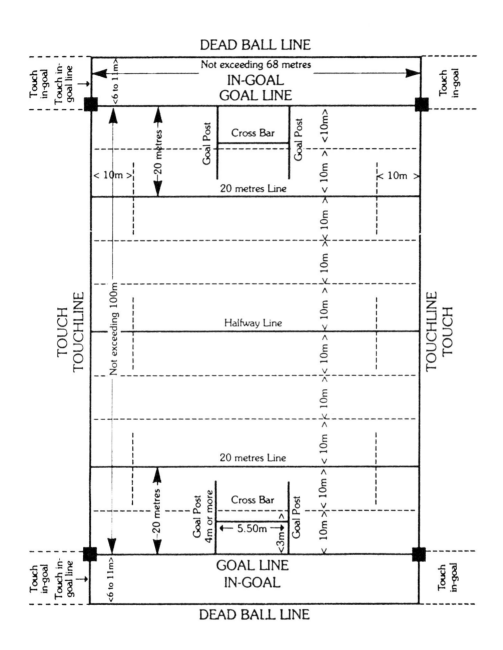

PLATE 17. Rugby League pitch (professional or amateur).

RUGBY UNION FOOTBALL

The colour of lines is unspecified by the Rugby Union, but white is suggested. A line width of 3" (15 cm) is preferred.

External dimensions shown in the diagram exclude width of lines - touch lines are therefore in touch. Goal lines are in the 'in goal' area. Dead ball lines are not in the 'in goal' area. The distance from goal line to dead ball line should be not less than 10 m where practicable and 22 m maximum.

The six short dashes 5 m in front of and parallel to the goal lines are each 1 m long.

The goal posts are on the goal lines and should be 5.6 m apart (inside dimension), with 3 m from ground level to the TOP of the crossbar. Posts should be at least 3.4 m (11'6") high.

Flags marking half way and 25 yd lines should be at least 1 m (3') outside the field of play. These and the flags at the junctions between touch lines and goal lines should be a minimum of 1.2 m (4') high.

PLATE 18. Rugby School, the birth place of Rugby football, showing a game in 1870. : note that the H–shaped goals have already appeared.

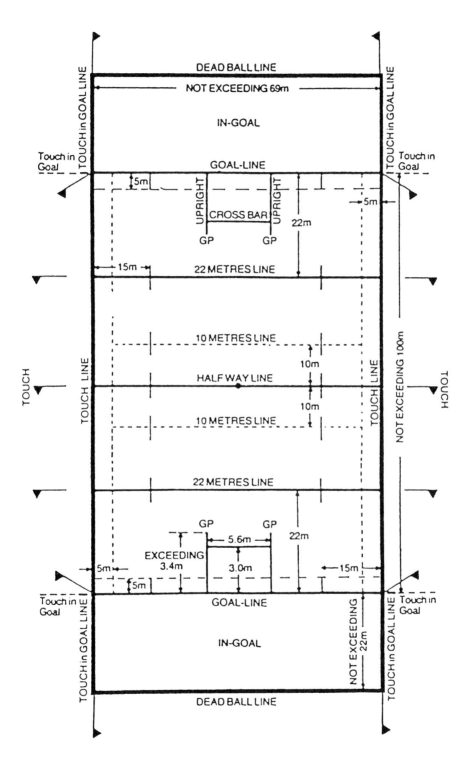

PLATE 19. Rugby Union pitch.

SHINTY

Governed by the Cammanachd Association based in Fort William, shinty is the native Scottish stick and ball game, having strong ties with the Irish sport of hurling. Control of the game was established with the formation of the above-mentioned association in 1893.

Lines may be of any distinctive colour (usually white) and are 40 mm minimum, 75 mm maximum width, except the goal (hail) lines which should be marked the same width as the posts - 75 mm minimum, 100 mm maximum.

Pitch dimensions should include the width of the lines. The 9 m arcs are measured from the inside of the goal posts and the outside of the goal line.

Four corner flags should be 1.1 m (3'6") high.

Goal posts are 3.66 m (12') apart and the crossbar (measured to its underside) is 3.05 m (10') above the ground. Nets are fitted.

Pitch size:

Standard of play	Length	Breadth
Competition	128 m – 155 m	64 m– 73 m
Senior competition	146 m minimum	73 m
U14 age group	91 m maximum	46 m maximum

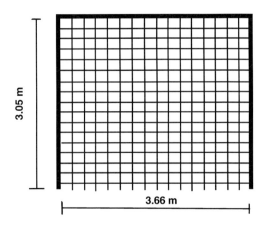

PLATE 20. Plan of shinty hail (or goal).

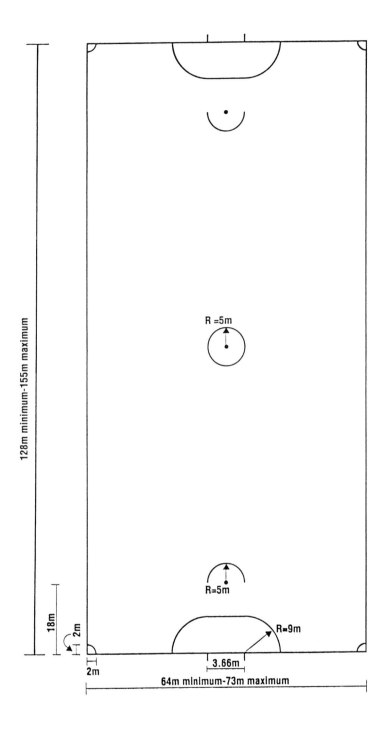

128m minimum-155m maximum

18m

2m

2m

R =5m

R=5m

R=9m

3.66m

64m minimum-73m maximum

PLATE 21. Shinty (Cammanachd) pitch.

OTHER SPORTS AND GAMES

The above series of pitch layouts will, it is hoped, give the sports ground developer and the groundsman a clear idea of the space and line-marking requirements for most of the outdoor sporting activities likely to be encountered in the British Isles. They do not, however, represent a fully comprehensive catalogue of the winter games played on coarse turf pitches in the UK and it may sometimes prove necessary to cater for other minority pastimes which deserve mention, although not full coverage here. Australian Rules Football springs to mind, with its unique oval pitch boundary and public school groundsmen may also be required at times to cope with Harrow football, Winchester College football or the Eton wall game. Polo crosse, a combination of polo and lacrosse played by teams of six riders, has been played in England since 1939. Pitches or courts for games such as touchball, korfball or field handball may also be sometimes required. The Indian game of kabaddi is increasing in popularity amongst ethnic communities in this country and requires a pitch 13 m x 10 m.

Some sports grounds may also feature archery ranges and turf areas may be used for summer activities, such as softball, rounders, Irish rounders or baseball (not forgetting the distinctive Welsh variety of the last-named game, played in Cardiff and Newport area of South Wales). The types of turf surfaces described in these pages may be regarded as suitable for all the above activities, although drainage requirements may of course be significantly reduced in the case of areas where usage is confined to the summer months.

PLATE 22. A football game in the Elizabethan era, before rules were formulated and playing areas defined.

THE EVOLUTION OF TEAM GAMES, GROUNDS AND GROUNDSMANSHIP

The origins of team ball games in the British Isles are buried in the remote past, but primitive football-type games or ball-and-stick competitions probably extend back to Roman times or earlier. The Romans played a game called harpastum played on a rectangle of land, each opposing team attempting to take a small, hard ball across their opponent's base-line. The Roman soldiery probably brought the game with them to the British Isles during the 55 BC invasion. Later, native populations played for less organised games where team numbers were unlimited, rules virtually non-existent and playing areas only vaguely defined. The format of such activities varied from locality to locality, but usually consisted of a contest between neighbouring villages or parishes and involving almost the entire able-bodied male population of each rival community. A ball or bladder would be kicked, punched, carried or thrown over a playing area consisting of the entire tract of land between participating villages, the opposing goals consisting of little more than a conveniently sited tree, market cross or gateway at each end. Games were disorderly and dangerous, injuries and even deaths being by no means unknown and played over areas of ground which might feature rivers and streams, tracts of woodland, meadows or heaths.

PLATE 23 Early football was a rowdy and dangerous affair. A street game portrayed in a Gloucestershire manuscript.

In more urban communities, games were played along streets and through market squares, endangering life and limb amongst the population as a whole, damaging property and occasioning general mayhem and lawlessness. As might be expected, the authorities made repeated attempts to ban such activities, but generally with only limited success. Ancient games of this kind have survived to the present day as folk traditions, for example, at Ashbourne in Derbyshire, where an annual game of primitive football is still played each Shrove Tuesday. Given such a scenario, it is obvious that no ground preparation was required, although it is probable that open tracts of land, where the turf was kept short by grazing animals, were to some extent preferable as a playing venue to woodlands or built-up areas. Confining rowdy play to areas of open land, where damage to property was minimised and so allowing more respectable citizens to go about their lawful business without interference, was clearly desirable. Thus, a monk named William Fitzstephen, writing about London life in the year 1175 wrote about Shrove Tuesday entertainments when "all the youth of the city go to a flat patch of ground just outside the city for their famous game of ball." By the late 15th century, there was a reference to "boundaries being marked" for a game - recognised playing pitches were obviously beginning to evolve.

31

For a considerable period of time, team games were frowned upon by the authorities, reflecting a belief that they encouraged hooliganism and extremes of irresponsible behaviour - a view which was often amply justifiable. On the other hand, pioneer educationalists, such as Richard Mulcaster, headmaster of Merchant Taylors' School from 1561 to 1586 and high-master of St Paul's School from 1596 to 1608, were beginning to put forward the idea that football and other team games should not be regarded as simply undesirable excuses for riotous behaviour and therefore suppressed. Mulcaster argues that such sports were a useful outlet for youthful energies, promoting health, strength and team-spirit. More control was obviously needed to eliminate vandalism, violence and other excesses linked with the playing of such games, but he felt that such activities could be turned into pastimes of benefit to public and participants alike. Here we have the beginnings of the English public schools' attitude to team-games and the subsequent wholehearted public acceptance of such outdoor sports as beneficial to mind, body and character development.

The 16th century also provides a reference to a "Fote-balle close" at Hitchin in Hertfordshire - an area of land actually set aside for the playing of the game. From then on terms such as pitch, playing field or sports ground in the modern sense began to be applicable to such reserved, open spaces. As early as 1514 a link between team games and the winter season had also been established as one of a series of short, pastoral poems by Alexander Barclay which described how

"The sturdie plowman, lustie, strong and bolde
Overcometh the winter with driving the foote ball."

By 1620, football was being played too at the universities, St John's and Trinity Colleges at Cambridge being particularly active in inter-college matches. Queen's College, Oxford was playing on reserved ground at Bullington Green by the end of the 17th century. In Ireland too, peasant sports were undergoing a similar evolutionary process to eventually form the basis of modern Gaelic football and hurling. A poem of 1720 describes a six-a-side game on "a wide extent of level ground" in County Dublin.

The Eton wall game is one of the oldest forms of football still to be played in this country and may date back to 1717 when the wall involved was built. Played on a narrow pitch bordered by the wall, the game features a door for a goal at one end and a rectangle marked in whitewash on an elm tree for the other. The surface begins the season as grass but is rapidly reduced to bare ground, dust or mud as the playing season proceeds - a circumstance still unfortunately often repeated in the case of more modern football games played in more conventional locations. Harrow school football is another version of the game, adapted to muddy conditions and from the 1850's played on the school Rugby fields in the Easter term. Winchester college football was played before 1790 on St Catherine's Hill, a prehistoric earthwork outside the college grounds, as the school had no playing fields of its own until that year. In 1790, however, the governing body made over to the college an area of land called the Meads, which was used for their traditional form of football. The survival of such archaic forms of football at public schools interestingly reflects the way that local versions of the game developed distinctive rules in isolation. Public schools were also pioneers in providing areas of land specifically for such games and in developing the ethic that sports were healthy and character-building as we have already seen. Evidence appears to be lacking as to whether public school's caretakers or gardeners carried out groundsmanship duties in the 18th century, but it may be imagined that some work was done on the playing surfaces of private school grounds - turfing perhaps, seeding and levelling of worn areas possibly and even some rolling or grass cutting with the scythe.

It was, however, not only in the public school environment that football and its associated ground facilities, was developing. Games were also popular amongst the emerging urbanised industrial working class at the end of the 18th century. In 1793 at Bent's Green in Sheffield a 3-day match was played between six Norton men, dressed in green and six Sheffield men outfitted in red. A considerable crowd watched this contest, passions ran high and a number of participants were injured. Again, in 1819, an attempt was made to deprive the pupils of the Free School at Hitchin in Hertfordshire of their football ground, where games had been played for as long as anyone could remember. The appeal of the game was spreading and not confined exclusively to one social class.

There is an interesting early reference to pitch construction or groundsmanship, which dates from 13 November 1810 and which concerns Westminster School. On that date, the Chapter of Westminster ordered "that Jonathan Green's bill of £3-1s. for marking out 10 acres of ground in Tothill Fields as a play-ground for the Westminster scholars, and for the use of his team of horses and plough two days, viz. the 28th and 29th of August last to mark the said piece of ground with a deep furrough, be paid." This presumably means that the boundary of the ground was delineated by means of a distinct furrow or trench cut with the horse-drawn plough, but some marking of individual pitches seems also to be implied.

The period spanning the years 1830 to 1860 was highly significant to the development of British football, as it was in this period that the schism between the handling game (the forerunner of Rugby and American football) and the foot-dribbling game (the forerunner of soccer) intensified. Prior to this date, teams simply played "football" - a single species of game which happened to have locally varying rules. At that time, Eton, Harrow, Westminster and Charterhouse favoured the soccer-type style, whilst Marlborough, Cheltenham and of course Rugby School itself, favoured the "pick up the ball and run" variety of football. At Rugby School the fact that ball handling was allowed was supposed to date back to an incident in 1823, but the story is quite possibly apocryphal. By the 1840-60 period, football of some kind was established as the winter sport for most boarding and grammar schools and as boys left school it spread with them to universities and cities. The conflict between the two diverging forms of the game came to a head at Cambridge University and resulted in 1846 of the drawing up of the "Cambridge Rules" which laid the foundation for modern soccer or Association Football. On the other hand, some adult clubs, such as Richmond and Blackheath near London, came down in favour of the Rugby version of football and by 1863 the difference between the two basic forms of British football had become clear.

As far as soccer was concerned, the situation was definitively clarified by a series of meetings, which commenced in October 1863 and which led to modification of the Cambridge Rules and the creation of the Football Association. The code of play decided upon spread slowly across the country, widescale acceptance being given a major boost by the FA Cup competition instigated in 1871.

Not to be outdone, those football clubs which followed the Rugby School version of football also formalised their Rule Book, the Rugby Football Union being formed as a result of a meeting of the representatives of 21 clubs in January 1871. Sometime later and in contrast to soccer's ruling body, the RFU came down firmly in favour of strictly amateur status for all its players. This proved unacceptable to a number of Lancashire and Yorkshire Rugby clubs, where coal-miner players were commonly financially compensated for missed shifts when involved in matches, so 22 North of England clubs broke away from the RFU in August 1895 to form the Northern Rugby Football Union, changing its name to the Rugby Football League in 1922.

Football had travelled to the United States of America with the early colonists, but as in Britain, it was not until the second half of the 19th century that standardised rules were formulated at the instigation of American Ivy League colleges. The Princeton Rules of 1867 were for a soccer-like game, but the ball could be picked up in the "Boston Game" played at Harvard from 1871 onwards. Yale and Harvard later adopted the English RFU rules. Further evolution of the game, however, took place amongst the US colleges, resulting by 1882 in the use of the distinctive and complex "Grid-iron" pitch. The evolution of the American game was complete by 1910 when the National Collegiate Athletic Association came into being. American professional football commenced with a game in 1895 and remained basically the College game, with modifications of rules governing forward passes. In 1933, goal posts were placed on the goal line of the grid-iron, not on the end line, for the professional game.

PLATE 24. Association Football : the first international match – England versus Scotland in 1872 (Scotland : nil – England : nil).

American football came to Britain in 1982 and after several years of exhibition matches a British professional team, the London Monarchs, were formed in 1991. The influence of television coverage of major US matches has fanned a growing interest in American football amongst participants and spectators alike and the game seems likely to enjoy growing popularity in the UK.

As is the case with England, Wales and Scotland, Ireland also has a tradition of folk-football playing, extending back to early unruly inter-village contests, although there is no written reference to the game in Ireland before 1527. Games known as field caid and cross-country caid developed from early beginnings. Later, English domination led to the soccer playing Irish Football Association in 1880 and to the Combined Irish Rugby Union in 1881. Irish nationalism reasserted itself in 1884, however, with the formation of the Gaelic Athletic Association, devoted to the preservation of native Irish games. The organisation saved, rejuvenated, reformed and organised Irish football, producing the 15-a-side game (played with a round ball) seen today. To the outsider, the modern game appears to combine elements of soccer and Rugby football - a mixture strikingly symbolised by the appearance of the goal posts of the Irish game. Firmly based on Irish soil, the game is, however, played in England and the USA and is closely related to Australian Rules football.

It is now appropriate to lay football-type games aside for a moment and turn to a consideration of the other group of winter team games, those played with some form of stick as well as a ball. For the British Isles as a whole, hockey is the most significant of these in terms of numbers participating and can appropriately be dealt with first.

As is the case with football, the origins of hockey lie shrouded in the shadows of pre-history, but an ancestral form of hockey called Bandy is referred to in written English records as early as the 14th century. Like early forms of football, bandy was played by a disorganised and violent rabble in a cross-country setting. The first hockey club was Blackheath, founded before 1861 when record-keeping began, who still at that time played over a vast area of heathland, using a squared piece of rubber for a ball hit with heavy oak clubs. The pitch appears to have been at least 270 yd. long and 70 yd. wide. This primitive version of modern hockey was refined by members of Teddington Cricket Club, who played using a cricket ball over the smooth surface of their cricket outfield, so providing members with a useful form of exercise during the cricket off-season and maximising usage of the available playing area. Such dual usage of outfields for summer cricket and winter hockey has of course continued to the present day. Middlesex Cricket Club also pioneered the game, with records of the winter use of their outfield for hockey going back to 1874. The Hockey Association was formed in 1886 and its influence rapidly spread throughout the country.

Despite much Victorian prejudice against the idea of girls and women playing team-games at all, hockey was considered more suitable for women than football and women students were playing the game at Oxford colleges in the early 1880's. The All-England Women's Hockey Association emerged from an earlier Ladies Hockey Association in 1896. Subsequently, the game spread around the world and internationally has become the most popular team game for women. It is particularly popular as a men's game in India where climatic conditions tend to favour the kind of hard, dry pitch surface ideal for the game. In the British Isles, deficiencies in the quality of grass pitches has led to an increasing use of artificial pitch surfaces in recent decades, although the game on grass is still widespread.

In the Irish Republic, hurling rivals Gaelic football in popularity and the modern game again owes its success to the efforts of the 1884 Gaelic League. Although obviously related to hockey and in the same family of ancient ball and stick games, the ball in hurling spends more time flying through the air than running along the surface of the pitch and from the groundsman's point of view, the kind of playing surface required is more akin to that of soccer than to the particularly fine and uniform surfaces needed for high class hockey. The same remarks apply to camogie, the women's version of hurling, which is organised by the Camogie Association of Ireland, founded in 1904 and reorganised in 1932. The Scottish version of hurling, shinty, was brought to Scotland by invading Irish Gaels and was described in 1769 as being played on large plains - the typical natural playing arenas of the period. Rules were codified in 1880 and the game's ruling body, the Camanachd Association, appeared in 1893.

The origins of the game of lacrosse are somewhat uncertain, but lie in the New World - it is the chief national game of Canada and there it is often played in the summer. The white invaders were playing the native game in Canada by 1844 and in 1867 the game was introduced into the USA and Great Britain, subsequently spreading to New Zealand and Australia. The English Lacrosse Union, governing the men's version of the game, stems from 1892 and the All-England Women's Lacrosse Association originated in the 1912 Ladies' Lacrosse Association. The men's and women's games have diverged to a point where the required pitch markings differ and the women's lacrosse pitch is unique in requiring no definite boundary markings.

Polo is also unique amongst the games dealt with in this book, as being of course the only team game described here which is played on horseback. The sport is an extremely ancient one, having its origins in Persia (Iran) perhaps 2,500 years ago, spread to India and was then taken up by the British who founded their first polo club in India in 1859. It was brought to Britain by a cavalry regiment, the 10th Hussars in 1870 and the Hurlingham Club was formed shortly afterwards. Polo presents extreme problems as far as ground presentation is concerned, not only from the sheer size of the area involved, but also because of the rapid surface damage caused by the ponies' hooves. Fortunately it is a summer game with the season extending from March to October, which at least allows some grass growth and recovery during the playing season and a chance of reasonably dry ground conditions. To include polo grounds in a book primarily devoted to winter games pitches may seem somewhat illogical, but the construction and maintenance of such grounds are more akin to those of winter games pitches than to the requirements for summer activities such as lawn tennis, bowls or cricket.

OF GROUNDS AND GROUNDSMANSHIP
The previous few pages have concentrated on the historical development of team games in the British Isles. At this point, it will be appropriate to switch our attention away from the games themselves and to consider the evolution of the grounds and pitches on which these sporting contests take place, with particular focus on the developing arts of pitch construction and groundsmanship. The above historical survey of team games makes it abundantly clear that most of them were not really organised or codified until the second half of the 19th Century and it is at this point that parallel progress in ground construction and maintenance techniques really commenced. Groundsmen probably existed before this period, but the historical record is sketchy and uncertain on this point. One or two early references to pitch preparation and care were included in the above account, but no detailed or coherent survey of groundsmanship before the mid-Victorian period seems possible, or even particularly relevant to the modern scenario.

In the days when team games were a riotous rough-and-tumble across country or through city streets and squares, ground preparation or maintenance was obviously neither needed nor considered. It was only when games became organised and controlled and playing skills honed, that the quality of playing surfaces became important, with increasingly expert players demanding truer and more uniform pitches on which their skills could be exploited to the full. Unfortunately the history of groundsmanship has not been well documented to date and detailed information is hard to come by. It is, however, hoped that the following account will give some idea of how the modern, highly scientific approach to both pitch construction and pitch care has developed and set the demanding and highly skilled work of today's groundsman in its historical context.

Even when team games moved away from the streets, or away from large tracts of countryside, onto relatively level and more limited areas of ground, such open spaces could hardly be referred to as recreation grounds or winter games pitches in the modern sense of these terms. Venues for games were generally not reserved for that exclusive purpose, whether common or private land, but were probably also used for village fairs and other gatherings as well as being grazed by sheep, horses or cattle. Maintenance aimed at producing an improved playing surface would have been largely non-existent and little, if anything, would have been done to improve natural drainage or surface contours. Before even primitive attempts at improving surfaces for team games could be worth-while, areas of land had to be reserved for that primary purpose and more importantly, enclosed by fencing or similar barriers to control access. In general, this did not happen until the second half of the 19th century and was a result of the formation of organised clubs, with a sufficiently keen and affluent membership to purchase the necessary land and contemplate its improvement. Cricket clubs were the pioneers here and this had some effect on creating better winter pitches as well - many cricket grounds were used for football, hockey or other winter pastimes as we have already seen.

For example, the Oval which was established by the Surrey County Cricket Club in 1845, was used for tennis, Rugby and soccer in the second half of the 19th century and summer grass growth was controlled by a flock of sheep. Again, Sheffield's Bramall Lane ground was first used for cricket in 1855 whilst soccer started on a pitch adjacent to and overlapping the outfield in 1862.

(In 1878 the world's first floodlit football match was staged there.) Nottingham's Trent Bridge cricket ground was the home of Nottingham Forest FC from 1880-82, whilst Derby County initially shared the Racecourse Ground with Derbyshire Cricket Club and then moved in 1895 to a ground also used for baseball, still known as the Baseball Ground. Such dual usage increased revenue and allowed ancillary buildings to be constructed - pavilions, changing rooms and committee rooms - although local public houses were also commonly used for such purposes. Passing the hat around amongst spectators was a way of supplementing club funds, but the obvious next step of securely enclosing the ground and charging admission was soon taken.

In the last 20 years of the 19th century, soccer tended to assume the lead as far as ground development was concerned, as breweries and other businesses began to invest in the game, advertising appeared at grounds and gate money increased. Three particularly old-established grounds still used by modern Football League clubs are Stoke's Victoria Ground (since 1878), Preston's Deepdale Ground (since 1881) and Burnley's Turf Moor (opened in 1883). Spectator facilities began to improve and sloping banks or terraces began to appear around the actual playing area to give a better view. Industry provided useful raw materials for such bank construction, mining spoil, ash, clinker or cinders being commonly employed as well as general rubbish - Fulham used road sweepings from the Local Authority at Craven Cottage in 1894-96 period.

PLATE 25. **Earth moving with a horse-drawn scraper.**

Many clubs in their search for a suitable venue were forced to accept sites where suitably level, natural ground for the pitch simply did not exist - uneven, overgrown wasteland, disused quarries or gravel pits were all used by clubs and Cardiff City were faced with a glass-strewn general rubbish tip during the development of Ninian Park in 1910. Industrial waste was therefore also commonly used for building up or levelling actual playing surfaces, laboriously graded by man or horse power, topped with soil and grassed over. The beginnings of pitch construction were obviously primitive by modern standards with little thought being given to drainage or ensuring healthy grass growth in the long-term, but the process of sports ground and playing surface development was definitely underway.

In the late 19th century playing field construction work began to benefit from developing agricultural mechanisation and technology, particularly as far as tractors were concerned. A steam traction engine for use on the farm had been exhibited at a Royal Agricultural Society meeting at Wolverhampton as early as 1871, but it was some time before such equipment became generally available for earth moving and cultivation work - horses remained the standard power source before the First World War. An oil-engined agricultural locomotive appeared at a Royal Agricultural Show in 1897 and by 1899 ploughing and other operations were being successfully carried out with an Ivel tractor - the Saunderson tractor was another early success.

PLATE 26. Agricultural steam traction engines were used to some extent in playing field development before the 1914-18 War.

The years of the Great War were inevitably a hiatus in the story of playing field construction and maintenance, but progress made in the design of military vehicles did have a useful spin-off when peace was restored and by the 1920's sports ground use of the internal combustion engine was firmly established, agricultural tractors being used for initial construction work, whilst smaller, specialised tractors specifically designed to meet the groundsman's needs were beginning to appear as aids to sports ground and golf course maintenance. Pattissons of Stanmore, Middlesex, established in 1896 and still active today, were prominent producers of sports ground power units, as were Annison Bull of Otley, Yorkshire - a firm founded in 1897. Allan Taylor & Co. of Wandsworth, London also produced a popular sports ground tractor in the 1920's, as did Moxons of Whetstone, North London.

The subject of the evolution of sports ground mechanical equipment will be returned to shortly, but first the question of the development of sports field drainage deserves mention. The fact that early pitch constructions involved only rudimentary drainage has already been touched upon, but it would be a mistake to assume that drainage work was neglected entirely in the period before the First World War. Agricultural drainage techniques using clayware tiles or pipes had after all been in use for centuries and there is no reason to suppose that agricultural-type systems were not placed under the pitch surfaces of early sports ground developments. These would, however, have been woefully inadequate by modern standards, following current agricultural practice rather than featuring the more intensive and efficient systems which would be considered essential today.

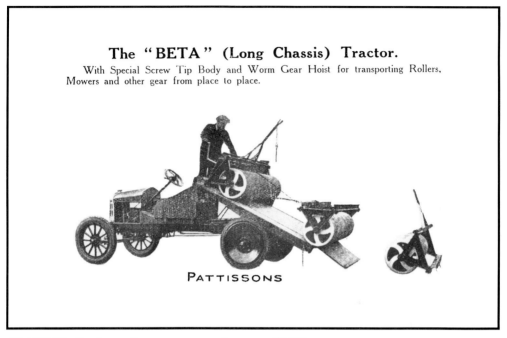

The "BETA" (Long Chassis) Tractor.

With Special Screw Tip Body and Worm Gear Hoist for transporting Rollers, Mowers and other gear from place to place.

PATTISSONS

PLATE 27. Pattissons Beta sports ground tractor of 1929.

Relying on the wisdom of hindsight, it is probably that pioneer drainage systems were laid with pipes at too wide a spacing and with inadequate stone backfilling over pipes, the latter preventing the all-important rapid transfer of water from surface to underlying drainpipe, particularly when dealing with compacted clay soils.

In the case of sports grounds built on made-up land where even-sized industrial clinker or hard ash was used as a foundation, it is possible that excellent drainage characteristics could have been achieved but the use of finer fly ash, subsoil or assorted waste must not uncommonly have resulted in waterlogging problems and perhaps occasional subsidence difficulties. Deep compaction-breaking subsoil cultivators were available for use with early tractors, as well as winch-drawn mole ploughs, but there are few mentions of such techniques in the context of playing field construction. For example, the Valley Parade ground in Bradford, now of course a soccer stadium but originally built as a Rugby ground by Manningham Rugby Football Club, was built in 1886 at a cost of £1,400. The work involved levelling a steep hillside, building up of layers of ballast, ashes and soil and finally turfing (not seeding) the pitch area, but there is no record of drain installation. Circular sectioned clayware drain pipes were, however, available around the turn of the century, having evolved from the variety of drain styles employed earlier and after the Great War were used for playing field projects with increasing frequency, until gradually superseded by plastic pipes in the 1960's. (Plastic pipe was actually first used in Holland in 1960.)

Drainage was installed at West Bromwich Albion's Hawthorns pitch in 1900, but the site was a particularly difficult one which sloped severely and which had a stream running diagonally across. One hundred and twenty men were required to culvert the stream, lay 1600 yd of drains and level with 300 loads of ash, topped by fresh soil and imported turf. The finished pitch still sloped markedly - possibly an advantage from the drainage point of view as the surface would tend to shed water onto the surrounding cinder track. Some pitches were given a severe camber, e.g. at Burden Park, built in 1985, where spectators at one side of the pitch could only see the top half of players on the opposite wing, again with the purpose of shedding surface water.

PLATE 28. Allan Taylor tractor of 1928 towing a 5-gang mower.

The development of pitch layouts and markings forms an interesting footnote to the history of team ball games and is best documented for soccer, although it is recorded that the Rugby Football Union specified in 1879-80 that the field of play should not exceed 110 yd in length or 75 yd in breadth and should be as near as possible to those dimensions. There was at that time no mention of a dead ball line. The first set of Football Association rules (December 1863) stated that the soccer pitch should be 200 by 100 yd maximum, marked with flags along the perimeter rather than lines marked on the pitch surface. Surface markings were introduced in 1882, delineating the main rectangle only. A half-way line then appeared and by 1887 there was also a centre circle and two 6 yd semi-circles in front of each goal from which goal kicks could be taken. A line 12 yd out from the goal line for penalty kicks was next added, together with an 18 yd line behind which players were obliged to stand when penalty kicks were being taken. Today's familiar soccer pitch markings were adopted in 1902, penalty arcs being added as a result of European suggestions in 1937.

The obvious advantages of white line pitch marking stimulated the development of line marking machines, which were widely available by the late 19th century. F.H. Ayres' Patent wheel to wheel paint transfer machine proved effective and its basic mechanism would be instantly recognised by users of many of today's machines which work on the same principle. Line markers were originally developed for use on country house lawn tennis courts - tiny 6" wide lawn mowers were also available, used to form a strip of close-mown grass prior to applying the marking paint. Some of these early line markers were built on a small scale for use by children - the gardener's boy might be as young as nine or ten years old, but larger versions were of course also made for adult use in the laying out of winter pitches.

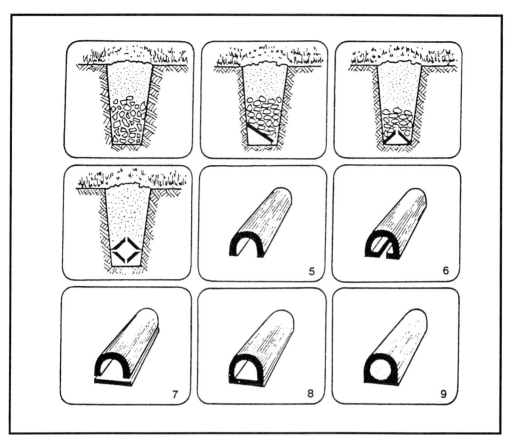

PLATE 29. A variety of drain styles were used before the circular-sectioned clayware tile became standard.

Goal posts evolved from a couple of conveniently sited trees or other natural features to two sticks driven into the ground. These were placed 2-3' apart in an account of football written by Joseph Strutt in 1801. The Cambridge rules of 1846 specified two poles of indeterminate height placed 15' apart. Rugby football's characteristic H-shaped goals had certainly appeared by 1851 as one formed part of a display at the Crystal Palace exhibition in that year. On its formation in 1863, the Football Association specified posts 8 yds apart, a rule remaining unchanged to the present day. Cross bars appeared in Sheffield around 1866 (the Sheffield Association's goals were 9' high but only 4' wide, making a straight wooden crosspiece feasible). For wider goals, a rope or tape stretched across proved practicable, but the FA finally adopted the rigid horizontal in 1882. The diameter of posts was fixed at a maximum of 5" in 1895. Elliptical sectioned posts and cross bars were developed by Standard Goals of Nottingham in 1920 and quickly became standard, although Scottish clubs have always tended to prefer goal posts of square section. Goal nets were the brain-child of Liverpool's City Engineer, J.A. Brodie, who designed them in 1889 and they were approved by the FA in 1892.

Returning to the subject of ground maintenance equipment, rollers had been in agricultural and horticultural use for centuries, the earliest having been laboriously-rounded natural stone, later superseded by concrete and cast iron models, the latter often water-ballasted. Horse-drawn rollers were used on sports grounds before and after the First World War to smooth pitch surfaces and it was probably not fully appreciated that although such treatment may produce a short-term improvement in playing quality, the repeated use of heavy rollers also results in soil compaction, loss of soil structure and consequently in impeded surface drainage.

41

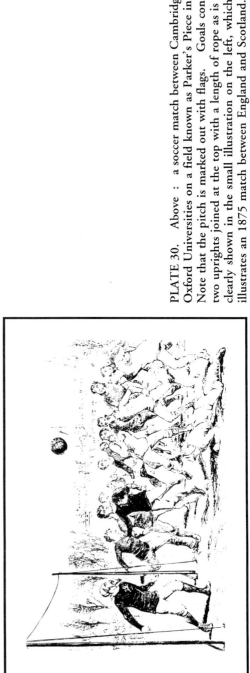

PLATE 30. Above : a soccer match between Cambridge and Oxford Universities on a field known as Parker's Piece in 1887. Note that the pitch is marked out with flags. Goals consist of two uprights joined at the top with a length of rope as is more clearly shown in the small illustration on the left, which illustrates an 1875 match between England and Scotland.

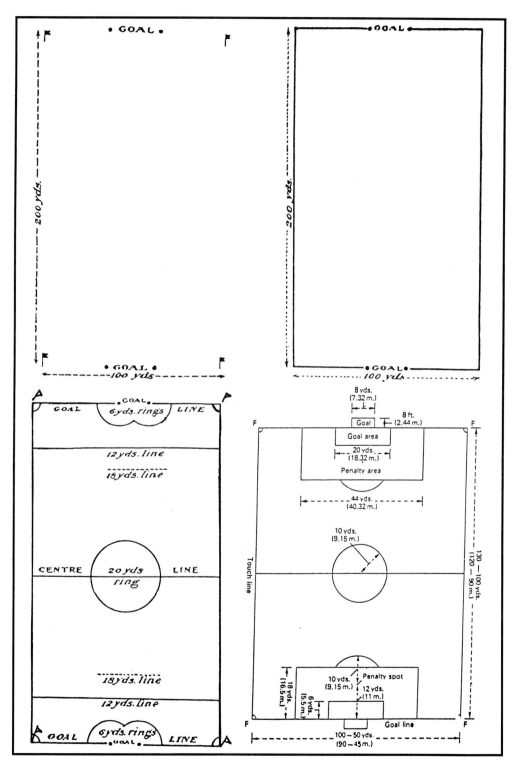

PLATE 31. The development of soccer pitch markings.   Top left – 1863 version.   Top right
– 1882.   Bottom left – 1892.   Bottom right – the perfected design used after 1937.

HOWARDS' NEW 'SAVAHORSE' ROLLER.

Drawn by a single horse, this roller will do the work of an ordinary two-horse roller. The draught is extraordinarily light, being reduced 40% to 45% by fitting a pair of cage roller bearings to each cylinder. The implement is almost unbreakable. The frame is of high carbon steel riveted together with corner gussets. The two cylinders are of steel plate electrically welded, with pressed steel corrugated ends riveted in position. (*Illustrated.*)

With shafts or pole. 24-inch cylinders.

5 feet across cylinders, weight 8½ cwt.	...	**£17 net.**
6½ feet ,, ,, ,, 9 ,,	...	**£18** ,,
7½ feet ,, ,, ,, 9½ ,,	...	**£19** ,,

Carriage paid in England and Wales.

PLATE 32. A horse roller from an 1883 catalogue and a Howard-Bedford design from the 1920's.

The most important mechanical advance which had a direct bearing on the maintenance of team game pitches was, however, the invention of the lawn mower. Prior to 1830, all ornamental and amenity turf was kept under control either by grazing animals or laboriously using a scythe. Of course, as far as keeping the grass reasonably short was concerned, those responsible for the maintenance of winter pitches were at some advantage over their contemporaries who cared for turf areas used in summer (cricket grounds, bowling greens, golf courses etc.) in that team games were largely staged in the winter when grass growth was not so much of a problem. For winter games pitches, it was feasible to control the grass by animal grazing in summer and to then clean up the surface for winter recreational use, when grass growth was naturally slackening off in the autumn. Mechanical mowing equipment was therefore more of an obvious advance in the improvement of summer games facilities and its usage for winter pitches spread only slowly. Indeed, summer grazing of the pitches of even top-class professional clubs was common until the inter-war period and even today, small and relatively impecunious clubs may still play on pitches which are grazed by sheep, cattle or horses in the summer growing season.

PLATE 33. Summer grass control by horses. The RFU's Twickenham ground in 1915.

The lawnmower was invented by a free-lance Gloucester engineer named Edwin Beard Budding, who obtained British Letters Patent on 25 October 1830. Finance was obtained by means of a partnership with John Ferrabee and manufacturing facilities were set up at the Phoenix Foundry, Thrupp Mill near Brinscomb in the inventor's native county. The largest version of the Budding-Ferrabee mower was, however, a two-man cylinder machine with a cutting width of 36" and although it was used with some success on ornamental lawns and bowling greens, it was not really big enough for the effective mowing of areas as large as a football pitch. Licence to manufacture the machine was obtained by J.R. and A. Ransome of Ipswich (now Ransomes Sims & Jeffries PLC) in 1832 and by Thomas Green of Leeds in 1835 and when patents expired in 1855, a number of other firms commenced production of the Budding machine. In the context of winter games pitch mowing, a significant development occurred in 1842 when Alexander Shanks of Arbroath in Scotland produced the first horse-drawn mower (at this time English Patent protection did not extend to Scotland). Shank's machine featured a 42" cutting width and now for the first time, it was feasible to mow an area the size of a winter pitch with a cylinder mowing machine. Similar horse-drawn mowing equipment was later produced by Ransomes in Ipswich, Greens in Leeds, Barford & Perkins of Peterborough, John Crowley & Co. Ltd. of Sheffield and Manchester and Samuelson & Co. of Banbury. Horse boots were manufactured by a number of firms, notably Pattissons of Stanmore, which prevented the animal's hooves from marking the turf surface excessively, particularly in wet weather when the ground was soft.

These early horse-drawn machines were roller driven and resembled enlarged versions of the hand-pushed domestic lawnmower, but they were usually equipped with side-delivery grass boxes fitted with a sliding shutter which pushed the clippings out to one side when the box was full. This emptying mechanism could be operated by the groundsman from his normal working position at the rear of the machine, so allowing him to avoid relinquishing hold of the reins and hence maintaining control of the horse whilst dumping accumulated grass clippings.

THE RANSOME GRASS SHEARING MACHINE, 1832.

The above engraving represents a new machine for shearing lawns, grass-plots, &c., which has been recently introduced into the Zoological Gardens, and where it may be frequently seen in operation. It is the invention of a Mr. Budding, and manufactured by Messrs. Ransome of Ipswich.

PLATE 34. Budding's mower shown in the *Mechanic's Magazine* 23 October 1832.

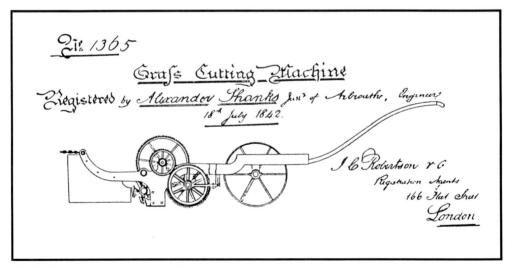

PLATE 35. Registration Certificate granted to Alexander Shanks in 1842 for the first horse drawn mower.

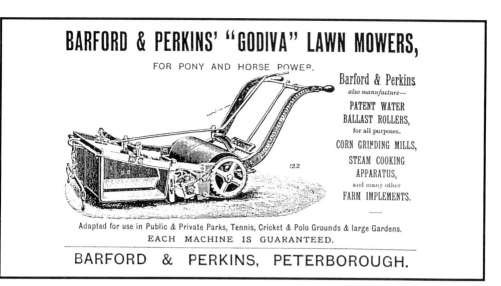

PLATE 36. Typical late 19th century roller driven horse mower with a side-emptying grass box.

The next development was the introduction of a side-wheel driven horse-drawn mowing machine, resembling a single unit of a modern gang mower. These were lighter machines than the earlier roller type and did not have grass-collecting facilities. Such machines were chain-driven and because they were easier for a horse to pull, allowed the operator to ride on the machine rather than walking behind. This class of machine was typified by the Ransomes "Ideal" of 1905, the Shanks' "Triumph" of 1922 and the Green's "Perfection", the last named being still available during the Second World War.

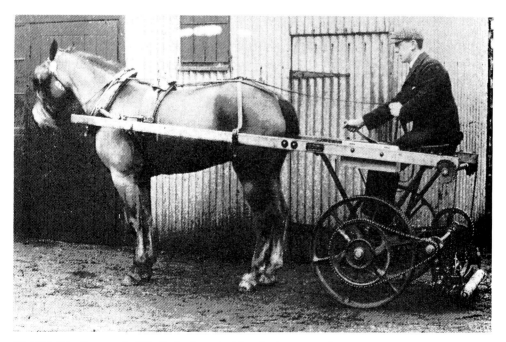

PLATE 37. Ransome's 'Ideal' single unit side wheel mower of 1905.

Units of this type were first linked to form a true gang mower by an American, Mr Worthington of Shawnee, who produced such a mower in 1919 (his company was later acquired by the Jacobsen Corp., still manufacturing mowers today). Gang mowers appeared in the UK after the First World War, some (such as the Shanks' Roller Triple) being roller rather than sidewheel driven, although the latter remained the norm. By this time, such machines were also available for use with tractors and the consequent availability of greater power meant that gang units could be linked into quintuple or even nonuple combinations - a single horse could manage only a triple gang mower.

As an alternative to horse or tractor drawn mowers, self-propelled machines were also produced for sports ground usage. Steam powered mowers were the first of these, initially designed by Elias Summer of Leyland, Lancashire and patented in 1893. Shanks' and Greens were both producing steam mowers around the turn of the century but by 1896 a petrol engined machine had also been produced, by W.J. Stephenson-Peach, a Burton-on-Trent engineer.

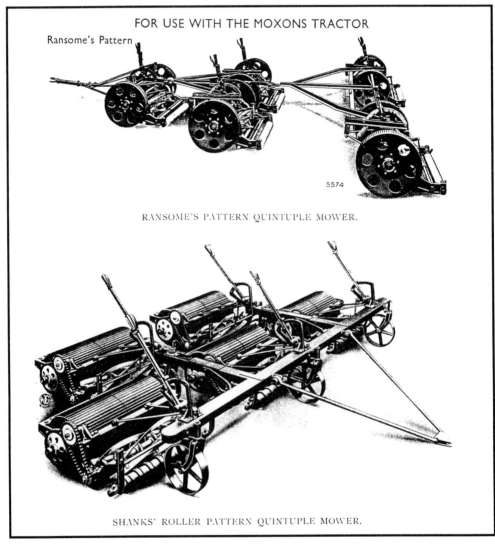

PLATE 38. Five-gang units were available for tractor draught in this 1932 advertisement.

In 1902 Ransomes of Ipswich introduced a commercial petrol engined mower with a 42" cutting width and a 6 hp Simms four-stroke engine, selling one of their first production machines to Cadbury Brothers for use on their Bournville sports ground.

PLATE 39. A 1902 Ransomes motor mower at Cadbury's sports ground.

Between the wars, a flood of new manufacturers entered the field of motor mower production, including a number of names which remain very familiar today. Dennis Brothers of Guildford produced their first machine in 1921 and about the same time Charles H. Pugh Ltd. launched the first "Atco" model from their Birmingham plant. J.P. Engineering of Leicester, Automower of Bath, Somerset and the Enfield Cycle Company also produced large sports ground motor mowers in the inter-war period, joined later by R.K. Allett of Stamford.

PLATE 40. Sports ground mowing with an Allen scythe and a set of miniature gangs.

Other mechanical equipment continued to evolve in the 1920's and 1930's – agricultural tractors tended to become lighter and more manoeuvrable and hence, more suitable for larger multiple sports ground complexes, particularly when fitted with smooth grassland tyres. Other agricultural equipment, sometimes modified specifically to meet playing field requirements, such as light rollers, grassland chain harrows and both spinner and belt-fed fertiliser distributors was in common use. For single pitches and smaller sports grounds, two-wheeled tractors proved a popular power source and machines such as the Ransomes Overgreen, Gravely X-Cel and Allen Motor Scythe could be fitted with a range of spikers, rakes, brushes and other tools. Similar small tractors produced after the 2nd World War were the four-wheeled Sisis Cinderella and the Auto-trac from the same Macclesfield firm.

The importance of forking as a method of relieving soil compaction and facilitating surface drainage was probably appreciated before the 1914-18 war, but attempts to produce a mechanical alternative to the hand fork commenced around 1930. An early and successful spiking machine was that designed by Ernest Smith of Manchester (British Patent 395467 of 20 July 1933) and produced in pedestrian, tractor-drawn and horse-drawn versions. Even more efficient was the somewhat similar machine designed by William Hargreaves of Cheadle, Cheshire and first marketed in 1932. Hargreaves' innovation was to mount the machine's tines on a square or polygonal roller which drove them into the ground as the roller jolted over the surface. The firm of W. Hargreaves & Co. Ltd. developed into Sisis Equipment (Macclesfield) Ltd., still one of this country's leading manufacturers of sports ground maintenance equipment.

A narrower machine could be supplied at a less price, but is not recommended

BECAUSE—the great value derived from turf piercing warrants the work being done in the most efficient manner, *i.e.* the greatest area covered in the least time, providing of course the pulling effort is not too great for the horse, and this is a point which has received careful attention.

At a speed of, say, 4 m.p.h., this means 3 acres per hour and 560,000 holes pierced.

PLATE 41. Sisis horse-drawn type H spiker, from a leaflet circa 1936.

PLATE 42. Aeration the hard way. Hand forking Tottenham Hotspur's White Hart Lane pitch during a downpour in 1937.

PLATE 43. The Dutch Verti-Drain machine is one of the most effective of modern aerators and was first produced in 1980.

Spiking is now considered one of the most essential routine maintenance operations in winter pitch management and conventional equipment remains basically the same as it was in the 1930's, although the development of weight transference systems allows part of the weight of the tractor to bear on the aerating machine, so achieving deeper penetration than was formerly possible. A major step forward in the development of aeration equipment was taken in 1980 by De Ridders in the Netherlands with the invention of the Verti-Drain, a deep sub-aerator capable of penetrating up to 16" below the surface using round, solid tines (hollow tines were subsequently also developed). The machine effects a prising motion on the turf, imitating exactly the old-time groundsman's hand fork and is an extremely effective way of relieving deep seated compaction and hence overcoming problems of slow surface drainage. The Verti-Drain became available in the UK in 1982, largely as a contractor's tool, imported by Charterhouse Turf Machinery Ltd. of Milford, Surrey.

As yet, no mention has been made of systematic scientific research into the problems of playing field construction and maintenance. Much knowledge has in fact been gained pragmatically with groundsmen learning by trial and error how to gain the best results from their labours, although since the 1920's organised research has been carried out in the UK, which has had a valuable and significant influence on practical sports ground management.

Turf research commenced in Great Britain in 1929 when the British Golf Unions' Joint Advisory Committee set up the Board of Greenkeeping Research. A research station and experiment ground were founded at the St Ives Estate at Bingley in West Yorkshire and activities commenced under the leadership of the Board's first director, R.B. Dawson. In 1951 the Board was reconstituted as the Sports Turf Research Institute, so formally extending its work to cover all turf surfaces for sport and amenity purposes, but even before that date its activities had not been confined to studies of golf course management alone. Advice was, for example, being given to the Hurlingham Club on the management of its polo fields as early as 1931. To Arsenal Football Club Ltd. goes the distinction of being the first soccer club to subscribe to the Bingley Research Station – the fact that they paid a 2 guinea subscription is recorded in the Board's Journal of March 1931, joined by Aston Villa FC the following year. Bradford Park Avenue AFC was visited by an advisor in 1932, together with a number of school, local authority and industrial welfare sports grounds. Articles by groundsmen concerned with the maintenance of winter pitches were first included in the 1948 Bingley Journal – one by J.C. McDowell of the Royal Academical Institution, Belfast and one by Arsenal Football Club's Head Groundsman, G.S. Rutt. The latter mentioned that his best friend was a spiked roller and that he refused to roll his pitch with anything heavier than a $9^1/_4$ cwt motor mower. When the Bingley organisation was reconstituted as the STRI in 1951, representatives of the Football Association, Football League Ltd, Rugby Football Union and Rugby Football League took their seats on its Board of Management and pioneering advice was given in 1950-51 on the reconstruction of Bristol Rovers' pitch at Eastville Stadium. During the 1950's the staff of the STRI gained much valuable experience in advising on playing field construction projects, working particularly on Local Authority and Education Authority sports ground developments and were able to offer project supervision and consultant-in-charge services to clients contemplating pitch constructions.

Such practical services were backed up by continuing research into improved grass varieties, disease control, fertiliser requirements, drainage problems and so on. As early as 1947 a significant leap forward was made in the testing of recently introduced, selective weed killers in the context of sports ground maintenance. An innovative six year trial of electrical soil warming as a method of frost protection was completed in 1954 and systems of this kind were subsequently installed at a number of professional grounds. An alternative method of pitch protection was tried from November 1960 – February 1961 at the STRI experiment ground in the form of a nylon cover, inflated by low pressure air blowers.

Slow release fertilisers (in the form of urea formaldehyde resins) were first investigated in 1961 and the effects of sand amelioration on the infiltration rate of winter games pitch soils was first studied at Bingley in 1971, similar work being done at the University College of Wales, Aberystwyth at that time. 1974 saw the commencement of a series of comparative studies of perennial ryegrass (*Lolium perenne* L.) varieties under a research contract from the National Environment Research Council and much-improved strains of the grass subsequently appeared, which have been of immense value for both the initial establishment and end-of-season renovation of winter pitches. Low-growing dwarf Dutch varieties of perennial ryegrass have proved particularly successful and since 1977, have been competitively classified (along with cultivars of other grass species) in the Institute's *Turfgrass Seed* booklet, now the definitive annual guide to the subject. In 1975, techniques were developed to simulate the wear and tear caused by players on grass swards and the use of wear machines on the Institute's trial plots have since that time given additional data on the suitability of various grass varieties for sports turf environment.

In May of 1982 the Football Association and Football Trust set up a new soil physics laboratory at the STRI and this facility has subsequently proved invaluable for scientific investigations of soil permeability and drainage, suitability of various sand types for pitch amelioration and other related investigations into the factors which underlie pitch quality.

An interesting survey of Football League and local authority grounds, involving the sending out of appropriate questionnaires, was reported in the STRI's 1983 Journal. The results showed that poor drainage continued to be one of the overriding problems of Britain's winter games pitches, despite the advances which had been made in the design of pipe drainage systems and the increasing use of slit drainage and sand amelioration. By 1985, attention was focused on methods of assessing the playing quality of sports surfaces, with consideration being given to such factors as ball bounce and surface speed as it affects the roll of the ball. The interaction of the player's foot with the playing surface was also considered in terms of the shear strength of the surface, characteristics such as traction and the likelihood of player injury. These techniques were later applied to studies of pure sand and sand-ameliorated pitch constructions and more refined techniques for testing the wear tolerance and playing characteristics of such pitches were gradually developed. Recent studies have investigated the cost effectiveness of different designs of winter games pitch constructions, the effects of sand top dressings on pitch performance and the effects of sward height on ball-roll properties for Association Football. The effects of slit tine spiking and other forms of aeration are also to be studied as, recently, some doubt has been cast on the value of routine slit tining for the improvement of surface drainage in some circumstances.

PLATE 44. Machine developed at STRI, Bingley in 1975 for simulating football-type wear on experiment plots.

Another factor which has contributed significantly to improvements in winter pitch standards in the post-war decades, has been the increased professional standing, enhanced skill and better training of the groundsman. Before the last war, very few amongst even the professional football clubs boasted a full-time specialist groundsman. Work on the pitch was often carried out in a haphazard and inexpert manner by trainers, junior players, club members or temporary labourers. (Prisoners of war were widely employed during the war and allowed to see the match free as a reward.) Work on the pitch was often of a rudimentary standard, involving little more than mowing, excessive rolling and the emergency hand forking of the inevitable wet areas on the morning before play. The staffing situation did, however, gradually improve, with better equipment being acquired, until most multiple-sports industrial welfare grounds and better quality clubs were employing full-time groundstaff specifically to look after grassed areas. A notable step forward was the creation in 1934 of the National Association of Groundsmen, thanks to the efforts of W.H. Bowles, H. Linsell and L.W. White amongst others. This ensured an exchange of hard-won knowledge and experience among members (initially in the London area) and facilitated future training schemes and higher work standards. The organisation flourished again after the war years with Charles Littlefield and Archie McTaggart proving particularly forceful figures and the Sheffield NAG was instituted as the first provincial branch, with the Hurlingham ground in London forming the venue for the first of a continuing series of annual exhibitions. Now reorganised as the Institute of Groundsmanship (the title was changed in February 1969), the association continues to provide an excellent service for its members and sport in general.

PLATE 45. Reconstruction of Blackpool AFC's ground in May 1951.

SECTION 2
DESIGN AND CONSTRUCTION OF WINTER GAMES PITCHES
By S.T. Pool

The work to be carried out during the construction of winter games pitches varies according to the site conditions and the type of construction involved. There are various options and quite marked differences between types of pitch. In addition to the production of the playing surface there may be ancillary works, such as the installation of irrigation and heating systems or, on many modern stadium pitches, the installation of ducts and cabling for score boards, starting equipment and television.

It is essential, if the finished playing surface is to perform satisfactorily, that all handling and cultivation of soils is carried out in suitable, i.e. dry, conditions. Virtually all soils will suffer damage if handled or worked in wet conditions and once the soil structure has been damaged, recovery is slow. The likelihood of delay in the programme of works has to be allowed for in any timetable of construction and first use. In some cases where little time is available before the playing surface is required or works have to be carried out at an unsuitable time of year, these immediate problems may play a major part in the choice of the type of pitch to be built.

SITE INVESTIGATION
Before the playing field design is considered and any work is commenced, a full and detailed investigation of the site is required. Some of the points which have to be looked into include:

SOILS
The nature of the existing topsoil and subsoil must be assessed. The range of materials which may be encountered on sites is substantial.

In England and Wales there are some 10 major soil groups, 67 sub-groups with approximately 300 different soil associations further divided into soil series. The type of soil will play a large part in the drainage characteristics of the pitch, influence cultivations and establishment.

The proportions of silt, clay and sand, together with the soil's structure and organic matter content, will determine its natural drainage characteristics and the way in which it reacts to handling and earth works. The lime content, as well as playing a role in the soil's fertility, can influence structure and the earth worm population. The pH and nutrient status will need to be taken into account when formulating fertiliser requirements.

The stone and gravel content of the soil will be important in terms of player safety. Rock, running sand or peat found on the site will be a major factor in determining the choice of construction method and the long-term success of any project. Such features are also likely to increase costs as they make the works more difficult.

DERELICT LAND
Despoiled, reclaimed or contaminated sites need special attention. Former household refuse tips are often chosen for playing field developments, but are frequently far from suitable. Decay of the tipped material can lead to settlement which disrupts both the immediate playing surface as well as any drainage system and produces water collecting hollows.

The presence of products of decomposition, such as methane, can lead to dangerous situations both on the field and the surrounding area, as well as leading to death of the sward. Trapped gases in manholes may be explosive or prove fatal to workers through asphixiation. Drainage works may lead to breaching of the tip cover and water percolating through the tipped material may produce a toxic leachate. Glass and other debris in the surface soils are hazards to players with a risk of both injury and disease. The presence of asbestos, heavy metals, toxic chemicals or even in some cases radioactive material can be further complications.

Underground fires which may or may not be apparent can be very serious, especially on the larger sites.

Colliery or other mining spoil heaps may pose particular difficulties with extremes in pH and the presence of harmful chemicals, as well as poor drainage, all making the production of a healthy sward difficult. The chemicals may also cause physical damage to drains, drainage aggregate and constructions such as man holes, silt traps and headwalls. The discharge of polluted water from drains can be a hazard and a legal liability.

The presence of mine shafts and the possibility of settlement, due to old underground works, can prove both short- and long-term dangers.

Former building sites with old foundations, roadways and cellars still intact can be quite expensive to develop.

Earth moving and drainage work can only be carried out following thorough breaking up of all hard material and even then the presence of residual stone, brick or concrete fragments will slow the operation down. The introduction of pipe drainage can be a particularly vulnerable operation. The removal of large pieces of stone during trench excavation leads to ragged, wide trenches which require extra quantities of expensive aggregates when filled.

Topsoil may need to be imported and even where topsoil does exist, this may have become contaminated. In some cases it may, in addition, be necessary to import clean subsoil.

Whilst despoiled sites may initially seem attractive for sports field development, it is almost inevitable that the construction works required to produce a satisfactory and safe surface will be much more extensive than where dealing with a green field situation. On all such sites, pitches should only be constructed after very careful consideration and site investigation.

DRAINAGE
This is of course a key factor in the development of surfaces capable of being used in winter months. Whilst generally soils with high silt and clay contents are likely to be less well drained than those with a high sand content, there are exceptions. Clay or silt loams overlying limestone or chalk may be quite well drained, whereas fine sandy loams with weak structures may well suffer from compaction. Some sands when saturated may be extremely difficult to work with.

Low lying land may be liable to flooding during the winter months. Coastal areas are often affected by high tides. Uplands, because of a combination of high rainfall and low temperatures, may have peaty water-retentive soils. Specific problems affect individual sites, surrounding developments may physically prevent any drainage system being connected to a satisfactory outlet. Local authority drainage boards or the River Authority frequently impose further restrictions on development work.

RAINFALL
In the United Kingdom annual rainfall figures range between under 600 mm to over 2.5 m. Weather stations throughout the country provide information as to the overall rainfall pattern, but even within a limited area there can be distinct local variations.

In general, the west of the country is wetter than the east; the south is drier than the north and uplands are wetter than lowlands. A similar pattern emerges when considering the maximum likely rainfall within a 24 hour period.

On similar soils pitch constructions which are quite adequate in a "dry" county, such as Lincolnshire, may fail abysmally in Cumbria or Lancashire. The more rain which falls on a pitch the higher the standard of pitch design required.

TOPOGRAPHY AND ASPECT

The shape and features of the land form will determine the extent and nature of levelling works required. Grass growth may be adversely affected on very exposed sites, whilst conversely excessively shaded pitches, particularly those surrounded by large stadiums and stands, can be very cold and slow to dry out, even where drainage is excellent.

SERVICES

A water supply is desirable for most pitches. Where pavilions, club houses or stands are to be developed as part of a playing field complex, there will also be a need for electricity, telephone, sewers and possibly gas supplies. Where such services have to be brought long distances, installation costs will be high. The presence, however, within the actual area to be developed of these and other services can be a major problem. The re-routing and disruption of power supplies and the like, whether above or below ground, can be very expensive. In some cases it may be better to design facilities around the routes of major services, although subsequent disruption through repair or maintenance work on pipelines remains a constant risk.

Accidents caused whilst working around services are, as well as being dangerous, very unpopular with the service companies and neighbours who understandably tend to resent having their electricity or gas supply cut off.

A thorough search should always be carried out before development work takes place and even before land is purchased. Ordinary searches by solicitors do not necessarily cover this aspect, unless details have been recorded in the deeds of the property

ACCESS

Access to sites is required for players' cars and coaches, but is also needed during the construction work. The ability of roads to take the likely traffic, road widths and restrictions caused by bridges, both weight and height, on both the immediate access and the route to the site must be considered. Where large quantities of material have to be moved onto site, disturbance to neighbours must be kept in mind and it may be necessary to provide road sweeping and/or wheel cleaning facilities.

PLANNING PERMISSION

Any new development will require planning permission. This will involve the submission of detailed drawings. Flood lighting, if required, may be a contentious issue. Car parking, access and the effects on neighbours will be considered. Conditions may be imposed particularly with regard to landscaping and protective fencing. Environmental factors, including the existing ecology of the land, the presence of ponds and wildlife have increasingly to be taken into consideration.

FACTORS AFFECTING THE CONSTRUCTION PROCESS
WEATHER AND GROUND CONDITIONS

In common with all sports turf work, weather and ground conditions during the construction period and establishment have a direct and major effect on the success of the project.

Weather conditions alter from year to year and there are substantial variations between different parts of the country. Records are kept and are available from the Meteorological office or in summary in various publications. It is therefore possible to predict the likely weather conditions for any area during the programmed construction period. It is of course impossible to forecast exact conditions during any particular period, but the risk of adverse weather occurring can be assessed. It is, however, not just rainfall which is important but temperature, day length, cloud cover, relative humidity and wind. These factors alone or in combinations must be considered as they will bear directly on grass germination and establishment.

RAINFALL

Certainly the most important of all factors is precipitation during the construction process and the period of establishment. Heavy and prolonged rain is generally disruptive and can adversely affect the long-term performance of the pitches. In wet conditions all operations become more difficult and except on the most freely-drained soils, are likely to result in damage to soil structure.

Earth moving equipment inevitably damages the soil structure even in dry conditions, but in wet weather smearing, compaction and the production of mud and slurry can have a most detrimental effect. The natural recovery of the soil structure can be very slow and poor playing surfaces may persist for years if not decades. Even ordinary cultivation work can cause substantial damage, particularly if it is carried out when the soil is too wet. Heavy rainfall within a short period can result in physical damage to the works by erosion. During thunderstorms around 25 mm of rain could quite easily fall in a very short time and over a hectare of ground this amounts to 250,000 litres of water. When this volume starts to move down slope and concentrates particularly on bare soil, erosion can be spectacular. The soil particles carried by such a water flow can cause problems by blocking drains, ditches and gullies and often leading to flooding.

Conversely extremes of drought, often coupled with high temperatures, may cause difficulties. In such conditions, dust thrown up following the passage of vehicles can be a hazard causing discomfort to plant operators, labour and neighbours. Coupled with windy weather it can lead to erosion of the surface. Sand type constructions are particularly vulnerable with dry sand blown from the playing surface leaving marked irregularities and the sand blown onto neighbouring properties or work resulting in complaints. Great care must be taken with pitches being constructed in new stadiums where running tracks are also in the process of construction. Sand blown onto a surrounding track during laying of the surface can be very damaging. Some types of natural soil also tend to suffer erosion through the action of wind, these include fine sands and some fenland soils.

In dry weather certain soils with a high clay content may not break down well during cultivation. Also with such soils subsequent shrinkage can lead to the collapse of drains or slit drain lines and through shrinkage and movement of large blocks of soil lead to more general surface disruption.

In very dry conditions use of the mole plough is unlikely to be successful although conversely subsoiling may do a better job with extensive soil fissuring.

Drought will of course delay establishment of the sward and where turfing is involved can easily lead to the death of the grass. Seeded swards are slightly more resilient but even with seeding, extended drought can result in major loss of grass cover. Weeds, however, often flourish. Sand or very sandy types of construction are most susceptible because of the lack of moisture retention and for such pitches, irrigation may well be needed at least in the early stages.

TEMPERATURE

High temperatures associated with dry weather can, as outlined above, result in damage to young or germinating grass. High temperatures in more humid weather can help in promoting rapid growth, although diseases may be more troublesome. Extremes of cold with temperatures well below freezing can damage, or in the extreme, kill young seedlings and newly turfed swards, particularly if accompanied by winds.

Plastic drain pipes become less flexible in cold weather and in freezing conditions may well fracture. Manufacturers usually stipulate a minimum working temperature of −4-5°C for UPVC pipes. Soil structure suffers if worked in the frozen state. Frosts can, however, help in breaking up heavy soil left over the winter months as well as checking disease and pest activity.

Prolonged, cool weather below 40°C may result in poor germination and growth of young grass. Seeding either late or early in the year can easily be adversely affected by such conditions.

OTHER FACTORS

Extremes of humidity in combination with other factors can as indicated, result in damage to young or germinating grass. Cloud cover may help by moderating the extremes of temperature, either by cutting down sunlight or by insulation, reducing radiation frosts.

Windy weather tends to accentuate problems caused by other factors such as heat, cold or drought.

CONCLUSION

The construction and establishment of winter pitches are heavily affected by weather and ground conditions. Planning of projects must take into account the weather conditions likely to be encountered. Extremes of weather do, however, occur at unpredictable times and in these cases, work must cease if to proceed would be detrimental to the end result. This can be very frustrating, particularly in Britain with its variable island climate. There are times when such delays have to be accepted, however undesirable this may be. There are no alternatives unless of course one can afford to cover the site in a tent, provide artificial heating and lighting and even then the result may not be perfect.

CONSTRUCTION OPERATIONS
EARTHWORKS

Unless existing ground levels are acceptable, sites will require regrading to desired contours. This usually involves stripping off the existing topsoil, grading out of the subsoil on a cut and fill basis before replacement of the topsoil. In certain circumstances there may be a need for the importation of fill or alternatively the removal of surplus material from the site in order to achieve the desired level.

Such work must be done so as to minimise damage to the soil structure and this includes both top and subsoils. Before embarking on such a procedure it is desirable to check the materials which are likely to be encountered (see under site investigation).

The equipment used to carry out the earthworks must be of the appropriate size to do the work efficiently and should be in good working order. Breakdowns are annoying and disruptive and can easily lead to missing good weather conditions.

Rock, running sand and peat will require specialist treatment. The end result should be a stable, level and smooth plateau on which to spread preserved or imported topsoil.

Surround banks should preferably be to gradients less than 1:3. When, because of lack of space, steeper slopes have to be constructed this may necessitate the provision of fences or safety barriers. Maintenance work will of course be more difficult in these situations.

Soils should only be moved when ground conditions are sufficiently dry (see weather and ground conditions).

DRAINAGE WORKS

A good pipe drain system is the foundation on which the success or failure of many winter pitch construction will depend.

Pipe drainage systems can be introduced using a variety of different techniques and equipment. Improvements or additions to existing drainage layouts on a small scale may be laid by hand. Excavation using special drainage spades and scoops is often very effective. Indeed, before the development of mechanical excavators, all agricultural drainage projects were carried out in this manner. For any substantial drainage scheme today, however, mechanical equipment will be employed to excavate the drain trench , lay the pipe and backfill with aggregate.

MECHANICAL EXCAVATORS

A variety of equipment is employed for the excavation work. General purpose excavators, such as the ubiquitous JCB and similar, together with a host of small diggers fitted with narrow trenching buckets, are effective for small to medium scale works. They are also often able to deal with difficult digging conditions and can be used to transport and deposit backfill materials, in addition to carrying out the trench excavation.

CHAIN EXCAVATORS

The majority of drainage work is carried out using specifically designed trench excavators of this type. The drain trench is excavated using teeth or blades fitted to a continuous belt, rather in the manner of a chain saw. Machinery of this type ranges from the small pedestrian operated unit to large-scale agricultural equipment, capable of laying thousands of metres of drains per day. Varying degrees of sophistication and modifications are incorporated. The provision of infra-red or laser levelling facilities allows precision excavation and laying of pipes. Indeed, many machines both excavate the trench and lay the drain pipe in one operation. Plastic pipes are more easily laid in this fashion, although some machines can lay clay tiles. Different types of teeth or cutting blades are available for difficult working conditions, for example specially hardened teeth for dealing with rock. The smaller, less powerful machines do, however, have limitations in working on very stony soils.

Most of the equipment designed, primarily, for agricultural use deposits the spoil at the side of the trench and indeed, may be fitted with horizontally mounted augers to spread the spoil over the surface. Operating at depth, however, this material will almost certainly be subsoil and the deposition of this over the playing surface is unacceptable. Whilst it is possible to remove the spoil as a separate operation, this is a slow process and easily disrupted by weather conditions. After rain the topsoil and subsoil often become inextricably mixed. The preferred alternative is to use machinery fitted with an elevator and conveyor to deliver the spoil directly into a trailer and away. This does have the disadvantages, however, of slowing down the operation and being liable to stoppages when stones or debris are encountered.

In all cases depth and width of trenching can be varied.

ROTATING WHEEL EXCAVATORS

Although there are some slow turning wheel type excavators used to lay pipe drains, the majority rotate at high speed, cutting trenches in this case as a circular saw cuts into wood. Very high rates of trench excavation can be achieved, but there are limits imposed on trench width and depth because of the means of operation. The equipment can be difficult to operate in very dry conditions. This type of machine is very useful in cutting slit drain trenches. As with chain trenchers, elevators and conveyors to dispose of the spoil are fitted when carrying out playing field work.

TRENCHLESS DRAINAGE

So called trenchless drainage equipment operates by forcing open a channel through the soil compacting the soil into the side of the "trench", rather than excavating it. The pipe is laid as part of the process. In some cases porous aggregate may be fed in over the pipe, in other cases the pipe alone is laid. Such an operation frequently leads to major surface heave. The resultant compaction and surface disruption makes this technique largely unsuitable for winter games pitch drainage work.

SURFACE DRAINAGE

A number of different types of machines have been adapted to introduce a variety of sand bands, slots, gravel slits and slit drains to improve the surface drainage of winter games pitches. Small versions of the chain or rotating wheel excavators are particularly useful in this respect. On a small-scale the trenchless system can also be adapted. A further development has been of the straight bladed rotovator type introducing multiple slits or slots at one pass.

When spoil is produced this is frequently removed by elevator and conveyor as with the larger versions. Usually such slits, slots and bands are backfilled with small stone and/or sand, but without the need for the laying of pipes. The backfill may be placed through a hopper fitted to the excavator or as a separate and second operation. As the equipment has of necessity to be comparatively small and of limited power, ground conditions are critical and operations are easily slowed just because the ground is dry and hard.

BACKFILL PLACEMENT
For small-scale operations barrows or small loading shovels may be used. For larger-scale works special stone hoppers are available feeding the porous aggregate direct into the trenches. Often the stone is fed by conveyor and clinched by a shute into the trench, minimising the spillage of stone onto the playing surface. Hoppers may be fitted direct to excavation equipment or may be separate. Some of the smaller trenching machines used for surface drainage may have two stage hoppers, the first for stone, the second for sand. In one pass the trench is hence filled with gravel and topped with sand.

THE OPERATION
As with all playing field work, the ground must be sufficiently dry for the works to be effective. The operation involves the passage of heavy plant over the surface and equally importantly, the movement and placement of tonnes of aggregate. The excavation of the trenches themselves involves teeth or blades cutting through the soil, often at speed, with ample opportunity for smearing and compaction of the trench sides if conditions are unsuitable.

The presence of rock or other underground obstruction or debris, will slow the works down.

It is important that drain trenches be excavated, pipe accurately laid and porous backfill placed with the minimum delay. Trenches left open for any period of time are very vulnerable. Sides may fall in with or without the aid of rain. Silt and mud can easily be washed into the trench if heavy rain falls before either pipe or backfill is placed in the trench. Such contamination can seriously prejudice the success of the work.

It is essential that drains are laid accurately to the required falls depth and spacing. The pipes must be laid to a true line and be free from contamination as must the backfill material. The stone or other porous backfill must be laid to a uniform depth properly blinded with selected material. Variation in the construction of the drains can have profound implications. For example secondary slit drainage work may fail if the slits do not make contact with the porous backfill over the drains because of variations in their depth.

Junctions must be correctly fitted where possible using purpose made units allowing clear, unobstructed flow of the drainage water.

Once drains have been laid they should be protected or allowed for in subsequent operations.

MATERIALS
Clay pipes or tiles
Clay tiles are still used satisfactorily in playing field drainage schemes and are well-proven with systems still functioning after many decades. Clay tiles are, however, heavy and subject to breakage both before, during and after laying. The pipes come in short sections and each has to be correctly aligned with its neighbour. Whilst mechanical laying is quite possible, it is by no means as easy as with plastic pipes.

Ground movement after clay tiles have been laid may severely affect the ability of the drain to carry water and may obstruct maintenance by rodding or jetting.

Plastic
Perforated, flexible, plastic pipe is most frequently used at the present time. Light and easily transported in large rolls, it is readily laid by medium or large-scale equipment. It does become

less flexible and more fragile if laid in cold weather. Laying by hand has its difficulties and in a wide trench the pipe will tend to snake about in the trench bottom.

The pipe comes in a range of sizes although above 225 mm in diameter the pipe is usually rigid and is produced in shorter 6 m lengths. Double walled pipe is available for added strength.

Concrete
Not normally used for playing field work, it is heavy and expensive. Large diameter pipe above 250 mm may be used to carry substantial volumes of water from diverted streams, ditches or as part of the local authority main drainage system. It is available in various strengths depending on the load it is expected to carry.

Pitch fibre
Rarely used at the present time.

Box section drains
Recently introduced, box section drains consisting of a central plastic egg box type, around which is wrapped a geotextile fabric have been applied to the winter pitches situation. Whether these are of any value at all only time will tell.

Standards
British Standards exist for clay, plastic and concrete pipe and wherever possible the pipes used should conform to the appropriate standard.

Backfill
Materials used to backfill drain trenches or to provide drain layers must have two characteristics. Firstly, they must transmit water rapidly down to the pipe drain. Secondly, they must be stable and not break down over time.

Natural gravels and crushed stone, provided that they are reasonably free of fine material, are very successful. Limestone can be perfectly satisfactory, but some soft limestone materials will break down, particularly in acid soils. The more durable materials are of carboniferous origin.

Ash has long been used and where it is available, can still be satisfactory. Materials with a high proportion of fines or which are likely to crush are less desirable. The material is lighter than crushed stone or gravel.

Processed materials, often derived from power station ash, such as Lytag, can be of great value.

Rounded aggregate can be more difficult to work with when forming layers under the entire playing surface, rather than just filling drain trenches. Care should also be taken about the choice of blinding materials used over such materials.

Various size ranges may be specified, all material should be uniform.

Blinding materials
Coarse sand or fine grit can be used to provide blinding layers over coarser aggregates. It is again important that the materials are durable and do not break down over time. Choice of the correct size is critical. (See section on 'Sand' for full details - Ed.)

Manholes and silt traps
Located at appropriate points within a drainage scheme, these provide access for inspection and cleaning out of the drains. The exact size and detail design must be appropriate for the size and depth of pipe work to which they are to be fitted. Constructions may be of concrete, brick, glass fibre, reinforced cement or even plastic with reinforcement where they are to be load bearing. Units may be pre-cast or built *in situ*.

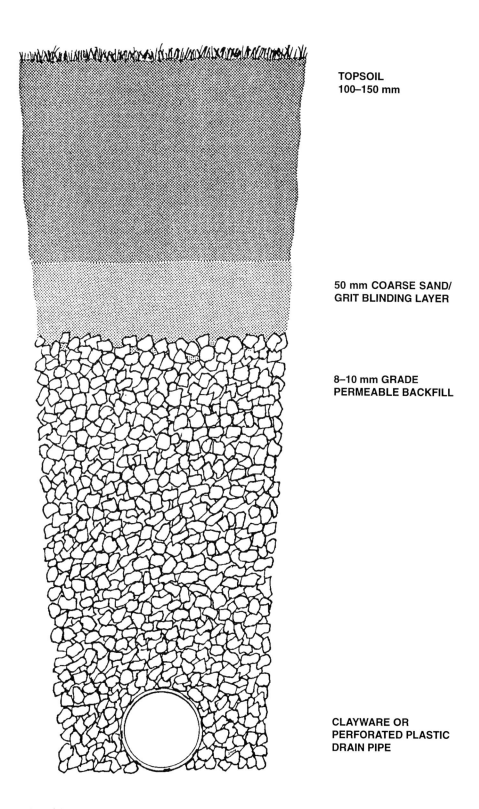

TOPSOIL
100–150 mm

50 mm COARSE SAND/
GRIT BLINDING LAYER

8–10 mm GRADE
PERMEABLE BACKFILL

CLAYWARE OR
PERFORATED PLASTIC
DRAIN PIPE

PLATE 46. Cross-section of typical pipe drain.

Headwalls and ditch units or similar construction are frequntly required to prevrent erosion at outfalls and within ditches constructed as part of the playing field works.

CULTIVATIONS

SUBSOIL CULTIVATION AND MOLE PLOUGHING

Deep cultivation is most important in alleviating compaction within the subsoil, particularly following earthworks. Whilst primarily implemented as part of general cultivation work, it can be carried out on existing pitches although care has to be exercised. Surface disruption can be a problem as can stones which may be brought to the surface. On cultivated sites the work is best done both before and after drainage. The subsoil tines can be set at varying depth although where drains exist they should be set well clear of the pipes to avoid damage, otherwise the depth should be around 450 mm with a spacing of 600 mm and several passes may be required.

Various designs of subsoil tine are available which accentuate the lifting and shattering effect on the soil. Operating at depth entails the use of powerful tractors and the number of tines which can be fitted to the tractor is limited. Tracked vehicles can be used on difficult sites.

Subsoil cultivation should not be confused with mole ploughing, although both can assist the passage of water through the soil. The former is intended to shatter the soil and alleviate compaction; the latter is intended to introduce a semi-permanent, smooth-bored channel through the subsoil. Subsoil cultivation is therefore most effective in drier conditions, whilst slightly more moisture helps in the moulding of the mole channel. Mole ploughing is useful on clay subsoil, but is not as effective on stony ground where the channel is easily disrupted. Mole ploughs should be run through to permeable backfill over pipe drains or to ditches. Water always has to flow to an outfall.

SURFACE CULTIVATION

General cultivation work is an essential part of seed bed preparation. The amount of work and the number of passes required will vary from soil to soil and with soil moisture content. Cultivation equipment often adapted from agriculture is diverse with many different forms of tines, discs, ploughs and harrows. Powered equipment can speed up the operation although care needs to be exercised when using rotary cultivators which can produce damage to the soil structure and smearing of the soil through the high speed of the cultivating blades. The tilth produced by rotary cultivators is often too "puffy" for the playing field. Rotovators can, however, help in breaking up established turf.

The final seed bed should be produced to form a smooth surface and the seed bed should be firm but not over-compacted. Stone and debris with one dimension over 35 mm should be removed. Where angular or sharp stone is present smaller stone may need to be removed. Some soils containing a high clay content do not break down readily and form clods, this does make grading of the final surface more difficult, but is not a major problem. Soils should not be overworked producing an over-fine dusty surface. Apart from the damage to the soil structure, such fine material may subsequently cap, restricting germination. Sandy soils are best well rolled to allow water to be drawn to the surface. Sands must always be well rolled and must be moist when seeding takes place. Sand constructions will normally not require any cultivation.

SEEDING

It is essential that seeding is uniform, the quantity of seed to be sown is therefore divided in half and each half sown in transverse directions. Areas which are missed will often take months to catch up and so doing the job right at the first attempt is important.

Agricultural seed drills and distributors can be satisfactory for seeding. The seed should be harrowed or rolled into the surface. It is rarely satisfactory to leave seed on the surface where even a few hours of dry weather can damage the plant as it germinates. A sand dressing applied immediately after seeding can ensure the seed is covered and give a very good take, 6-10 mm of sand is probably ideal, but the sand must be applied as quickly as possible as the passage of trailers and tractors will damage germinating seedlings.

For satisfactory establishment on sand pitches, the seed must have 10 mm or so of cover to ensure that it is not subject to rapid drying out. As previously stated, the seed bed should be left firm.

FERTILISER

Adequate supplies of plant nutrient must be available for the establishment of a healthy sward. Laboratory analysis of soil will assist in formulating an adequate seed bed fertiliser. On pure sand pitches slow-release materials are very useful as nitrogen and potash in particular can be rapidly washed from sand.

Processed seaweed products improve the water holding capacity of the sand and greatly assist establishment on sand or very sandy material.

TURFING

Pitches can be established using purpose grown imported turf. There are, however, certain factors which require attention.

[a] The turf must have been grown using correctly chosen wear-tolerant cultivars of ryegrass and where appropriate, other species such as smooth-stalked meadow-grass. General landscape or meadow turf is not suitable.

[b] The turf should be substantially free from weeds including annual meadow-grass. Pests and disease should not be present.

[c] The soil on which the grass is grown should be as close as possible to that on the pitch rootzone. The turf should be cut thinly and preferably with less than 15 mm of soil attached. Washed turf which has the soil removed before laying may be used provided that it holds together.

[d] The turf should not be excessively fibrous.

[e] The turf must be laid as soon as possible after lifting and not left in stacks or allowed to dry out.

[f] The turf bed must not become over-compacted and the turf must be laid working from boards. A good standard of turf laying is required. Irrigation must be on hand if the turf is laid in dry weather.

[g] Most important, except perhaps for washed turf, the pitch must receive an intensive programme of hollow tine aeration work starting as soon as the turf is sufficiently anchored, the cores being removed. Over a period of 2 or 3 months 3-4 passes with a hollow tine corer fitted with 12 mm tines on a 50 mm spacing are required. The pitch should then receive a liberal dressing of sand.

This work is to minimise the layering effect which automatically comes with the turf and to remove as much imported soil and fibre as possible and to work sand into the surface to improve as far as possible the speed of drainage through the immediate surface.

As a general point, however, turfing is not suitable for most pitch constructions. The advantages in the speed of establishment are not that great. Although the sward can look well, the grass still has to produce a root system. Newly turfed swards are much more vulnerable to damage or even death in the early weeks through drying out than a seeded turf. Very poor playing surfaces can be produced in the first season of use through water-holding in the introduced turf layer, even when the underlying material drains quite well unless a porogramme of intensive hollow coring is implemented.

SAND AS A ROOTZONE

As outlined elsewhere, some types of pitch construction involve growing grass on more or less pure sand. Sand does not behave or have the same properties as rootzones based on natural topsoils.

When attempting to establish grass on sand constructions, there are certain key points to bear in mind:

[a] Grass growing in sand has no greater requirements for nutrient and water than any other sward. The sand does, however, have a limited ability to retain reserves of nutrient and moisture.

[b] The germinating seed and young seedlings with a very limited root run are very susceptible to nutrient and moisture deficiency. As the plant matures with a more extensive root run, it can draw on supplies from a much greater volume of rootzone and thus becomes less vulnerable. It is therefore essential to provide adequate moisture and fertiliser in the first few weeks after seeding.

After this period there is a greater margin of safety, particularly as far as watering is concerned. Indeed, it is undesirable to irrigate too frequently as the roots will have no incentive to search out water in the base of the rootzone. Heavy watering will leach out nutrients, particularly nitrate and potash. Where a layer of sand is spread over topsoil, the roots can tap the reserves in the underlying soil.

[c] The surface of a newly seeded sand pitch will dry out in a matter of hours. Once the top 10 mm or so has dried out, the rate of water loss drops and even after several days of dry weather, moist sand can be found less than 20 mm from the surface.

Unless given virtually continuous irrigation, seed within the top 10 mm has little chance of survival if weather conditions are dry.

If the seed bed is firm, moisture can draw moisture up from below through capillary action. Loose sand contains more air which speeds the rate of evaporation.

[d] Slow release fertiliser, such as those based on IBDU or resin-coated materials, are of great assistance in establishing grass on sand, but regular monitoring of the grass should take place, especially in hot weather when the speed of fertiliser release is increased.

[e] Processed seaweed products, such as "Alginure", greatly in increasing the moisture holding capacity of the sand.

[f] The choice of the correct type and grade of sand is essential.

TIMING
Earthworks and cultivations should be carried out in dry conditions, usually between April and August. It is worth checking meteorological data in advance to determine the likely rainfall for the construction period. In the wetter parts of the country the working period may be more restricted.

Seeding can be carried out at any time when the temperature is sufficient for germination and there is some prospect of rain or the soil is adequately moist. Germination is most rapid in humid, warm weather. The ideal time for seeding is between mid-July and mid-September, but seasonal and geographic variations are substantial.

Under ideal conditions it is possible to produce a wear tolerant sward in 10 or 12 weeks from seeding, but as a normal rule a full 12 months is required. Whilst slit drained pitches can be constructed and made usable within this period, the playing surface may be uneven for the first playing season.

Sand pitches, unless turfed, require close to 2 years before the sward is fully mature.

Whilst the sward may be sufficiently mature to take play, within a comparatively short period the soil structure and hence the drainage, may not fully recover for several years. The vulnerability of construction works and establishment to prevailing weather conditions cannot be over-emphasised.

TYPES OF WINTER GAMES PITCH CONSTRUCTION

The following represent the main forms of construction which can be considered:

[A] UNDRAINED PITCHES

On naturally well-drained soils, pitches may not require any supplementary pipe drainage. This type of pitch can be very successful but it is not a suitable method of construction for the majority of sites. Sand, soils over gravel, shallow soils over limestone or chalk are the most suitable.

[B] PIPED DRAIN PITCHES

The vast majority of existing pitches are constructed with the *in situ* soils, graded on a cut and fill basis if necessary and with a basic pipe drainage system. Given reasonably permeable soils, quite good playing surfaces can result, but in many sites use in the winter months can be severely restricted. This type of pitch may not perform well in the first five years or so after construction, particularly if earthworks have been involved.

Properly constructed pipe drain pitches can be upgraded, either by adding further pipe drains to give a more intensive system or by supplementary slit drains.

Pipe drains are commonly installed with laterals at a spacing of 3-15 m.

[C] PIPE DRAINED AND SLIT DRAINED PITCHES (SEE PLATE 56 IN FOLLOWING SECTION)

A very popular form of construction whether as a means of upgrading existing pitches or as an initial design. The pitches are usually constructed on native soils if necessary, being subject to regrading. The foundation of the system is the pipe drainage which must have porous backfill to within 200 mm or so from the surface and at a spacing between 5 and 15 m centres. These then form the outlets for the slit drainage system. Slit drains consist of a series of narrow (commonly 50-60 mm) trenches cut across and into the porous backfill of the drains. The trenches are backfilled with small 6-8 mm hard aggregate and topped off with sand. Importantly the pitch is dressed heavily with sand both immediately after the initial slit drainage work and subsequently as a part of routine maintenance works. For a 7,000 m² pitch an initial dressing of 100 tonnes of sand, followed by annual applications of 60-100 tonnes, would be reasonable.

The above type of slit drain is best installed at a spacing of 600 mm to 1 m, although a wider spacing may be acceptable in less intensive situations.

There are a number of variations on the above basic principle with varying depths, widths and spacing of slits. Some slits are formed with just sand, although lateral movement of water along the slit is not as rapid as where a gravel or small stone is used.

The advantage of these systems are that they do not rely on the drainage capacity of the soil and high drainage rates can be achieved on poor draining soils. For the system of slit drains to function, it is essential that: [a] the slits make good contact with the porous backfill over the pipe drains where they intersect and; [b] the slits do not become capped even with mud, either through play or through worm casting. The sand dressings are designed to ensure that capping does not occur. Where necessary, worm control measures may be required. It is also essential that maintenance results in the production of a vigorous and dense grass sward overall, in order that bare soil is not produced.

There are three common problems associated with this type of construction. The first is that during the playing season, after introduction, the surface will be uneven. The second is that soils with a fairly high proportion of clay shrink in dry summer conditions. The slit drain being the point of weakness, crack open as the soil draws back from the edge of the slit. As the slit widens the gravel and sand backfill settle. This may become even more marked in prolonged, dry weather where the soil cracks below the bottom of the slits, causing gravel and sand to disappear into the void. The uneven surface so produced has to be topped up with sand. This is normally only a problem in the first year, although on some soils in drier parts of the country, it can be a recurring phenomenon. The third problem is that the slits do become capped over if adequate sanding is not carried out. Where practicable, lime-free sand should be used to avoid encouraging worm activity.

[D] SAND SURFACES OVER SOIL

Sand is used in winter pitch construction to improve playing conditions in wet weather. Where slit drained pitches are involved, frequent and intensive dressings are required in the early years after construction to prevent the formation of mud and the sealing of slits. The provision of approximately 25 mm of sand on the surface of such constructions has been shown to increase markedly the wear tolerance and performance under play.

The provision of greater depths of sand over the native and frequently quite heavy soils has been used to provide playing surfaces with higher drainage rates and longer life expectancy.

Pipe drains are normally first introduced into the base soil at an appropriate spacing with or without supplementary slit drains before the sand layer is spread. The sward is established in the sand, but roots should be able to penetrate and make use of nutrient and water reserves in the underlying soil.

This type of option has a number of advantages, together with some disadvantages and problems in construction.

To facilitate the passage of roots from the sand into the underlying soil, it is important that the surface is broken up by cultivation prior to spreading of the sand. Frequently roots will not pass from one rooting medium to another with the formation of distinct root breaks. Whilst the formation of the cultivated and graded surface on which the sand is to be spread is not a major difficulty, subsequent work such as slit drainage and/or the passage of plant used to transport and spread the sand, often results in marked compaction, smearing and sealing of the surface. The introduction of slit drains is a slow operation, leaving the surface vulnerable to wet weather over an extended period. Any cultivation carried out after slit drains are introduced all too easily results in capping of the slits and an immediate reduction in their effectiveness. Techniques for introducing the slits in this situation should be simple to speed the operation. Both excavators and trenchless machines have been used to introduce slits into the seed bed.

The above procedure is most likely to be successful in dry conditions, however, establishment of the sward in the sand requires moist, if not wet, weather. It is by no means impossible to both establish and maintain sand surface pitches without irrigation, however, the provision of a good water supply and distribution system is undoubtedly an advantage, particularly in the drier parts of the country.

Grass seed must be covered and the surface well firmed for successful and uniform establishment. If the sand is moist at seeding, cool, cloudy weather over the first four weeks may be all that is required for successful establishment. As with all sand pitches, the sward becomes less vulnerable to drought as the grass matures.

[E] SAND-SOIL SURFACES

For many years, attempts have been made to produce artificially well-drained soils by mixing varying quantities of sand into the existing soil.

In its simplest form, such pitches comprise a basic, although intensive, pipe drainage system at a spacing of as close as 3 m. The indigenous soil is mixed with imported sand.

The success or otherwise of these types of construction largely depends on the choice of sand and the ratio in which the sand is mixed with the soil (see Section 3).

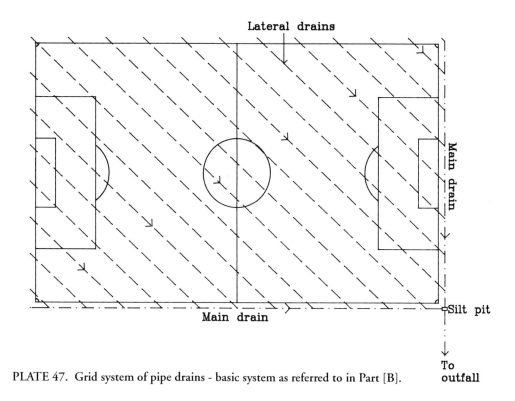

Lateral drains

Main drain

Main drain

Silt pit

To
outfall

PLATE 47. Grid system of pipe drains - basic system as referred to in Part [B].

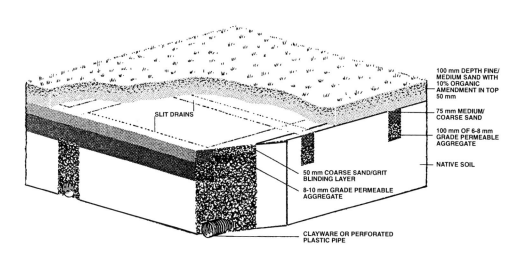

SLIT DRAINS

100 mm DEPTH FINE/
MEDIUM SAND WITH
10% ORGANIC
AMENDMENT IN TOP
50 mm

75 mm MEDIUM/
COARSE SAND

100 mm OF 6-8 mm
GRADE PERMEABLE
AGGREGATE

NATIVE SOIL

50 mm COARSE SAND/GRIT
BLINDING LAYER

8-10 mm GRADE PERMEABLE
AGGREGATE

CLAYWARE OR PERFORATED
PLASTIC PIPE

PLATE 48. Sand surface over soil construction as described in Part [D].

69

Even with drains at close spacing the drainage characteristic of the underlying soil is important. Whilst the surface may drain freely, the results will be less than ideal if the water cannot readily penetrate into the underlying material. Thorough subsoil cultivation is usually essential.

This type of pitch has proved very successful, performing creditably on professional Football League grounds.

[F] STONE CARPET/SUSPENDED WATER TABLE CONSTRUCTION

When the subsoil is not suitable by being impermeable or contaminated, or for other reasons a very high standard of pitch performance is required, it may be necessary to provide a layer of free-draining aggregate over the entire pitch.

This permeable layer usually stone, gravel or in the past ash, will be laid to a depth of at least 100 mm and be tapped by a series of pipe drains, normally at a spacing of 5-10 m. On soft or unstable ground, geotextile is often laid beneath the stone to preserve the integrity of the layer and prevent any of the stone working its way or being pushed into the underlying material. The drain trenches must be left uncovered to prevent any possible restriction in the passage of water down to the drains. In the case where odd soft pockets are found, these may be dug out and filled with stable material. The only requirement for the sub-base is that it should be stable. The stone layer must of course be durable and except where the smaller 4-5 mm materials used, blinded with a grit or coarse sand material matched to the size of the aggregate. This layer should be approximately 50 mm thick.

Having provided such a porous platform over the entire pitch, it is usual to provide 250-300 mm of either a very sandy rootzone or a more or less pure sand. If the pitch is constructed using correctly selected materials, a very high standard of playing surface is produced. The pitch should take very heavy rainfall and still provide a dry surface. The sward will, however, in most circumstances need more irrigation and particularly with the pure sand varieties, a fully automatic system is highly desirable.

The term suspended water table refers to the fact that water will, in theory at least, be held in the lower part of the rootzone and above the drainage layer. The soaked sponge analogy is often cited. This reserve of moisture should help sustain the sward during dry weather. Recent research on similar constructions in golf has, however, cast doubt on this theory, at least for some rootzone materials.

In the first half of this century many pitches of this type were constructed using the then readily available ash and whatever soil came to hand. Results were variable but many of these pitches are still in use today. Provided that the permeable base has not broken down, such pitches respond readily to deep aeration work and sanding, even if the topsoil used is not particularly permeable.

[G] SEALED SYSTEMS

A number of patented forms of construction have been designed where the pitch construction is contained within a plastic liner.

The cell system

The pitch is divided into a series of sections or cells. Each cell is lined with plastic sheet. Irrigation/drainage pipes are set in the bottom and the pitch constructed with sand; the surface being a soil/peat mixture.

Water which falls on the pitch as rain percolates through to the drains/irrigation pipes. During the summer such water can be retained by stopping the pipe outlet, this is to provide moisture reserves for grass growth. During wet weather the pipe outfall can be allowed to flow, thus surplus water is discharged from the system.

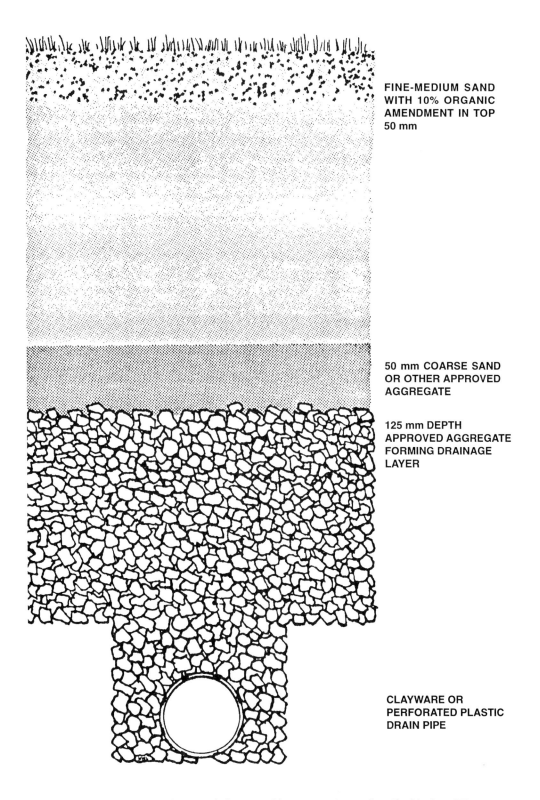

FINE-MEDIUM SAND
WITH 10% ORGANIC
AMENDMENT IN TOP
50 mm

50 mm COARSE SAND
OR OTHER APPROVED
AGGREGATE

125 mm DEPTH
APPROVED AGGREGATE
FORMING DRAINAGE
LAYER

CLAYWARE OR
PERFORATED PLASTIC
DRAIN PIPE

PLATE 49. Stone carpet and suspended water table construction as described in Part [F].

The PAT system (prescription athletic turf)

Designed by Bill Daniel at Purdue University, Indiana, the PAT system was a development of the Pur-wick system, also designed by Mr. Daniel.

As the Pur-wick system and unlike the cell system, the entire pitch is one complete unit lined with a plastic sheet. Pipes are again laid in the pitch base with a sand rootzone and a surface 50 mm of soil/peat. The drains are connected to pumps which can be operated in wet weather to suck water from the rootzone. In dry conditions the pumps can be reversed, pumping water into the base of the pitch.

Pur-wick system

The forerunner of the PAT system, but without the pump feature.

VACUDRAIN

A PVC lined system with a pump attached to perforated pipes throughout the construction. The rootzone is sand with nutrients being supplied to the surface 150 mm. Water can be either pumped into or out of the system.

Other patent systems have been designed involving sand surfaces.

Prunty-Mulqueen

Developed in Northern Ireland, the Prunty-Mulqueen or PM pitch, involves a carpet of unameliorated sand overlying a slit and pipe drained base.

REINFORCEMENT MATERIALS

Various materials have been developed in order to improve the stability of natural soils, sand or soil/sand mixes.

These include Fibresand, polypropylene fibres mixed with and used to stabilise sands or soil/sand mixtures. Netlon Advanced Turf (pieces of plastic mesh mixed with selected rootzone materials) has been shown in America or STRI trials to improve water infiltration rates, soil moisture retention and overall turf health and to have some positive effects on surface traction, hardness, resilience and durability. VHAF (vertical and horizontal fibres) in the form of sheets has been used to stabilise the playing surfaces.

MOBILE PITCHES

The modern sports stadium or arena is extremely expensive both to construct and maintain. The natural grass pitch, even at its best, can only take so much wear and the surface may be totally inappropriate for some functions which would otherwise be held there.

The possibility of constructing a natural grass pitch in square or hexagonal boxed sections, which can be moved into and out of a roofed stadium to maximise its use has become an attractive proposition. There are no technically insoluble problems in achieving this, indeed some World Cup soccer matches staged in 1993 in the USA utilised such a pitch installed at the Pontiac Stadium. The weight of the entire pitch being several thousand tonnes makes it desirable to break the pitch up into smaller, more manageable sections. Care must of course be taken to ensure that the sections fit together with an imperceptible joint. The pitch must be left to grow in the open air and has to be maintained as an ordinary pitch. It is therefore necessary to have sufficient space outside the stadium to accommodate the pitch.

THE CHOICE AND DESIGN OF WINTER PITCH CONSTRUCTIONS

Great care needs to be taken when designing any type of pitch for use in a particular situation. The conditions found on the site and the anticipated level of use envisaged must form the basis for the proposals modified by conditions likely to be encountered during the construction period and the proposed timetable, followed of course by the availability of funding.

Having in principle established the general type of construction required, consideration must then be given to the detailed requirements. The depth, width, spacing and falls of any pipe drainage work must be determined. Similarly, calculations must be carried out to determine the design of any slit drainage works. Depths and types of any drainage layers and rootzones must be assessed.

Costs must in the majority of cases be a consideration, but great care needs to be exercised in any reduction in standards to meet a budget figure. Whilst it is clearly essential not to waste money the works must be solidly constructed. All too often money is thrown away on projects where corners are cut, compromises are made and cheap substandard materials used. It is worth bearing in mind that when building anything it is absolutely essential that the foundations are soundly constructed. For the winter pitch the foundation is the drainage system. Where funds are limited, it is essential that what work is done is sound, then at least if problems arise this basic work can be added to or be supplemented by further operations at a later date and work is not simply abortive.

The design details having been finalised, it is important not to forget the practicalities of the constructional work. Can all the materials, plant and labour be transported to the site? Is there space and time for the work to be done? Is the access adequate and will disturbance cause difficulties with neighbours?

IMPLEMENTATION
The vast majority of winter pitch construction work is carried out by contractors. Clear and precise specifications, drawings and Bills of Quantities will be required to enable competitive tenders to be obtained. All companies invited to tender should be competent (in this particular sphere of operations), reliable, honest and financially sound. If the firms are not known directly then references should be sought.

Having selected the most suitable contractor, the works should be independently supervised. Having schemes professionally designed and supervised is well worthwhile, particularly for sizeable projects where substantial expenditure is involved. The STRI can offer a variety of services in this respect.

DESIGN AND BUILD CONTRACTS
Briefly, this means that contractors are invited to both design and build the pitch. Whilst this system has the advantage that if anything goes wrong there is only one company responsible for the work, for playing fields there are certain complications. Firstly, because of the range of options available for the construction of a winter games pitch, it is likely that a range of options and prices will be offered. Unless these are very carefully vetted there will be a tendency for the cheapest form of construction to be chosen and this may not be appropriate. To ensure that the end result is to be satisfactory, it is essential that a perceived design brief is provided with minimum standards set. Again during the work, professional advice and quality control is required to ensure that standards are adhered to.

COMMISSIONING AND MAINTENANCE
It is generally important to avoid over-use of a facility once it is brought into commission. In many cases the pitch will still be comparatively immature and at this stage, it is best not to abuse or over-use the pitch. Restraint in the first season will be repaid in subsequent years.

With regard to maintenance it is essential that any type of pitch is maintained with skill and care. After spending what may amount to several thousands of pounds on providing a playing surface, maintenance must be of a respectable standard. Given good maintenance, adequate fertiliser, aeration, top dressing and renovation work the pitch should perform well. If, however, the sward is maintained with less care, doing little more than mowing the grass, all playing surfaces will deteriorate.

SECTION 3
SANDS FOR PITCH CONSTRUCTION AND TOP DRESSING
By S.W. BAKER

INTRODUCTION
Sands are widely used in the construction of winter games pitches and for top dressing, mainly because the majority of soils have inadequate drainage in conditions of heavy wear. Apart from those soils which are naturally sandy in texture, most soil materials rely on aggregation to create a system of large pores for adequate drainage and aeration. This aggregation is brought about by physico-chemical processes associated particularly with the clay and organic matter fractions. It is the large soil pores between the aggregates which remain air-filled at field capacity and which are responsible for rapid drainage of the soil. If the soil is compacted these larger pores are lost and the soil becomes poor draining and waterlogged. On most natural soils used for winter games pitches it is the inability of the compacted surface layer to transmit rainfall rapidly from the surface which causes poor playing conditions or cancellation of games.

Sand-based materials, on the other hand, do not rely on structure for drainage. Instead there is a stable network of pores between the sand grains and, as long as the sand is chosen carefully with respect to its size and uniformity of grains, this can provide a growing medium with high rates of drainage and adequate aeration for plant growth. In addition, because of its high permeability, sand material can be used in slit drainage, allowing rainfall to bypass the compacted soil layer and enter the drainage system below.

SAND FOR ROOTZONE CONSTRUCTION
SOIL AMELIORATION
Additions of sand can be used to improve the physical properties of soil during construction work, either by rotovating prescribed amounts of sand into the surface of an existing pitch or by preparing a blend of sand, soil and sometimes organic matter to be used as a rootzone material. It is very important that the correct sand is selected. Firstly, the sand must be uniform in character - if it consists of a wide range of particle sizes it will simply interpack (Plate 50), leading to a loss of pore space, poor drainage rates and restricted grass rooting. Secondly, the sand must be of the right size. If it is too fine drainage suffers and the material will be highly water-retentive. If it is too coarse it will be droughty and very unstable if grass cover is lost.

Sufficient quantities of a uniform sand must be added to the soil so that a permanent network of large pores is formed between the sand grains. The amount of sand is critical and, for example, Plate 51 shows the effect of different mixing rates with a sandy loam soil on various aspects of turf performances. After three seasons of simulated wear infiltration rates were still over 400 mm/h on the pure sand (0:1) treatment, 11 mm/h for the mix of 1 part soil:2 parts sand and only 3 mm/h on the 1 part soil:0.5 parts sand mixes. The low infiltration rates on the 1:0.5 and 1:1 mixes meant that standing water was a severe problem and during 1986-87, ponding was recorded on 20% and 16% respectively of measuring dates. This compared to a 4% incidence of surface water on the 1:2 mixes and the sand plots were effectively free from ponding. The unfavourable physical conditions meant that grass cover was lost more quickly on 1:0.5 and 1:1 mixes and these mixes also gave a poor quality surface for play.

Adding too little sand in amelioration work can sometimes produce worse results than just using the soil without addition of sand. This can arise because soil structure is lost during the mixing process. Instead a critical threshold of sand is required before there is any significant improvement in the soil physical properties of the mix: this threshold is reached when the sand grains begin to abut with adjacent grains forming large pores between the grains. Inadequate sand contents probably account for the rather limited success of amelioration projects in the past: an STRI drainage survey in the early 1980's for instance found that over 40% of sand ameliorated pitches still had inadequate drainage.

As a minimum specification for amelioration work it is suggested that sufficient quantities of a clean, uniform sand should be added to dilute the finer fractions to:

Clay	(particles <0.002 mm diameter)	< 5%
Silt + clay	(particles <0.063 mm diameter)	<10%
Fines	(particles <0.125 mm diameter)	<20%

74

UNIFORM SIZE DISTRIBUTION   MIXED PARTICLE SYSTEM

PLATE 50. The effect on sand uniformity on particle interpacking.

For more free-draining mixes, the amount of clay is usually reduced below 3%, silt plus clay below 6% and the amount of fines below 15%.

Heavier soils will of course require more sand. For example, to meet the minimum specifications above, a sandy loam soil with an initial content of 15% clay and 20% silt would require at least 2.5 parts of sand for each volume of soil, whilst a loam soil, initially with 20% clay and 25% silt would require a mix of at least 1 part soil:3 parts sand. Soils with a silt plus clay content of more than 45% or a clay content of more than 20% should not normally be considered for amelioration as it is unlikely that such a material could be mixed accurately and it is doubtful whether the material would ever be sufficiently friable to get a good quality blend.

Projects involving soil amelioration need detailed laboratory testing to establish an optimum rootzone mix. This would normally involve the measurement of the hydraulic conductivity of the proposed rootzone materials as well as optimising its particle size distribution.

Pure sand rootzones
The next progression from soil amelioration is to dispense with the soil altogether and just use the sand as the construction material. Sand-based constructions for winter games pitches require greater skills with respect to irrigation and fertiliser management and there can be problems of surface stability if ground cover is lost through wear and the surface is allowed to dry out. However, sand constructions have advantages of good drainage, the rootzone is well aerated and in the construction work the laborious operation of mixing sand and soil can be omitted.

The type of sand which is used is critical. Plate 52 shows the effect of four contrasting sands on water infiltration rates, traction (i.e. the potential grip for the player) and moisture retention in dry weather. The medium-coarse sand had a very high drainage rate but was unacceptable because it had very poor moisture retention and when grass cover was lost, traction values fell below the level acceptable for play (<20 N m). The sand with the wide range of particles had the lowest drainage rate of 68 mm/h and tended to compact more readily than the other sands giving a much harder playing surface. For winter games pitches the medium-fine and medium sands were the optimum construction materials.

SAND SELECTION FOR ROOTZONE MATERIALS
In this section, the specifications for grain size and uniformity are given in the form of a grading

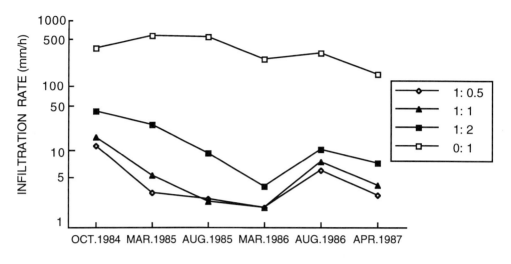

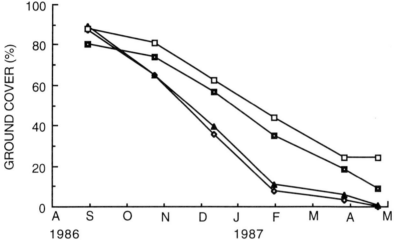

PLATE 51. The effect of sand content on infiltration rates, ground cover and firmness of football turf receiving artificial wear. The 1:0.5 mixes had a sand content of 79% and the 1:1, 1:2 and 0:1 (pure sand) materials had sand contents of 86, 90 and 100% respectively. (Adapted from Baker [1988] and Baker et al. [1988]).

envelope, i.e. a set of upper and lower size limits to which the sand should conform. This is considered to be more suitable for general application than, for instance, a system based on indices of grain size and uniformity. It is usually easier to plot the size distribution on a grading diagram than to calculate the relevant size and uniformity indices and the latter are often difficult for users to comprehend.

The grading envelopes which are presented in this chapter give a recommended and acceptable particle size distribution. If all the data points fit within the central band as in Sand A (Plate 53) the sand would be considered to be in the recommended range for the specified application. If some of the data points fall outside the central band but within the overall grading envelope as in Sand B the sand would be considered to be a potentially acceptable material but careful consideration of the particular conditions at the site would have to be made before its use could be confirmed. Sand B, for example, falls within the acceptable range but is slightly coarser than the preferred range. Obviously if there were sand available which fell entirely into the central band (i.e. within the recommended limits), this should be chosen. To avoid any sands with a very wide size distribution being used for applications where there are likely to be high levels of compaction, a further stipulation is made. If the sand is within the acceptable range but part of the distribution is coarser than the preferred limits and part

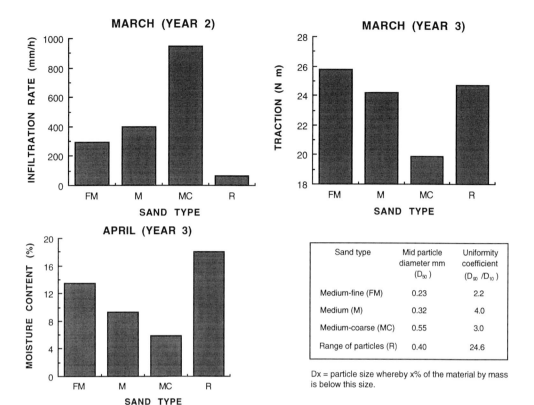

PLATE 52. The effect of four different sand types on water infiltration rates, traction and moisture retention (adapted from Baker [1988] and Baker et al. [1988]).

finer than the preferred grading (e.g. Sand C), this material would not be acceptable. Finally, sands with any data point outside the acceptable grading envelope (e.g. Sand D) would not be considered acceptable.

It is suggested that if the sand falls within the recommended range this sand could be used with confidence for the intended application. If the sand falls within the acceptable range it will be suitable in many cases although agronomic factors may preclude its use on certain sites or there may have to be slight modifications in, for example, a construction specification to accommodate the material. If there is any doubt about a sand's suitability, professional advice should be sought which can take into account the particular circumstances for which it is intended to use the sand.

In general, it is accepted that a coarser sand should be used for soil modification on a winter games pitch than in a pure sand construction and accordingly two sets of grading curves are given.

The following specifications are given for sands for winter games pitches:

Grading : soil modification and top dressings (see Plate 54), pure sand constructions (see Plate 55)
Lime content : <15%. Furthermore soft limestone fragments must be avoided
Particle shape : not specified, although sub-rounded to sub-angular materials are preferred

SANDS FOR SLIT DRAINAGE
Sands for slit drainage must fulfil a number of requirements. They should be of high permeability to allow the rapid transfer of water to the drains, they should be sufficiently water-retentive to support grass growth, they should be sufficiently stable so that if grass cover is lost on say a winter games pitch the sand will not kick out of the slits nor detract from the playing quality of the surface. Coarse particles in the sand should not affect the quality of the surface and finally, if the slit is a layered

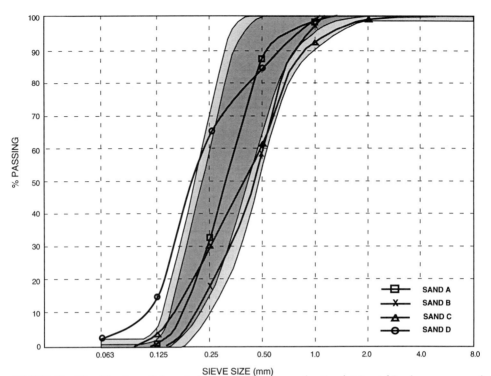

PLATE 53. Classification of the suitability of different sands: Sand A is within the recommended range, Sand B is potentially acceptable although the exact circumstances of its use would have to be carefully consideredand. Sands C and D are not acceptable.

construction of sand over more permeable gravel then the sand must not filter downwards into the gravel.

Where slits are installed without a lower layer of gravel (e.g. secondary slit systems based on sand injection or surface grooving) it is possible to use a relatively uniform medium sand with the majority of particles in the range 0.25-0.75 mm diameter.

However, in most slit drainage designs, the Sports Turf Research Institute would recommend slits consisting of sand over gravel (Plate 56). An example could be 100 mm of sand over 125 mm gravel depending on the slit and drain spacings and the target drainage design rates. The gravel is preferred because of its capacity to transmit water laterally to the drains, for example, a slit drain of 100 mm sand over 125 mm of 5-8 mm gravel would have a lateral drainage capacity over five times that of a slit of 225 mm medium sand.

If very coarse gravels are used in the slit drains the sand would also need to be relatively coarse to prevent the sand filtering into the gravel. However, sands may be rather unstable and abrasive to players and re-establishment of grass over the slits could be difficult. It helps therefore if slightly finer gravels of approximately 5-8 mm are used in the slit drains and it is for this type of material that the sand specification is derived.

For sand used in a slit drain over a 5-8 mm gravel, the grading given in Plate 57 is suggested. For soccer and Rugby pitches, lime content is not usually critical, although any calcareous material which is present must not break down and affect water transmission. On any hockey pitch with a fine fescue/bent sward and particularly where the native soil is rather acid, sand with a lime content >0.5% should generally be avoided otherwise a striped pattern across the pitch could result because of more vigorous growth over the slits and possible changes in species composition.

BLINDING SANDS
The function of the blinding layer is to prevent soil over drain trenches from contaminating the gravel

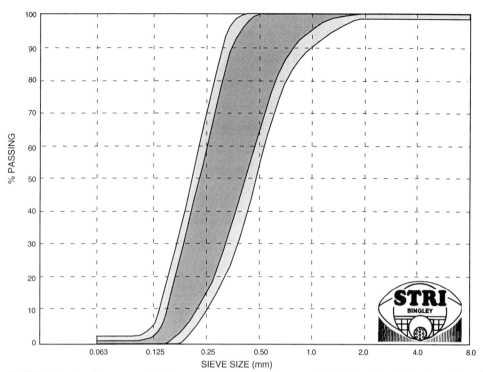

PLATE 54. Grading curve defining recommended and acceptable limits of sand size for soil modi-fication and top dressing of winter games pitches.

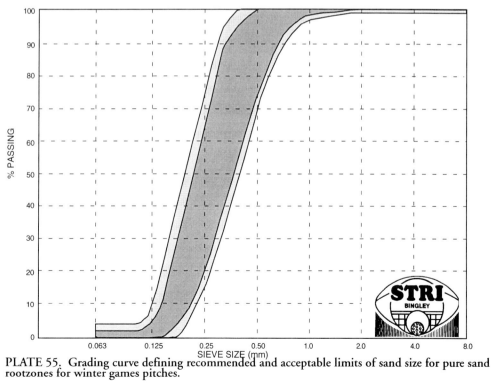

PLATE 55. Grading curve defining recommended and acceptable limits of sand size for pure sand rootzones for winter games pitches.

79

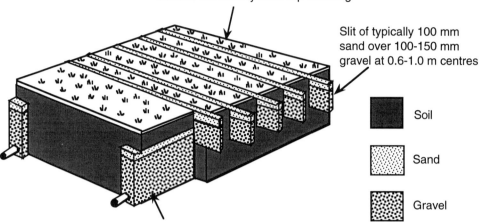

Surface with heavy sand top dressing

Slit of typically 100 mm
sand over 100-150 mm
gravel at 0.6-1.0 m centres

Soil

Sand

Gravel

Pipe drains at 5-15 m centres

PLATE 56. **The layout of a typical slit drainage system with excavated slits fitted with sand and gravel.**

backfill in the trench or, in the case of a construction with a gravel drainage carpet, the blinding sand prevents the finer rootzone material from filtering into the gravel.

In theory, a material will not migrate downwards into the underlying layer if the following bridging factor is satisfied:

D_{15} (lower layer) $\leq 5 \times D_{85}$ (upper layer)

where:

D_{15} (lower layer) = particle diameter below which 15% of the particles in the lower layer (by weight) are smaller.

D_{85} (upper layer) = particle diameter below which 85% of the particles in the upper layer (by weight) are smaller.

For a layered construction where a rootzone sand is placed over gravel it follows that the blinding layer must be compatible with the gravel but also that the rootzone sand must not filter into the blinding sand. It should be noted, however, when soil is added over a drain trench, aggregation of the soil particles is usually sufficient to prevent migration of particles into the blinding layer overlying the gravel backfill of the trench, but considerable care should be taken with poorly structured soils containing a lot of coarse silt or fine sand.

Specifications for blinding sands cannot be considered in isolation from the size distribution of the gravel material which requires blinding. In general, gravel materials in the range 5-10 mm are used in sports turf drainage and the specification which is given is based on a gravel falling within this range with a mid-particle diameter (D_{50}) of no more than 8 mm. For a coarse gravel in range 8-10 mm the points on the grading curve should fall within a zone coarser than the finer recommended limit. Similarly if the rootzone sand is relatively fine (i.e. with a D_{50} value <0.25 mm), the blinding sand should be finer than the upper recommended limit with no points in the coarse but acceptable zone.

If a drainage aggregate is coarser than 10 mm it may be necessary to double blind the material, e.g. for a 20 mm gravel, a layer of say 4-5 mm grit could be added and then this is in turn covered with a blinding sand of, say, 300-2000 µm before the rootzone layer is added. In most situations this is an unnecessarily complicated procedure and can only be justified if no suitable 5-10 mm aggregate can be obtained.

A suggested specification for blinding sands over a 5-10 mm drainage aggregate would be as follows:

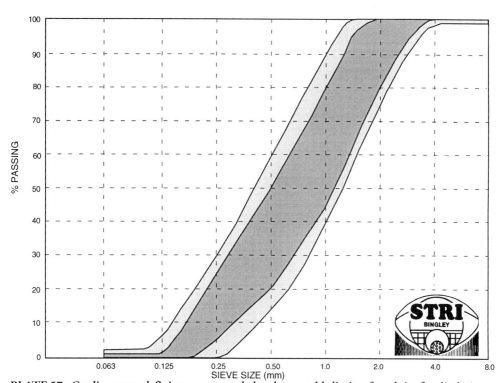

PLATE 57. Grading curve defining recommended and acceptable limits of sand size for slit drainage sands for placement over a 5-8 mm gravel in the base of the slit.

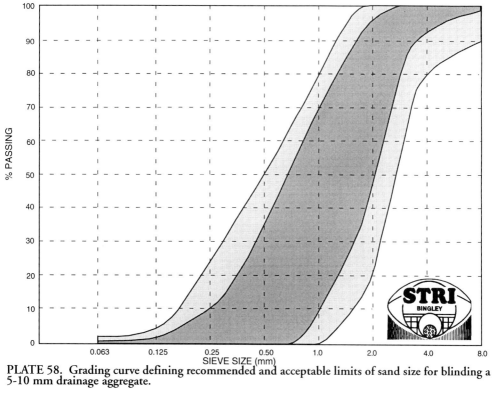

PLATE 58. Grading curve defining recommended and acceptable limits of sand size for blinding a 5-10 mm drainage aggregate.

81

Grading   : see Plate 58
Lime content   : <15%. Furthermore soft limestone fragments must be avoided
Particle shape : not specified

SANDS FOR TOP DRESSING

Sports turf is a dynamic system with the properties of the turf varying according to the amount of play and level of compaction to which it is subjected. A build up of compaction will tend to reduce the permeability of the surface layer and this will be exacerbated if finer particles of mineral matter migrate to the surface as a result of wear and fine organic residues accumulate from the breakdown of grass material.

The main uses of sand in the maintenance programme for a winter games pitch is to dilute accumulations of fine mineral and organic matter at the surface to retain the permeability of a pitch and to provide a firmer surface in wet weather. In these circumstances pure sand, with no soil amendment, is the preferred top dressing material. Sand or a sandy compost is also important to repair divots kicked out by the players, thus restoring the levels of the surface.

The advantages of sand are clearly seen in Plate 59 which shows the effects of different rates of sand on a pipe drained sandy loam soil, the same soil with slit drains at 600 mm centres and a sand carpet construction. The sand rates of 0, 4, 8 and 16 kg/m^2 per year correspond to annual applications of 0, 25, 50 and 100 tonnes of sand per year to a pitch of 6,250 m^2. The advantages of higher grades of construction are evident with the sand carpet pitch retaining more cover during wear than the slit drained and particularly the pipe drained pitch. The sand carpet pitch also has a dry, firm surface where ball bounce, for example, is good. However, players find ball rebound values less than 15% unacceptable and the wet, muddy surface on some of the pipe drained and slit drained plots gave very low values indeed.

Sand application is important on all types of construction: where topsoil is present sand makes the surface layer less plastic in wet conditions giving a firmer and drier surface and on sand constructions it can be important in maintaining surface permeability by diluting organic material which can accumulate in the areas of lower wear, e.g. on the wings. On a slit drained construction the absence of protective sand dressings causes the slits to be sealed by play preventing rainfall from entering the slit system and causing waterlogged surfaces. In the example shown in Plate 59 the grass cover on the sub-plots with no sand was zero compared to 43% where the equivalent of 100 tonnes per year was used and the wet, muddy surface on the slit drained plots with no sand gave a ball rebound of only 1% compared with 30% on the area with the highest rate of sand.

The results for the slit drained plots with no sand are similar to those of the pipe drained area, in other words the advantages of a slit drainage scheme can disappear in less than 1^1/$_2$ seasons of wear because of the lack of adequate sand dressing. Indeed this trial and observations on actual pitches show that even a few months of play on a slit drained pitch with no sand dressing can negate the value of the drainage work.

Specifications for sands for top dressing would normally follow those for soil amelioration given in Fig. 5. If only relatively light applications of sand are used (<25 tonnes per pitch per year), it is generally more effective to use a sand within the coarser range of the recommended limits.

THE IMPORTANCE OF SAND TESTING

Sand deposits are never totally uniform in terms of the grain size distribution. The variability of particle size in a deposit is a function of the agents of transportation and settlement at the time when the sand was deposited. Similarly processing of sands can vary. Sands developed for certain industrial applications, e.g. glass making, filter beds etc. will be consistent because they are processed to satisfy the grading requirements of these industries. However, many of the building sands have less stringent requirements and variations in the degree of washing can affect the quality of the sand.

It is important therefore to recognise the fact that although a sand may initially satisfy gradings given in this book, further supplies of material from a different part of the quarry may, unless processed to stringent requirements, not satisfy the same grading curves. If there are doubts whether a sand still meets a given requirement, further testing is required.

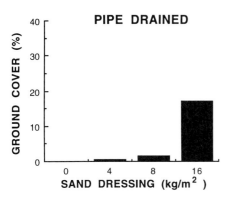

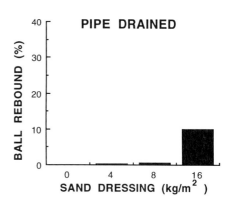

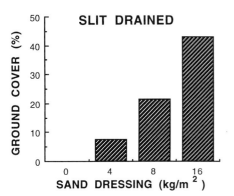

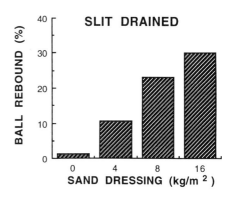

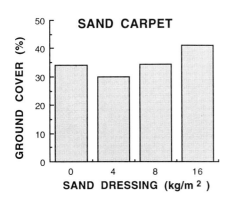

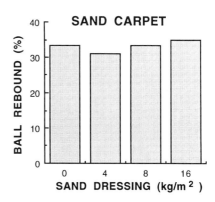

PLATE 59. The effect of sand top dressing rate on ground cover and ball rebound on pipe drained, slit drained and sand carpet constructions receiving simulated football-type wear. (Adapted from Baker & Canaway [1989, 1990] - data for December 1988.)

SECTION 4
FROST PROTECTION AND SOIL WARMING
By D.F. Boocock

HISTORICAL

From the very earliest beginnings of winter games such as Association football and Rugby football, ground conditions on the day will have had a marked influence on the participants' enjoyment of the match and indeed, on occasions, the outcome. Many a bright hope for victory must have sunk without trace in the mud of playing surfaces such as Cardiff Arms Park and the Baseball Ground, Derby, not all that many years ago. Whilst the most common cause of postponed matches when STRI conducted a survey of League grounds in 1982 was a waterlogged pitch, postponements due to frost and snow grab the headlines sometimes, most noticeably in the seasons 1962/63 and 1978/79. The latter season, remembered for the infamous "pools panel" which presided over the outcome of matches for many weeks on end, precipitated a meeting organised by the Football Association to discuss various means of protecting pitches against adverse weather conditions.

Long before that enthusiasts would have explored means of protecting grass pitches from severe frost, if only for safety reasons, with such robust games as soccer and Rugby. Once the professional game came into being there were distinct financial inducements to solving the problem. However, it was to take many long years and many trials before effective and efficient means of protecting grounds from frost were determined.

NATURAL PROTECTION

All surfaces take part in exchanges of heat with their surroundings, resulting in net gains or losses. These occur by radiation and convection with the atmosphere, conduction with layers of soil below the surface and evaporation or condensation of water at the surface.

Under severe weather conditions, radiation and convection are by far the most important means of heat loss from winter pitches.

On a calm, cloudless night the net radiation loss is enough to keep the temperature of short grass at about 5°F or more below that of the air only a few feet above ground. It follows therefore that by maintaining as dense and as long a cover of grass as is compatible with the requirements of the game, the better the surface will be protected from freezing. The grass cover, trapping still air between leaf blades, acts as a protective "blanket". Groundsmen have long appreciated this fact and those blessed with a co-operative manager, who will accept a sward length of say 1½" at the start of the season, will be less affected by frosts up to December when natural wear and tear have reduced grass length and exposed more soil. Even then, with judicious use of tarpaulin sheets or similar material in goal mouths and centre circle overnight, the effects of frost can be minimised. Couple that with a good programme of surface restoration following games, including light rolling of a surface which has become cut up if the forecast is for frost, and the average winter will pose relatively few problems. Knobs of soil or lumps of turf on a disturbed area of the pitch freeze first and hardest and can sometimes result in a cancellation if they are slow to thaw out, whereas the same pitch rolled beforehand and with a smoother top would have far more chance of being judged acceptable for play.

The construction of stands, especially tall structures, to the south side of football grounds has added to problems keeping half the pitch or more in shadow for long periods during the winter, so there is less chance for natural thawing by sun and of course, slower drying.

For many years Twickenham has enjoyed a good reputation for staging major games when freezing weather has forced cancellations elsewhere. That success was achieved without recourse to expensive techniques to keep the ground frost-free and by simply leaving a good length of grass, up to 2½-3" being acceptable for Rugby, at the start of a season.

Snow also has excellent insulation properties and falling on an unfrozen or slightly frozen pitch will help to keep the surface in good condition for lengthy periods. Problems arise where there is a depth of snow cover and the difficulties imposed clearing and disposing of any quantity. Mechanical shovels or tractors with grading blades are crude, but the only effective approach nowadays where large volumes of snow have to be shifted quickly. Timing of the move needs to be closely related to the local weather predictions and of course, inevitably there is some loss of grass cover which can exacerbate problems with frost afterwards.

A prolonged period of harsh weather, resulting in many match cancellations, also brings with it a wealth of ideas to prevent pitches from freezing. One idea tried at Bingley, that of using "deep heat" from the earth by driving in lots of metal rods, came to nothing.

CHEMICALS

The most frequently used chemical for thawing pitches has been either agricultural grade salt or the rock salt used on roads. Assuming a moisture content of 25%, the freezing point of the soil moisture in a layer 1" thick could be depressed 1°C by applying salt at 1 tonne per acre. At that rate there would be severe leaf scorch, with concentrations of salt high enough in the surface layer of soil to damage turf root systems. Worse still, the effect of sodium is to deflocculate clay particles which wrecks soil structure, never very good on a winter pitch anyway and results in long-term ill-effects on soil drainage rates. The latter is not easily corrected by applying remedies such as gypsum either.

Calcium chloride, sometimes with an additive, is widely used in America in pelleted form for breaking up ice on roads and this product is also available here. A few pellets sprinkled onto ice quickly melt small holes in it, making the ice easier to break up and clear. Used on football pitches, however, quite large quantities are needed to thaw out frozen soil and the turf is often completely killed, although damage to soil structure is not as serious as with common salt.

More recently, a natural salt product consisting mainly of magnesium chloride and potassium chloride has been marketed for defrosting. This causes virtually no scorching of grass leaves when used at the maker's recommended rate, unlike the two materials mentioned above. However, its long-term effects on soil structure and drainage have not been determined.

There have also been attempts at defrosting using chemicals such as urea, which is a nitrogenous fertiliser. Unfortunately, at the high rates required to achieve significant defrosting (up to 16 times those normally employed), this too can cause significant turf damage.

All the above chemicals have to be used at rates which raise the concentration of salts in the immediate surface soil. That in turn raises the osmotic pressure at the turf roots, which leads to damage and possibly death. Even when much lower rates of the materials are applied, these may thaw the top quickly but leave a hard layer below. The result is a very soft surface which is prone to severe disturbance in play and any rainfall at all can only make matters worse, since the water cannot get away underneath. Even motor car antifreeze has been tried in experiments, but with predictably extremely severe turf damage.

INSULATING PITCHES

If heat loss by radiation from a turf surface can be checked or stopped in some way, the chances of the pitch freezing up badly are much reduced.

Straw, with its entrapped air, is an excellent insulator. Applied at 10-20 tonnes to the pitch before frost gets into the ground, it can be counted on to give protection against almost any frost. Wheat straw was always regarded as the best material and it needed to be well fluffed up, especially if you were attempting to economise. This approach has a long history of use with pictorial records of the pitch at Tottenham being strawed down in 1925. In the 1950's the Rugby League pitch at Headingley was regularly kept covered in this way from 1 December to the end of

February. In those days removal for matches and replacement cost £20 for the two operations and took 20 men 3 hours each time.

Handling the straw on and off pitches could be a problem, especially with wet material, although under dry conditions a hay sweep was used. There were difficulties with weed seeds and of course, storage problems for a bulky loose material like this. These days public health and safety regulations would rule it out immediately on grounds of fire risk.

The story goes that Newcastle once tried to thaw out their pitch by covering it with straw and then setting fire to it. Unfortunately, once the fire got going rain started to fall and left the pitch in a terrible state. The whole lot had to be covered with sand, but United did not postpone their match!

Within the last 12 years an insulating blanket called 'Polystraw' has been on the market. This consists of a mat of loosely packed straw enclosed between two lengths of polythene and stitched at intervals like a quilt to prevent movement of the filling. Sheffield Wednesday use them with some success for protecting the 6 yard boxes. Various other materials and methods of covering have been tried, e.g. using expanded polystyrene sheets. Recently a lightweight blanket, Tildenet Fleece, has been promoted for this job. Weighing only 17 g/m it comes in widths between 2-15 m and in 100 m lengths. In all cases, difficulties in handling the sheets on and off the pitch, securing lighter materials effectively and storage problems, especially for full pitch covering, have reduced interest in this approach. Another drawback, especially with numerous sheets, is that they can concentrate rainfall at the gaps which can lead to localised softer patches.

PLATE 60. Trial of polystyrene insulating cover at STRI, Bingley in a hard winter - February 1963.

AIR HOUSES AND COVERS

Around early 1960 the possibility of using covers (of polythene or nylon), laid directly on the pitch to keep off rain and prevent freezing, was investigated. Polythene was tried experimentally at Bingley, albeit on a small scale, although at least one League club tried it out over their pitch. Difficulty was experienced keeping the polythene secure during windy weather and it was found in practice that handling problems and even bird damage were encountered.

In Sweden, the idea was taken further and in a more severe winter climate, the plastic covers were used in conjunction with an "electric blanket" of heating wires laid in the topsoil surface to gain maximum efficiency. In the late 1960's the stadium at Solna and the south stadium in Stockholm were protected in this way. The plastic sheet used was transparent, UV stabilised and 0.15 mm thick. The size used was 80 m x 110 m, rolled on a steel cylinder with a diameter of 0.5 m. The cylinder was driven by an electric motor at each end and the set-up was stored on one of the long sides of the pitch, where it could be protected from sunlight and heat. It was found necessary to provide for the disposal of water which collected on the sheet when it was rolled up. This was achieved with catchwater drains at both ends of the pitch. It was found that heat input via the undersoil heating wires could be halved and the sheet also gave protection against heavy autumn rains.

Over 2 separate winters (1960/61 and again in 1969/70) a trial was carried out at Bingley to examine pitch protection using an air house. The first trial used a green nylon cover, comprising 36 m wide strips sewn together, with taped seams to make them water-tight. The sheet covered about 850 m² and was secured by digging a trench around the cover and then threading metal conduit tube through nylon loops attached to the outside edges of the cover. The loops were drawn tight over the edges of the trench and held by spikes driven into the trench face. The fan used to inflate the cover had a potential input of 1,000 cu. ft/min. and was run on a time clock to achieve an acceptable degree of inflation. Entry was achieved via an air lock.

Soon after erection, it became apparent that too little light passed through the green nylon for satisfactory grass growth and the sward deteriorated. Conditions were also favourable for the development of fungal disease, especially fusarium patch, although satisfactory control of this with fungicides was possible.

Good protection against rain was achieved, apart from 1 or 2 poorly finished seams. Little frost penetrated the cover and on only one occasion when temperatures dropped to 14°F, was it necessary to run an industrial heater, with a capacity of 300,000 BTU's per hour and that coped very effectively. In fact, snow gave more problems than frost, although that winter there was never more than 2 or 3" and the heater was operated to melt what did fall. Even so, partial collapses due to the weight of thawing snow and water occurred even with heating and maximum air input. Wind effects that winter were the most serious and wind speeds of 20-25 mph could only be coped with provided the air fan was boosted to maximum immediately the wind got up. Anything over that, i.e. a strong breeze or near gale with winds of 32-38 mph, brought the cover to the ground. The second trial undertaken with a more transparent nylon and stronger fabric tapes met with no more success in winter gales and heavy snowfall than the first.

During 1971, Leicester City installed an "air balloon" manufactured by Boyspan International Ltd. of Nuneaton. The one-piece, 2½ ton membrane measured 250' x 360' and was made from 1,000 gauge polythene. One end was attached to a wall where four 3-phase propeller fans were sited. The other end was secured by steel cable, nylon cord and clips. Fifty cables across the width were anchored every 7'. The polythene allowed 98% light transmission and needed renewing every 3-5 years.

The balloon took 20 minutes to inflate, rising to 15' height in the centre. It could deal with frosts and snow and was also used in wet spells to keep rain off the pitch. Good drainage at the sides and ends of the pitch to cope with water off the cover were essential. During frosty conditions, 2 oil-fired industrial heaters could be used, one at either end. The balloon was taken down about 4

PLATE 61. Air house trial at STRI, Bingley during the 1960-61 winter. A fan used to inflate the cover.

PLATE 62. A similar experimental pitch cover at the same location – winter 1969-70.

hours before a match to allow goal posts to be reinstalled and it took 16 men 2 hours to remove. When not in use, the cover was stored in a trench running the width of the pitch. The club had the latter well organised, had few problems and gained great benefit. In extremes of wind or snow, the balloon was deflated until the adverse weather was over.

Perhaps the most famous cover of them all, in Houston, Texas, opened in 1965 with a natural grass surface. Because of problems with scorch and glare from bright sunlight through the glass roof panels, these had to be painted over. That soon affected grass growth and the pitch became a hard, dry dust bowl. Conversion to an Astroturf artificial surface took place the following year.

As recently as 1979, Aston Villa toyed with the idea of installing a fabric tent based on the civil engineering material Terram 3000. The method of support was to be a combination of simple winches, terylene fibre ropes and compressed air pistons.

During 1985 a Dutch company promoted a system misleadingly called "All Weather Protection". In fact it was a partial covering system, based on gutter tracks and tent shaped supports with covering fabric drawn over them. The covering "tent" is fitted with rollers which run in the gutter tracks and mounted on a special cart pulled by a compact tractor. The gutters are raised on legs and designed to provide a fall to the central cross gutter which removes water. It was claimed to protect pitches from excess water and at the same time, enhance grass growth. No mention was made of possible problems with frozen strips on a partially covered pitch, heavy snowfall, or high winds.

As recently as January 1993, a massive tent was imported from Germany and used almost like a greenhouse, to establish newly laid turf on Denmark's national stadium in Copenhagen. The tent was kept in place almost 3 winter months with artificial light and heating to speed up root establishment and grass growth prior to the Denmark -v- Spain football match on 31 March. Whilst the tent achieved what was required of it, sheer cost and time involved erecting and dismantling it would rule out its use on a regular basis.

SPACE HEATING
Various ways of heating from above the surface have been tried, especially when games have been in danger of cancellation due to frozen surfaces, perhaps only over a part of the pitch, e.g. the side shaded by stands. Ideas tried have included various types of industrial heater, ashphalt burners, which are normally used for repairing roads and even a jet engine. All achieved some degree of success and frequently a well cooked turf into the bargain! Where heavier vehicles, such as ashphalt burners, were employed there was also a tendency to damage the pitch.

Dickie Jeeps (a fruit farmer) used some of the space heating candles, marketed by BP for use in orchards at flowering time, on the Twickenham pitch one year. Results were moderate, with some harder patches left and costs were pretty high.

None of the above approaches has proved very efficient, since a large proportion of the heat is lost directly into the atmosphere before it can do any good for the pitch.

ELECTRIC BLANKET
Heating the pitch from below ground was a much more practical approach and the first trials with electric soil warming at Bingley started in 1947 and continued through until 1960. In the preliminary studies, we considered forms of undersoil heating, other than electric soil warming and came to the conclusion at that time that sufficient uniformity of heating could only be obtained through electric wires, where every inch of heating cable gave out the same amount of heat, whether near the supply or at the far end of the pitch. We worked on the assumption that the electricity boards might allow use at night for 12 hours, which was important in relation to cost per unit and the availability of the large electrical load required for the whole pitch. We had a good deal of co-operation from the General Electrical Company and their technical representative. We came to the conclusion that 10 watts/ft^2 was the right load. That meant

PLATES 63 & 64. Early soil warming experiments at the STRI trial ground at Bingley. Soil warming wires being installed using a modified mole plough and (left) the resulting wire depth and spacing.

PLATE 65. A series of four photographs showing the installation of soil warming wires at the SRFU ground, Murrayfield, in 1959.

PLATE 66. Scottish Rugby Football Union ground, Murrayfield.

PLATE 67. SRFU Murrayfield : David Brown equipment.

PLATE 68. SRFU Murrayfield. : close-up of wire installation.

warming wires inserted at 6" depth and 6" spacing, in itself a compromise between the most economical loading and putting wires more deeply so as to be well out of harm's way from spikers etc. In practice, the plastic covered warming wires were installed from the surface using an adapted mole plough, designed by David Brown Tractors, and remarkable accuracy was achieved in both depth and spacing.

We worked with the idea that the system would be switched on for the whole of the frost risk period, input being controlled by time clocks to run at night and by thermostats in the surface of the pitch. Even so, it was appreciated that practice would differ from theory and clubs would switch off when no major game was due for economy reasons. The loading of 10 watts/ft^2 was fairly tolerant of that and usually if heat was put on over Wednesday night and successive nights, the Saturday game was secure unless, of course, the pitch was hard frozen to depth on the Wednesday.

The system kept grounds frost-free, even in the severe conditions experienced during 1981. It would also deal with light to moderate snowfall, provided that it was switched on early enough, so that the snow melted slowly almost as it fell. Heavy snow 24 hours before a game or severe drifting caused problems. The first installation was at Murrayfield in 1959 where the system performed admirably for over 20 years. A system was also installed in the Rugby League pitch at Headingley in 1963 and at Leeds United in 1971 and gave good service for many years. In 1971, installation cost was around £21,000 and in the severe winter of 1981 running costs were £18 per hour using off-peak electricity. Because of the wires, all maintenance operations have to be confined to the soil surface and spiker tines needed to be trimmed to 4" in length, which restricted options if soil drainage was not sound. In all the trial work there were no signs of problems with soil becoming baked around the wires or with drainage, although the latter aspect gave the system a bad name following a couple of ill-fated ventures on pitches where soil drainage was poor.

There have been other brief flirtations with electric undersoil heating, including a proposal by Charlton ThermoSystems in 1981. This used their unique heating unit and steel rope laid 9" below the surface and it was claimed to maintain soil at a pre-set temperature with great economy, but it never caught on.

In Sweden, soccer is not played in the hardest winter months, but in less severe weather a number of grounds have used a combination of underground electric heating, with a cover of moderate insulating properties. The latter is drawn over the pitch in a few minutes by an electrically operated winding drum. The great benefit of this is in retaining more heat in the soil, so keeping heating costs to a minimum.

SOIL WARMING : WARM AIR
During the late 1960's and early '70's, Land & Water Management Ltd. of Cambridge, were experimenting with warm air soil heating. Perforated plastic pipes were laid 15" below the surface and 1 yd. apart. The number of perforations was pre-determined by computer so that there were more holes further away from the pumping source. This ensured that an equal amount of warm air was carried to the extremities of the system. A lightweight aggregate was utilised to provide permeable fill in the trenches, which provided for permanent drainage and facilitated access of warm air into the soil. The topsoil was required to show good drainage characteristics. A warm air heating plant under the stands fed warm, moist air into the plastic pipes.

The first installation of this type was at the Arsenal ground in 1970 by a firm called Sureplay. This gave reasonable results, although there were slight disadvantages. The side of the pitch near the control unit and the boiler was warmer and water percolating through the soil carried silt with it, which could block the holes in the pipes. Again, soil drainage was the key to good performance, whether or not the soil heating was effective and in later years, this system was replaced with a different type when the pitch was rebuilt. Experimental areas were installed in the practice pitches at Everton and Leicester City football clubs, but the approach was never to go further.

PLATE 69. Above :
installation of
Warma-turf warm
water pipe system by
Wilco Heating Ltd.

PLATE 70. Right :
the Wirsbro
Meltaway warm
water pipe system,
pictured in 1979.

practice pitches at Everton and Leicester City football clubs, but the approach was never to go further.

SOIL WARMING : WARM WATER

The severe winter of 1978/79, when many sports were affected by freezing conditions, prompted a reappraisal of methods of protecting pitches from extremes of weather. Low pressure, warm water circulation through PVC pipes had been used successfully for some years in horticulture, both to force outdoor bulbs such as tulips and daffodils and under glass for tomatoes. A variation of this approach was first tried at Coventry Football Club with the Warmaturf System by Wilco Heating Ltd., closely followed by Manchester City using the Wirsbro Meltaway System (E.A. Yates Ltd). Since then many other football clubs have followed suit.

The system is powered by an oil or gas fired boiler, rated at around 4.5 million BTU/hr installed off-pitch in a boiler house. This supplies water at 40°C to 160 mm polyethylene header pipes at one end of the pitch. From here water is distributed via 25 mm polyethylene pipe loops running the full length of the pitch and back, the other end connected to a return header in the same trench as the supply header for recirculation to the boiler. The most effective depth and spacing for the pipes within the pitch was found to be a constant 250 mm. Three pipes are installed on each run using a modified subsoiler pulled by a 4-wheel drive tractor unit.

The stadium itself will determine how pipework is laid, the flow pattern usually being from the cold or shaded side to the warmer sunny side.

The lessons learned from earlier ventures with electric wire soil warming were heeded and any drainage and pitch upgrading work necessary was completed first. Accurate pipe laying is important as well, to allow routine maintenance work to proceed without risk of damaging the pipes.

Control of the system is usually governed by sensors buried in the turf. The first is located at the coldest point in the pitch and is 37 mm below the pitch surface and set to switch on the system to heat up the water when the surface soil temperature falls to 2°C. When the second sensor, some 37 mm deeper in the soil, detects the same temperature a 3-way valve is automatically opened and the circulating pump draws hot water from the boiler into the distribution pipework. In practice, it is usual to maintain close links with the local Met. Office and their up-to-the-minute forecast, together with readings from the under-pitch sensors at the control panel, provide the information to determine when to switch on. Usually in cold weather conditions, the system has to run for about 3 days to be absolutely sure the pitch will be match-fit.

In general, the warm water systems have proved cheaper to run than the electric wire method, at around £25 per hour in 1992. Over the last 5 years, installation costs have varied from between £90,000-130,000. Apart from minor variations, such as installing the pipes in sand bands, or surrounded by gravel in surface slit drain trenches, the systems are basically the same.

This form of undersoil heating has been taken up by many football clubs now and the general consensus is that properly laid and operated, with good pitch drainage to start with, it is satisfactory. Possibly the next step forward will be to combine under-soil heating with a really effective pitch cover for economy.

Section 5

GRASSES FOR WINTER PITCHES
By A.J. Newell

INTRODUCTION

Thirty years ago there were very few grasses which had been specifically selected for amenity uses. Twenty years ago there was perhaps ten which could be described as amenity cultivars. Today at Bingley 14 species of grass and 365 different amenity grass cultivars are being tested. Of these, 192 are commercially available and listed in *Turfgrass Seed 1994*. Many of these grasses are used in seeds mixtures for winter pitches.

The major objectives of this section are: to describe the appearance and performance of the major amenity grass species; to provide information to help in the selection of the best types or species of grass for a winter pitch; to give guidance on choosing individual cultivars from within each type of grass and; to suggest seeds mixtures for different categories of winter pitch.

Before going on to do this, it is well worth stressing that the very best grasses for winter sports will perform badly on under-fertilised and poorly drained pitches. However, if the management and construction are good then the choice of grass can have a profound affect on the durability and playing quality of that pitch. If poor quality grasses are sown the performance of the turf will be limited by those grasses, irrespective of how good the subsequent management is. Cheap grasses can become very expensive if they wear away quickly, require extra maintenance and invariably early replacement.

DESCRIPTION AND CHARACTERISTICS OF GRASSES USED IN WINTER PITCHES

In this sub-section grasses which have been used historically in seeds mixtures for soccer, Rugby and hockey pitches are described. Please note that their inclusion here is not necessarily a recommendation that they continue to be used in the future. Suggested seeds mixtures are discussed later. The grasses described below are: perennial ryegrass, smooth-stalked meadow-grass, Timothy, red fescue and bentgrasses. Before discussing these grasses individually, their performance in a football wear trial is compared in Plate 71. This trial was sown in 1990 and worn for two consecutive seasons, 1991/92 and 1992/93. The data presented are for the second season. In this season the relative wear tolerance of perennial ryegrass and smooth-stalked meadow-grass was markedly higher than that of the other grasses and smooth-stalked meadow-grass showed better recovery during the latter part of the season. Similar trends were found in the first season, with the exception of perennial ryegrass performing better than smooth-stalked meadow-grass, up to February of that season.

PERENNIAL RYEGRASS (*Lolium perenne* L.)

Perennial ryegrass has been cultivated for 300 or more years in the UK. During this time numerous strains have been selected, initially for agricultural uses. However, in the mid-1970's cultivars of this grass specifically selected for amenity uses also started to become available. This has increased from 3 in 1977 to in excess of 50 today. It is strongly suggested that the choice of cultivars of this grass for amenity use is restricted to these grasses, which have been specifically selected for sports and general amenity uses.

In mown turf perennial ryegrass is medium fine to coarse leaved (leaf width 2-6 mm). However, new material is now being bred with very fine leaves (less than 1 mm in width). Cultivars selected from this material should become available in the future. The leaves themselves are folded when young, strongly ribbed on the upper surface and very shiny on the lower surface. The mid-point of the lower surface also has a distinct rib running along its length. Other identifying features include a red or purple base to the shoot and auricles (claw-like projections), which are visible on the collar of the leaf where the blade meets the main body of the shoot. These structures are often very difficult to see in the amenity varieties.

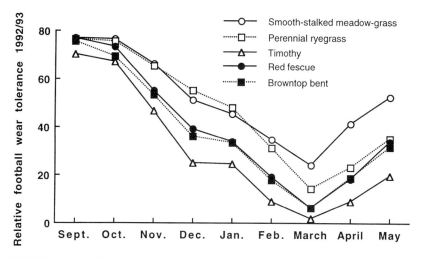

PLATE 71. Relative football wear tolerance of smooth-stalked meadow-grass, perennial ryegrass, Timothy, red fescue and browntop bent. The data presented are averaged monthly reflectance ratio measurements, which are strongly and positively correlated with ground cover.

Perennial ryegrass has a tufted growth habit in that it does not produce creeping stems. Some cultivars, however, have been shown to produce aerial tillers which may root. Being tufted in its growth habit, perennial ryegrass cannot spread as rapidly as creeping grasses into bare areas, nor can it repair damage as quickly. In addition, turf produced solely from perennial ryegrass does not tend to hold together very well. It does not have a strengthening web of creeping stems like that produced from some other grasses. As a consequence this grass is rarely grown on its own by turf producers. If it is, it often has to be cut very thickly when sold.

In turf, perennial ryegrass has a fairly open sward when grown on its own. As a result, other grasses are often sown with it to thicken the sward. In this respect grasses such as red fescues, bentgrasses and even smooth-stalked meadow-grass can improve the appearance of ryegrass turf, but they do not necessarily improve the performance or durability of the sward when used in a soccer or Rugby pitch. In terms of football wear tolerance, perennial ryegrass is markedly more wear tolerant than red fescues, bentgrasses or Timothy. Only smooth-stalked meadow-grass can be considered its equal in terms of wear tolerance.

No description of perennial ryegrass would be complete without discussing its speed of establishment following sowing. Its speed of establishment is markedly faster than all other amenity grasses commonly used in northern Europe. In good conditions this grass will show signs of life in 3-4 days after sowing and need cutting within two weeks. As perennial ryegrass establishes very quickly, it is the best and probably only grass to use for overseeding when there is only a short period between the end of play in one season and the start of play in the next. In a mixture the rapid establishment of the ryegrass proportion can swamp out the other grasses, particularly if the ryegrass plants are allowed to close the sward. Early topping of a new sward at 25-37 mm can prevent the sward closing and thus give other grasses a chance to establish.

Once mature, perennial ryegrass cultivars do not withstand persistent very close mowing, although breeders are continually improving this characteristic and newer cultivars which have better tolerance of close mowing are available. These should be selected for use in pitches which double up as cricket outfields (as long as their football wear tolerance is also good). The main disease of perennial ryegrass is red thread. Resistance to this disease varies amongst ryegrass cultivars, and its occurrence will affect the appearance of the sward and subsequent performance. Turf diseases are discussed in detail in Section 8 of this book.

SMOOTH-STALKED MEADOW-GRASS (*Poa pratensis*)

As mentioned previously, smooth-stalked meadow-grass is the only grass other than perennial ryegrass which can be considered for use in winter pitches on merit, assuming that the only characteristic used to decide its inclusion is tolerance of football wear. In turf this grass is medium fine to coarse-leaved (leaf width 2-5 mm). The youngest leaf is folded in the shoot and the tips of the leaves are blunt and commonly described as being 'boat shaped'. This grass has a ligule - a fleshy structure, which can be found at the upper junction of the leaf blade with the main body of the shoot. It also has tram lines running down the middle of the upper surface of the leaf. These can be hard to see, but they are an important distinguishing characteristic for all meadow-grasses. When looking for tram lines, the leaf should be rolled across the finger and then held up to the light. The central groove running up the middle of the upper surface of the leaf should then be examined carefully, if two parallel lines make up this central groove then it has tram lines.

The above features are also common to annual meadow-grass (*Poa annua*) which is considered to be a weed. Smooth-stalked meadow-grass can be distinguished from annual meadow-grass by its darker colour and shorter ligule. In addition, if it is producing seed heads after mid-July and before May it is definitely *P. annua*.

Poa pratensis is well suited to sandy soils and is very drought tolerant. It also seems to tolerate low fertility situations better than perennial ryegrass. Another important difference between perennial ryegrass and smooth-stalked meadow-grass is their relative tolerances of close mowing. Smooth-stalked meadow-grasses in trials at Bingley have tolerated mowing at a cutting height of 8 mm for four years, perennial ryegrass did not. This reasonable tolerance of close mowing would make *P. pratensis* a useful contributor to the sward where the pitch is used as a cricket outfield in the summer.

The main diseases which affect smooth-stalked meadow-grasses are rusts and leaf spot. This grass is most prone to attacks of rust in the autumn and leaf spot in the winter. Cultivars do, however, differ in their resistance to these diseases. This should be taken into account when selecting grasses where occurrence of the "disease" is likely to be high and/or if the use of pesticides is limited.

As stated earlier, tolerance of football wear is very good in smooth-stalked meadow-grass, with the best cultivars being comparable with the best ryegrasses. Like the ryegrasses, there is a range from average to very good amongst the different smooth-stalked meadow-grass cultivars. As such, care should be taken to choose cultivars with a good wear tolerance rating for use in a winter pitch. Unlike ryegrass, smooth-stalked meadow-grasses produce rhizomes. These creeping underground shoots allow this grass to repair damage to the surface very quickly. It is possible to completely destroy the grass surface and still achieve complete recovery from these underground shoots. In football wear trials at Bingley new shoots were evident in February and very strong recovery of the sward was noted in March - a time of the year when new growth would be greatly appreciated by most groundsmen.

This grass is much prized by turf producers because of its rhizomatous growth. These underground stems have been shown to add strength to turf, allowing it to be lifted earlier and cut thinner. This is particularly true for turf which contains other grasses which are restricted to a tufted growth habit such as perennial ryegrass. The inclusion of smooth-stalked meadow-grass in turf sold for winter pitches should not be viewed as disadvantageous. The main drawback of sowing *P. pratensis* is its slow establishment. In turf someone else has dealt with this problem. However, in a seeds mixture the slow establishment rate of smooth-stalked meadow-grass can make it very difficult to establish. Because of this it is not suitable for inclusion in overseeding mixtures, but given time to establish it will make a useful contribution to the sward. As such, smooth-stalked meadow-grass should be considered for inclusion in seed mixtures for new constructions. The time of sowing can also make a large difference with the best results being obtained when soil temperatures are high in late summer and early autumn.

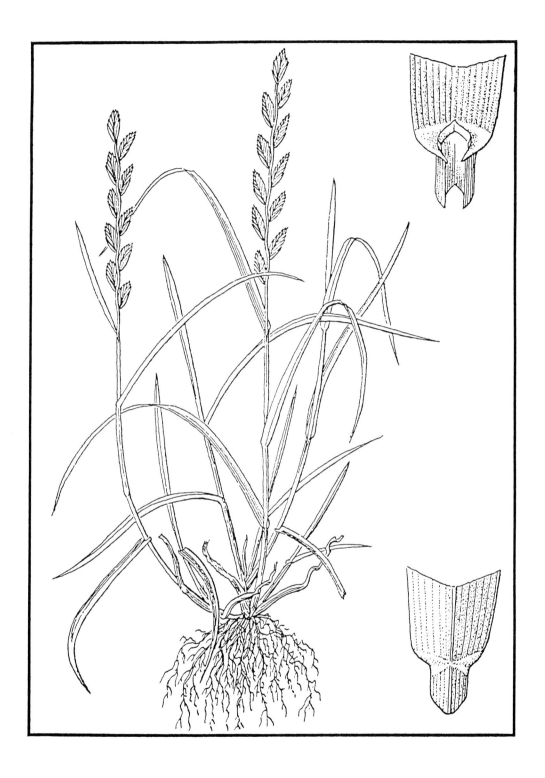

PLATE 72. Perennial ryegrass (*Lolium perenne*).

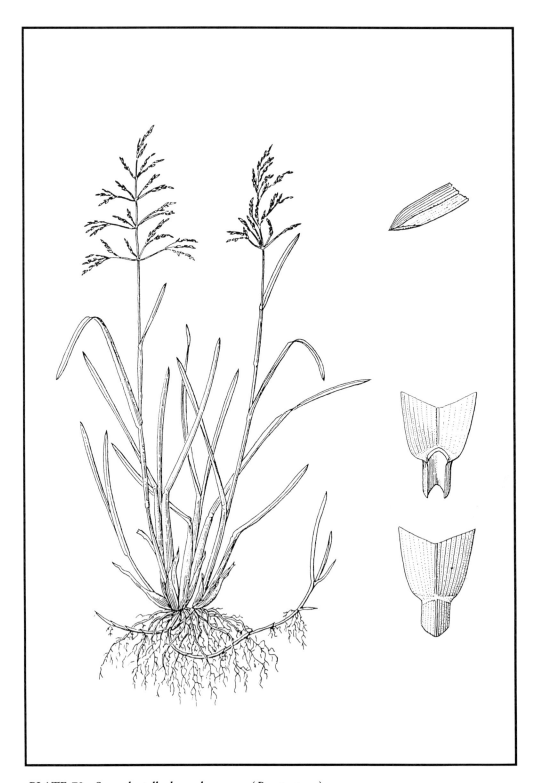

PLATE 73. Smooth-stalked meadow-grass (*Poa pratense*).

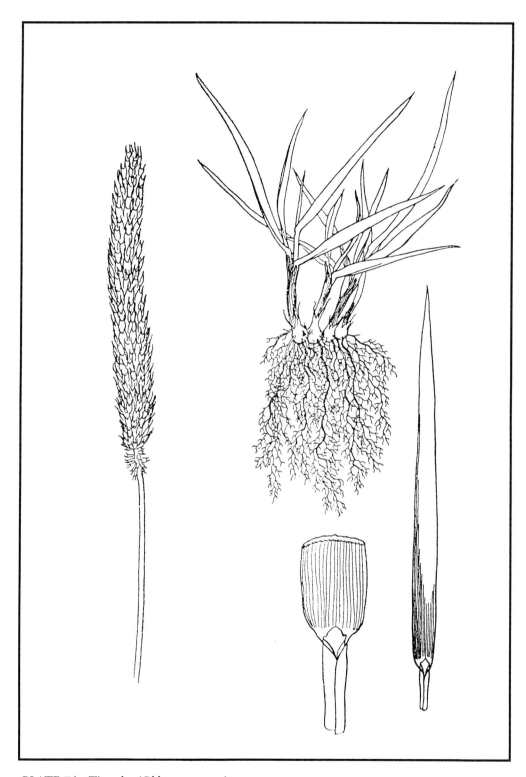

PLATE 74. Timothy (*Phleum pratense*).

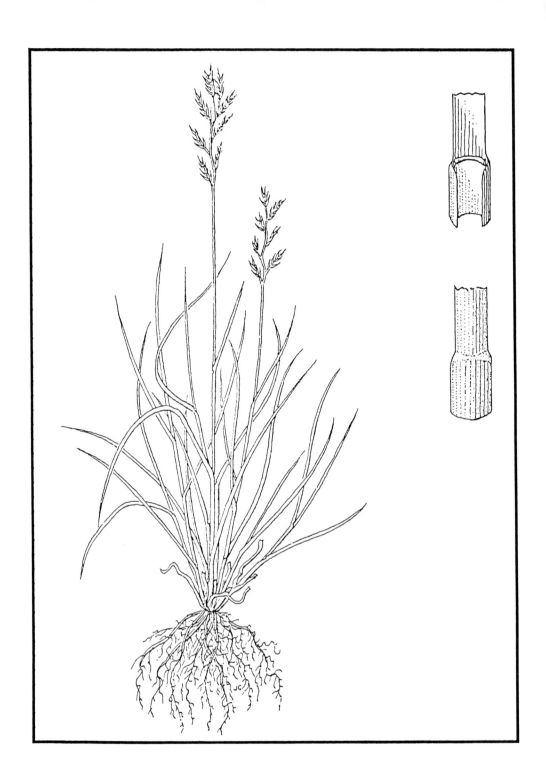

PLATE 75. Fescue (*Festuca* spp.).

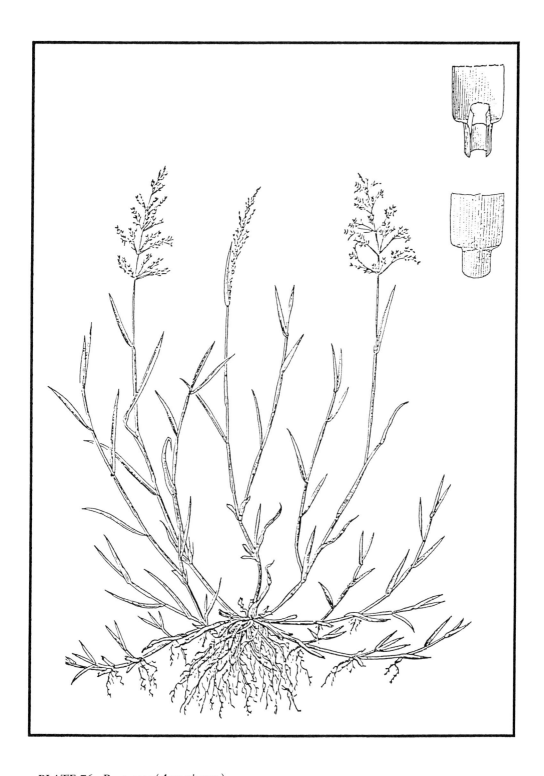

PLATE 76. Bentgrass (*Agrostis* spp.).

103

TIMOTHY (*Phleum pratense*)

The common name Timothy was derived from Timothy Hanson, who introduced this grass to the USA in the 1720's. In turf two types of Timothy have been used: large-leaved Timothy (*P. pratense*) and small-leaved Timothy (*P. pratense* ssp. *bertolonii*). Historically, these two types were considered to be distinct species, but now the small-leaved Timothy is classified by taxonomists to be a subspecies of large-leaved Timothy. In terms of leaf texture, small-leaved Timothy could be described as medium fine to coarse-leaved (leaf width 2-5 mm), whereas large-leaved Timothy can be described as medium fine to very coarse-leaved (leaf width 3-9 mm). In a mown sward these grasses look very much like large bentgrasses in that the leaves are yellow/green with a dull greyish hue. The youngest leaf is rolled in the shoot and the older, expanded leaves may twist. These grasses have a pointed ligule and the base of the shoot may become bulbous. They are also restricted to a tufted growth habit.

Ten years ago there were 15 cultivars of Timothy commercially available for use in amenity situations, as described in *Turfgrass Seed 1984*. Today there is one. This is a fair indication of the current importance of this grass for use in turf. Timothy is markedly less tolerant of football wear, in comparison with perennial ryegrass and smooth-stalked meadow-grass. Its advantage was its good adaption to wet, heavy soils. It is the view of the STRI that winter pitches should be better drained and better constructed, rather than sown with an inferior grass, even if it does tolerate poor conditions.

Timothy establishes readily from seed, not as fast as perennial ryegrass but much faster than smooth-stalked meadow-grass. It can be affected by leaf spot disease, but this does not tend to cause much damage to the grass. This grass does not in fact suffer any serious disease problems.

RED FESCUES (*Festuca rubra*)

There are three types of red fescue: Chewings, slender creeping and strong creeping. The Chewings fescues are restricted to a tufted growth habit, whereas the slender creeping and strong creeping fescues produce, as their names suggest, creeping underground stems called rhizomes. In a mixed sward these grasses can usually be recognised by their very fine leaves, they are often described as having needle-like leaves. In this respect their leaf widths rarely exceed 1.5 mm and they are usually finer than that. The leaves are also shiny in appearance and when inspected very closely inrolled. The leaf sheaths when viewed through a hand lens are covered in small, downward pointing hairs. The lower sheaths may also be purple.

In fine turf the Chewings and the slender creeping fescues are markedly superior to the strong creeping red fescues, both in appearance and performance. The strong creeping red fescues do not tolerate very close mowing. The better cultivars of Chewings and slender creeping red fescues will tolerate persistent close mowing down to 5 mm. However, in a football situation there is probably little to choose between these three types of fescue.

All red fescues tested in football wear trials have been fairly intolerant of this type of wear, particularly so when they have been compared with perennial ryegrass and smooth-stalked meadow-grass. They can nevertheless improve the appearance of ryegrass and smooth-stalked meadow-grass swards. Red fescues have been described as bottom grasses because of their ability to fill an otherwise open sward. So in simple terms red fescues can improve the appearance, but not the performance of a soccer or Rugby pitch.

In performance terms, red fescues can be usefully included in pitches which are mown down in the summer to form part of a cricket outfield. Although they decline rapidly during play in the winter, they do recover very strongly in late spring and early summer. Because of their tolerance of close mowing, drought and if needed low fertility, red fescues can add to the performance of a cricket outfield. In terms of close mowing, Chewings and slender creeping red fescues perform better than strong creeping red fescues. In relation to drought tolerance, Chewings and strong creeping red fescues are good but slender creeping red fescues are even better.

There are two major diseases which affect red fescues. These are red thread and dollar spot. Although there are cultivar differences within each type of red fescue, as a group Chewings fescues tend to be more resistant to these diseases.

BENTGRASSES (*Agrostis* spp.)
There are three types of bentgrass commonly in use. These are: *A. castellana* (browntop bent), *A. tenuis* (browntop bent) and *A. stolonifera* (creeping bent). There are a number of cultivars available within the creeping bent and *A. tenuis* types, but only one cultivar of *A. castellana*. This cultivar is called 'Highland' and it is the cheapest and most widely used bentgrass in amenity turf mixtures. Please note that its price is only low in relation to other bentgrasses. Weight for weight it is very expensive when compared with other amenity grasses. However, its very small seed size means that a mixture containing just 5% of the grass may well contain more individual bentgrass seeds than seeds of any other grass in the mixture.

All bentgrasses produce creeping stems. However, the type of creeping stems produced differ. Creeping bentgrass produce stolons which spread over the surface of the soil, whereas the browntop bents produce mainly rhizomes which creep below the surface of the soil. In turf the leaves tend to be rather dull in appearance with the youngest leaf being rolled in the shoot. Leaf fineness of bentgrasses varies from very fine to medium coarse (leaf width 1-6 mm).

As mentioned above, the most common bentgrass in amenity mixtures is 'Highland'. It is extremely unlikely that a football mixture which includes some bentgrass includes any bent other than 'Highland'. The better cultivars of the other bents do, however, tend to perform and look better in ornamental and very close mown turf. 'Highland' bentgrass is often described as having good colour in winter, it also shows growth in winter when other grasses are dormant. However, 'Highland' and the other bentgrasses are fairly intolerant of football wear and they cannot show good growth when they have worn away. Like red fescues, bentgrasses can improve the appearance of the sward, but not its performance during wear. Also like the red fescues, 'Highland' could usefully be included in pitches which form part of a cricket outfield in the summer.

A number of diseases affect bentgrasses and may reduce their visual appeal, such as red thread, leaf spot and fusarium patch disease. There is one disease which is capable of completely destroying bentgrass turf. This disease is take-all patch and there is no chemical treatment for it. Whereas there are cultivar differences in the resistance to other diseases, all bentgrasses are extremely susceptible to take-all patch disease.

CHOOSING GRASSES USING THE *TURFGRASS SEED* BOOKLET
The STRI is the only independent organisation in the UK which conducts tests on the performance of amenity grasses. Information from these studies are used to update the annually published *Turfgrass Seed* booklet. *Turfgrass Seed* is the most comprehensive and only non-trade guide to the performance of grasses for use in winter pitches. It also includes information on the performance of different grasses for other amenity uses.

In the booklet the characteristics and performance of amenity grass cultivars within the different types of grass available are described in one or more tables. Within each table there are a number of columns which describe individual characteristics such as wear tolerance, fineness of leaf, resistance to disease and shoot density. Information within these columns is presented in a numerical system based on a 1 = poor to 10 = good scale. Users of *Turfgrass Seed* can thus select grasses which score highly in characteristics which are important for their intended use. In selecting grasses for winter pitches a high score for tolerance of football type wear would be a good starting point. The booklet provides descriptive information on the colour of grasses in winter and summer. It also provides names and addresses for the suppliers of the different grasses. Tables in *Turfgrass Seed* for the different grass types have been placed in particular orders which reflect one or more of the most important uses of the different grass types. At this point please note that the following discussion will be limited to two types of grass; perennial ryegrass and smooth-stalked meadow-grass. In *Turfgrass Seed* there are two tables for cultivars of perennial ryegrass, one places the available grasses in order of suitability for use in soccer and Rugby fields (Table 1 in *Turfgrass Seed*), the other in order for finer turf uses (Table 2 in *Turfgrass Seed*). The order in Table 1 is determined solely on the basis of wear tolerance, it does not take into account any other factors. This needs to be borne in mind when cultivars of perennial ryegrass are selected from this list for particular sites. In individual situations, the groundsman may need to and should combine wear tolerances with other factors which are important for his particular site and management regime. If the maintenance budget is limited the groundsman may wish to combine wear tolerance under low fertility with short growth and disease resistance. Thus choosing a grass or grasses which will fit in best with a minimum maintenance regime in which cutting, fertiliser and pesticide application are likely to be limited. If the pitch is to be used as a cricket outfield in the summer, it would be best to combine wear tolerance with tolerance of close mowing. In this case it would be appropriate to choose grasses using both lists in *Turfgrass Seed* to find the grasses which have the best combination of wear tolerance for use in winter and finer turf characteristics (tolerance of close mowing, fineness of leaf) for use in summer.

In *Turfgrass Seed* the table for cultivars of smooth-stalked meadow-grass is ordered in relation to both finer turf and wear uses. As a result, cultivars towards the top of this list may be good all-rounders, but not necessarily the best available for heavy duty sports turf. As wear tolerance is the most important characteristic when choosing grasses for a soccer or a Rugby pitch, the choice of grass is probably better limited to the most wear tolerant grasses before other characteristics are considered.

Tables for cultivars of perennial ryegrass and smooth-stalked meadow-grass based on information in *Turfgrass Seed 1994* are presented below. The table for smooth-stalked meadow-grass is a reproduction of Table 8. Please note that this table, as pointed out above, is placed in order of the averaged suitabilities for use in winter pitches and other finer turf situations. As a result, the best grasses for a winter pitch may not be at the top of the list. The perennial ryegrass table is the same as Table 1 in the booklet.

TABLE 8 (from *Turfgrass Seed 1994*)
SMOOTH-STALKED MEADOW-GRASS (*Poa pratensis*)

Cultivar	Wear tolerance	Shoot density	Mean	Fineness of leaf	Short growth	Freedom from leaf spot	Orange stripe rust resistance	Summer greenness	Winter greenness
Limousine	7.3	8.4	7.9	7.5	5.5	6.2	3.7	DG	MG
Julia	7.6	6.3	7.0	6.1	4.8	7.8	5.8	MG	MG
Minstrel	7.1	6.1	6.6	5.4	4.4	5.9	7.2	MG	MG
Haga	7.2	5.8	6.5	5.0	6.7	6.1	6.8	DG	DG
Melba	5.9	7.1	6.5	6.0	6.2	6.4	5.8	DG	MG
Broadway	6.8	6.1	6.5	5.1	4.4	5.9	5.1	MG	DG
Conni	5.5	7.2	6.3	6.6	6.1	5.9	6.2	DG	MG
Cynthia	6.2	6.3	6.3	7.4	6.5	5.2	5.1	MG	DG
Trampas	5.4	6.4	5.9	5.8	6.1	5.9	–	MG	DG
Asset	6.1	5.6	5.9	5.2	5.9	6.6	6.4	DG	DG
Nimbus	6.0	5.7	5.8	5.3	6.8	5.8	6.8	DG	DG
Andante	5.6	5.9	5.8	6.2	6.1	6.9	6.5	MG	MG
Ampellia	5.7	5.7	5.7	6.8	4.0	7.4	5.9	MG	DG
Entopper	6.0	5.1	5.6	5.0	6.3	4.2	6.8	MG	MG
Fylking	5.1	6.0	5.5	7.4	5.6	5.0	6.5	–	–
Parade	6.2	4.8	5.5	5.6	6.4	5.5	6.7	MG	DG
Enprima	4.9	5.6	5.2	6.6	5.9	5.6	–	MG	MG
Baron	4.9	4.3	4.6	4.4	7.4	4.6	6.8	MG	MG
New cultivars									
Cocktail	7.5	8.0	7.8	7.7	5.5	6.3	5.0	DG	MG
Miracle	7.3	7.7	7.5	5.0	7.2	5.1	6.6	MG	MG
Rocardo	6.1	8.1	7.1	7.7	5.5	6.7	6.6	MG	LG
Barvictor	6.9	7.0	6.9	5.9	7.2	–	–	DG	DG
Star	7.0	5.5	6.3	3.7	6.3	–	–	MG	LG
Fortuna	5.1	7.0	6.0	6.3	7.9	5.7	6.3	DG	DG
Saskia	5.2	6.6	5.9	6.5	6.3	–	–	MG	DG
Cardiff	6.3	5.1	5.7	4.8	6.3	2.6	6.6	DG	MG

TABLE 1   (from *Turfgrass Seed 1994*)

PERENNIAL RYEGRASS (*Lolium perenne*) FOR HEAVY DUTY SPORTS TURF (SOCCER, RUGBY, etc)

Important: Read pages 2 and 3 before evaluating cultivars.

Cultivar	Wear tolerance Low N	Wear tolerance High N	Mean	Shoot density	Fineness of leaf	Cleanness of cut	Slow regrowth (regular mowing)	Freedom from red thread	Winter greenness
Master	8.7	7.7	8.2	4.9	5.6	5.1	5.8	7.1	DG
Meteor	7.6	7.9	7.8	6.3	6.7	4.6	6.0	6.9	DG
Allegro	7.9	7.2	7.6	5.1	4.7	6.2	6.4	4.8	MG
Barclay	6.7	8.2	7.5	6.9	7.0	6.5	6.6	6.2	MG
Cartel	7.3	7.2	7.3	6.1	5.5	3.8	5.9	5.5	DG
Barlow	7.3	6.9	7.1	5.5	6.7	5.9	7.0	6.1	DG
Danilo	7.3	6.8	7.0	7.0	6.7	7.7	6.1	5.8	DG
Barrage	6.9	6.9	6.9	5.0	4.3	5.7	5.9	6.2	DG
Queens	7.2	6.5	6.8	6.7	6.1	6.1	6.9	6.1	DG
Surprise	6.4	7.3	6.8	5.3	6.5	4.3	5.0	6.1	DG
Avenue	6.6	7.0	6.8	6.3	5.8	5.6	6.7	5.5	MG
Score	6.6	6.9	6.8	5.5	5.4	3.1	4.7	6.0	MG
Troubadour	6.9	6.4	6.6	6.1	7.0	5.9	6.4	5.8	MG
Cavalier	6.3	6.7	6.5	6.5	6.0	6.4	5.5	6.1	DG
Superstar	6.5	6.5	6.5	7.1	7.0	4.2	5.6	5.4	MG
Lisabelle	6.7	6.3	6.5	6.8	6.4	5.9	6.2	5.9	MG
Taya	6.0	6.9	6.5	5.1	5.2	5.9	7.0	4.2	MG
Mondial	6.6	6.3	6.5	5.4	4.9	6.4	5.5	5.4	DG
Liselotte	6.4	6.5	6.4	6.1	6.7	5.5	6.2	6.5	MG
Hermes	6.0	6.9	6.4	4.8	3.4	5.3	4.4	6.7	DG
Jetta	6.7	6.1	6.4	5.1	6.3	4.9	6.0	5.7	DG
Barcredo	6.8	5.7	6.3	6.8	6.6	7.3	7.1	6.1	MG
Elka	6.5	6.1	6.3	7.8	7.5	7.2	6.8	5.1	DG
Outsider	6.6	5.8	6.2	4.1	4.2	4.6	4.7	6.1	DG
Juwel	6.0	6.3	6.2	4.7	4.2	4.4	6.1	4.1	MG
Manhattan	5.6	6.5	6.1	4.7	5.1	5.3	5.9	5.2	DG
Barry	6.0	6.1	6.1	6.1	6.0	6.0	7.0	5.4	DG
Hunter	6.2	5.6	5.9	5.5	5.2	5.0	6.3	5.3	LG
Langa	5.8	6.0	5.9	5.8	5.8	5.9	5.9	7.2	DG
Lisuna	6.1	5.6	5.9	5.5	5.7	5.9	5.5	6.7	DG
Numan	5.8	5.8	5.8	6.8	6.7	7.0	6.0	6.5	DG
Prester	5.9	5.7	5.8	6.3	4.7	7.9	5.9	7.1	DG
Loretta	6.1	5.5	5.8	6.1	5.8	7.4	6.6	6.1	MG
Entrar	5.5	5.9	5.7	6.0	6.7	4.9	6.4	3.8	MG
Sprinter	5.5	5.9	5.7	4.6	5.0	4.7	4.6	6.4	MG
Gator	5.6	5.8	5.7	5.3	6.0	6.2	5.8	6.0	DG
Majestic	5.7	5.4	5.6	4.6	5.6	5.8	4.6	6.1	DG
Arno	5.4	5.7	5.5	4.9	5.2	5.2	6.7	5.3	MG
Lorina	5.9	5.1	5.5	7.6	6.1	7.5	7.9	5.4	DG
Wendy	6.0	4.5	5.2	2.8	2.9	3.8	3.5	7.2	DG
New cultivars									
Rambo	7.9	7.9	7.9	7.9	6.9	4.8	7.7	6.7	MG
Martina	5.7	6.8	6.3	6.3	6.1	6.6	6.1	6.5	–
Merci	7.2	4.2	5.7	7.9	8.3	6.1	6.8	6.3	–
Lissabon	5.8	5.6	5.7	5.8	6.4	6.4	6.8	6.1	–
Delaware	4.4	5.7	5.0	7.1	5.5	6.7	6.5	5.6	–
Hobbit	5.2	4.0	4.6	6.5	5.9	8.1	5.9	5.7	–

SEEDS MIXTURES FOR WINTER PITCHES

SEED WEIGHT

Seeds mixtures for winter pitches tend to contain a blend of perennial ryegrass cultivars, usually two or three, or a mixture of perennial ryegrass with one or more other types of grass. The proportion of the different cultivars and/or types of grass are described in terms of the percentage weight of seed. For example, a mixture may contain 60% perennial ryegrass, 30% red fescue and 10% browntop bent. If this mixture was divided into its constituents then 60% of the total weight would be accounted for by perennial ryegrass, 30% by red fescues and 10% by browntop bent. However, the number of individual seeds of each constituent would not follow these proportions. Perennial ryegrass seeds are heavier than red fescue seeds, which in turn are much heavier than bentgrass seeds. In this mixture for every 100 seeds of perennial ryegrass there would be 84 red fescue seeds and 398 bentgrass seeds. Average seed weights for grasses which have been used in mixtures for winter pitches are described below.

Average individual seed weights and numbers of seed in 1 g for cultivars of perennial ryegrass, smooth-stalked meadow-grass, red fescue, Timothy and bentgrasses

Type of grass	Individual seed weight (mg)	Number of seed in 1 g
Perennial ryegrass	1.67	600
Smooth-stalked meadow-grass	0.33	3,000
Red fescue	1.00	1,000
Timothy	0.25	4,000
Bentgrasses	0.07	15,000

Please note that what you sow and what you grow may be two very distinct things. The proportions of different grasses in a new sward will be affected by choice of seeds mixture, but it will also be affected by sowing conditions, germination rates and total germination of the individual constituents and early management of the sward. Relatively few perennial ryegrass seeds in a mixture can produce a sward which is predominantly perennial ryegrass. This grass germinates and establishes much faster than other amenity grasses. As a result it is able to stake a claim to most of the available spaces in a new sward before the other grasses get a chance.

SEED GERMINATION AND PURITY
All seed sold for use in a winter pitch is covered by the official seed regulations. These set legal standards for purity and germination for different grasses. In this respect all certified seed has to have been tested by an official seed testing station or a private licenced seed testing station prior to being sold. To be sold the germination and purity has to exceed certain minimum standards. These standards are set out below.

Percentage germination, purity and permitted seed content for perennial ryegrass, smooth-stalked meadow-grass, red fescue, Timothy and bentgrasses as set out in the 1993 seed regulations

Type of grass	Minimum germination (%)	Purity (%)		Other seeds (%)
		Normal	Higher voluntary standard	
Perennial ryegrass	80	96	98	1.5
Smooth-stalked meadow-grass	75	85	90	2.0
Red fescue	75	90	95	1.5
Timothy	80	96	98	1.5
Bentgrasses	75	90	-	2.0

For most grasses there is a higher voluntary standard for seed purity. This, as the name suggests, is a voluntary standard and mixtures of inferior purity can legally be sold. However, it may be worth paying more for seed with the higher standard. All reputable seedsmen will be pleased, if asked, to provide information on germination, purity and noxious weed content of the mixtures which they sell.

SEED MIXTURES
Before discussing the different mixtures it is appropriate to make a distinction between soccer and Rugby on the one hand and hockey on the other. Soccer and Rugby pitches receive intensive wear, but they are not, or should not be, mown at a cutting height of less than 25 mm. Ideally, soccer pitches should be mown at 25-38 mm and Rugby pitches at 25-75 mm. Hockey, however, makes demands of a pitch which real turf finds hard to meet in the winter involving close mowing and

heavy wear. Grasses which are most tolerant of heavy wear tend to be those which are least tolerant of close mowing. As a consequence seed mixtures for hockey pitches (and indeed for lacrosse pitches) tend to contain a mix of grasses which tolerate wear or close mowing, but not both. These mixtures are a compromise but efforts should be made to seek the best grasses in difficult circumstances. Relative tolerance of close mowing should be included in the calculation when choosing wear tolerant grasses. In addition, Chewings and slender creeping red fescues will probably be a better option than strong creeping red fescue. That said, hockey at the highest levels does now tend to be played on artificial turf in the UK.

Suggested seed mixtures for soccer, Rugby and hockey pitches are set out below. Please note that the suggested proportions of different grass types are just guide lines, they are not written in tablets of stone. Practically, differences of 5-10% from the suggested proportions would usually have little effect on the resulting sward.

Seed mixtures for winter pitches. The proportions given refer to percentage weight of seed

Type of grass	Mixture			
	[1]	[2]	[3]	[4]
Perennial ryegrass	100	60	40	50
Smooth-stalked meadow-grass	-	40	30	-
Red fescue	-	-	20	40
Browntop bent	-	-	10	10

Mixture [1]
This mixture is for overseeding existing pitches and new constructions where there is little time between seeding and play. It is suitable for soccer and Rugby pitches, but not hockey or other pitches which form part of a cricket outfield in the summer. Although 100% perennial ryegrass is suggested, this should be made up of two or more different cultivars.

Mixture [2]
Mixture [2] can be used in new constructions for soccer, Rugby, American football and Gaelic games, but is not recommended for hockey pitches or where the pitch forms part of a cricket outfield in the summer. Nor is it recommended for overseeding existing playing fields.

Mixture [3]
This general, broad mixture is suitable for most winter pitches, including hockey and those which are used as cricket outfields. It should not be used for overseeding. The red fescue portion should be split between Chewings and slender creeping red fescues for use in hockey pitches and where the pitch forms part of a cricket outfield. Strong creeping red fescues would be acceptable for soccer and Rugby mixtures.

Mixture [4]
Like mixture [3], this mixture is suitable for general use including hockey, lacrosse and cricket outfields, but not for overseeding. As above, the red fescue portion should be split between Chewings and slender creeping fescues for hockey and where the pitch forms part of a cricket outfield in the summer.

PITCH MAINTENANCE : MECHANICAL EQUIPMENT
By S.P. ISAAC

Any turf facility employed for sporting activity has to be managed to produce playing surfaces of acceptable quality for the nature of the game played upon it. Although winter games pitches may not require the finesse of a maintenance package designed for areas of finer turf, e.g. bowling greens, they must receive a certain level of attention to promote suitable conditions underfoot and adequate grass coverage.

Hockey is perhaps the one sport where the pitch has to be prepared to a high standard as ball to surface contact is fundamental to the game. The fact that all major hockey is now played on artificial surfaces highlights this fact. Soccer and Rugby may not be quite so demanding but the quality of preparation and presentation must increase as one works toward the professional theatre for either sport. A dominating aspect of pitch quality often commented upon is the appearance in terms of grass retention and aesthetic striping, particularly as the season draws to a conclusion and many pitches are boggy morasses suitable for little more than kick and chase. A groundsman's job is difficult at the best of times but there may be the added pressure of producing a pitch which favours the playing qualities of the home side; a well grassed, smooth surface for passing sides and running Rugby teams, or a more unpredictable, slower surface for the "up and under" experts of the soccer world or Rugby teams reliant on the heavyweights of the pack. To a degree local authorities are rarely put under such scrutiny but are responsible for providing pitches for many more matches per season and if they fail in this may suffer financially from a loss of revenue from pitch hire.

Winter pitches are, by the nature of the sport played on them, prone to the very worst the British climate can produce. Drainage must be sound to allow play at all, never mind play in wet conditions. The soil must be adequately cultivated to achieve annual renewal of a grass cover, ever more difficult with a seemingly never ending playing season. The elements of a management programme which relate to fine tuning of the sward, i.e. mowing and fertiliser, are totally reliant on those practices, essentially aeration, which sustain a dry, playable surface and thereby a grass cover.

The components of a management package for winter pitches revolve around the basics of mowing and aeration, but there are many other aspects of work which a groundsman is responsible for. There are key machines that a groundsman cannot do without but the demands on the pitch, in terms of expected performance and appearance, will determine the level of maintenance required and hence the level of mechanisation. More often than not the latter does not meet the needs of the former!

MOWERS AND MOWING
Effects of mowing
Mowing is one of the most frequent operations carried out on turf and has an important effect on:

[1] The growth habit of grasses – whether upright or procumbent. Cylinder mowers with rollers may flatten the grass. This is important as a cleaner cut will be achieved if the grass is standing up into the mowing unit. Lying grasses will smother weaker emergent ones producing a thinner turf and possibly encouraging weed ingress through the promotion of a shaded micro climate. This can be a problem during the winter as one of the affects of play is to flatten the grass.

[2] Root and shoot development and hence the density and wear tolerance of the sward.

[3] The botanical composition of the sward. For each grass species there is a minimum height of cut at which it can survive, e.g. perennial ryegrass weakens if regularly cut at less than 20 mm ($^3/_4$). No grasses survive satisfactorily under regular mowing below 5 mm ($^3/_{16}$") although this should not concern the groundsman as pitches should never be cut that closely.

Weed population and type of weed in turf also affected by mowing. Under close cutting only low-growing weeds can survive, e.g. rosette types (daisy, plantain), types with surface runners (clover), types with underground runners (sedges) and the mat–forming types (pearlwort, chickweed). Larger weeds are occasionally seen on winter pitches following end of season renovation or if the pitch is not cut frequently enough, e.g. docks and thistle, but they only thrive whilst the cutting level is relaxed to encourage grass seedling development and are generally mown out as the cutting height is reduced.

[4] Compaction within the soil. Different machines cause different amounts of compaction, e.g. tractor-mounted machines exert greater ground pressure than pedestrian cylinder mowers. This can be a particular problem on pitches where there is little room for turning beyond the boundaries of the playing surface itself, e.g. in stadia where there is only a narrow track between the pitch and spectators or large sports fields where as many pitches as can be fitted in are utilised. Here the choice of equipment must be given careful consideration.

Types of machine
[1] Cylinder mowers comprising a rotating reel of sharpened blades cutting across a fixed bottom blade (sole plate). Petrol-driven or electric (mains or battery) or tractor-driven. Pedestrian machines can be side wheel or roller types completely power-driven or cutting cylinder only driven. Dual clutch machines incorporate both mechanisms. Only the larger units are of interest to groundsmen looking after pitches, mainly used for hockey pitches, with or without a grass collecting box and have a trailing seat for ease of operation.

Ride-on cylinder mowers are becoming popular with sports clubs looking after a variety of areas due to their speed and quality of finish, particularly if there are tight corners or limited access. Triple and quintuple gang units are available with or without grass collection.

Mini-gangs for smaller areas and a fine finish. Tractor-drawn or tractor-mounted gang units for larger areas. Hydraulically driven gang mowers tend to provide a more uniform cut than gear driven and a better cut in wet conditions. The gang mounting rides on studded disc or pneumatic tyres, the latter should cause less surface impression and even if wet should not slide on a level area. If pitches are mown out of undulating or sloping ground then the studded discs may be more appropriate and they eliminate problems of tyre pressure, influencing height of cut.

[2] Rotary mowers have a sharpened horizontally rotating blade. Petrol-driven, electric or tractor-driven. Hand-pushed self-propelled wheeled or hover-type rotaries, roller types, tractor-mounted and ride-on available. Pedestrian mowers have a single or double blades, the wider the tractor-mounted or ride-on the greater the number of blades, although usually 2-3. Grass collection possible on some. Strimmers work on the rotary principle. A direct comparison between rotary mower cutting and a cylinder machine shows a superior finish from the cylinder, i.e. with the rotary the grass is torn rather than cut cleanly. The main difficulty with rotary mowers, in so far as routine cutting is concerned, is that they tend to leave lines of grass clippings. Developments in rotary mower technology has provided an improvement in the quality of cut and clipping collection usually through a suction effect from the cutting blades which draws the cuttings into a hopper. Even so the expert eye can, relatively easily, tell the difference between the cut produced by a quality cylinder mower and that from a quality rotary.

[3] Combination machines : interchangeable cylinder or rotary heads with or without grass collection.

[4] Flail mowers cut grass through the speed of vertical rotation of splayed blades. Self-propelled or tractor-mounted. There is a move towards an increase in the use of flail mowers for the cutting of winter pitches, advances in design have certainly improved the quality of finish, mainly a result of finer blades and grass collection. If used regularly these flail machines have a mulching effect although they are still inferior to the better cylinder machines. Combination flail mowers cum sweepers have an advantage in collecting cuttings and other debris and can produce a striped finish with their roller base.

PLATE 77. Ransomes Mastiff 76 or 91 cm motor mower. The operator on the steering seat can be seen raising the front rolls off the ground into the transport position. (Courtesy Ransomes Sims & Jefferies Ltd.)

PLATE 78. The 36" Premier mower from Dennis with suspension trailer seat. (Courtesy Dennis of Derby.)

PLATE 79. The Lloyds Standard Leda trailed gang mower. Units are available in 760 or 915 mm cutting widths, with 4,5, 6 or 9 blade cylinders. (Courtesy Lloyds & Co. Letchworth Ltd.)

PLATE 80. The Ransomes Sportcutter Mk II trailed gang mower in a 5-unit combination. (Courtesy Ransomes Sims & Jefferies Ltd.)

[5] Reapers : pedestrian, tractor-drawn or mounted motorised scythes. Only for use in reclaiming neglected sites where a silage cut is needed before better quality mowers can be used.

For routine mowing of pitches the mower to consider is a cylinder machine. The fine turf of top quality hockey pitches needs a machine capable of providing 60–80 cuts per metre (54–73 cuts per yard) and height of cut variable from 12–25 mm (½–1") for a good finish. This will also apply to the quality of machine for cutting premier arenas for other winter sports. Pitches taking a lower standard of play may be cut with a set of gangs capable of 25–35 cuts per metre (23–32 cuts per yard). The number of cuts per metre is related to the design of the cutting mechanism; the number of blades on the cylinder, diameter of the cylinder, speed of rotation of the cylinder and forward speed of the mower itself all influencing the quality of cut. For a striped finish the mower must have a roller, alternating stripes being produced by making cutting passes in the opposite direction. Rotary mowers have a role in topping emerging seedlings following renovation and may provide an acceptable finish for Rugby and other winter games where the quality of appearance is not critical. The same principle applies to the better flail mowers.

Whilst consideration of the quality of cut is paramount, speed of operation must also be a concern, particularly for those involved in mowing large areas. When comparing machines in the following table appreciate that one soccer pitch can involve an area of 1 hectare (2.5 acres).

Type of mower	Hectares per day (8 hour)	Acres per day (8 hour)	Suitable for areas of	
			Hectares	Acres
Pedestrian mowers				
91 cm (36")	4.0	10	2.4 –4.0	6 – 10
102 cm (40")	4.9	12	2.8 – 4.9	7 – 12
Gang mowers				
Triple (3)	8	20	sports grounds	
Quintuple (5)	14 – 16	35 – 40	playing fields	
Septuple (7)	20 – 24	50 – 60	large playing fields	
Nonuple (9)	36 – 40	90 – 100	exceptionally large areas	

The following factors influence the effect of the mowing machine on the sward:

[1] Height of cut. Different heights of cut favour different grass species in the sward. Very low heights of cut weaken almost all grasses and encourage moss and some weeds, e.g. pearlwort and rosette type weed. Excessively high cutting encourages coarse grasses, upright weeds and formation of a stubble-like sward of inadequate density.

The height of cut employed will have a direct bearing on the nature of the playing surface, becoming more important the greater the ball to surface contact for a particular sport. The cutting height should also vary according to season – cutting higher during the late autumn, winter and early spring when little growth is taking place. The recommended cutting levels for a variety of winter games are:

	Summer		Winter	
	mm	inches	mm	inches
Hockey pitches	12–25	½–1	12–25	½–1
Rugby pitches	25–50	1–2	50–75	2–3
Soccer pitches	25–38	1–1½	25–38	1–1½

The cutting height chart provides guidance only and the individual situation and requirements of each pitch must be taken into account before deciding on any particular mowing regime.

Uniform machine setting is essential and careful measurement of height of cut is required, using an "F.G.S." or similar mower gauge. The most convenient units are millimetres or sixteenths of an inch. For correct setting the cutting unit must be set on a level surface, most gang mowers have notches which adjust the rear roller and thereby the cutting height. The mower does not always give the same height of cut as the bench setting, e.g. on fibrous turf the mower may sink into the sward. Gang mowers with floating heads may require different settings in comparison to conventional single unit machines or those with fixed cutting heads.

[2] Frequency of mowing. There tends to be great emphasis placed on the importance of cutting height and too little to the actual number of cuts given to turf per week. The two factors are of equal importance to the production of a quality sward. The best playing surface will be one mown regularly at a suitable height, the exact requirement for each parameter related to the needs of the sport and standard of those playing upon it. Fine quality turf on a hockey pitch needs mowing twice per week in good growing weather, whereas coarse turf needs to be cut at least once per week. Cutting during the autumn and winter should not be neglected if growth is taking place.

[3] Return or removal of cuttings. If cuttings are boxed off then more fertiliser is required to restore soil nutrients. Allowing cuttings to fly produces a more drought-resistant sward of better colour. On the other hand it produces a softer turf more susceptible to disease and favours an increase in weeds, worms and weed grasses. For a top quality playing surface cuttings should be boxed off, e.g. for hockey and first class soccer.

[4] Direction of mowing. The direction of mowing should be varied where possible for each cut in order to reduce the risk of pile (grain or nap). Attractive striping patterns are produced by double cutting or other types of combination cut.

[5] Moisture. A clean cut will be achieved on a reasonably dry surface. Wet grass will tear and there will be a tendency for clippings to amass on the mower, dropping off irregularly to leave piles of grass and an untidy finish. On parched dry grass there is also a tendency to tear, especially on coarser cultivars of ryegrass.

For each winter sport the mowing patterns will vary in terms of cutting height and frequency. Once the end of season renovation work has been completed, a programme of regular mowing treatments will be the key to producing a fine, even surface ready for the start of the next season. The type of cutting programme possible at this time will depend on the amount of seeding work necessary. Hockey pitches requiring a minimum of repairs and which form part of a cricket outfield will, as a matter of routine, be mown at least once or twice a week, depending on the amount of prevailing grass growth. Inevitably, however, a conflict of interests arises when the cricketers demand a very closely mown surface to help provide a smooth and fast outfield. If the summer is very hot and dry there could be wide-scale droughting of the turf, particularly if watering of the pitches/outfield area is limited. In such situations a compromise mowing level should be employed, one which is short enough for the cricketers but at the same time provides enough grass cover to avoid severe drought stress occurring. Therefore, on dual use locations the cutting blades should not be set closer than 12 mm (1/2"). Where the finest quality hockey pitches are being maintained, dominated by fescue and bent, the smoothest playing surface may require a cutting level down as low as 8 mm (5/16"). For best results, an appropriate 90 cm (36") wide cylinder mower should be used with the clippings boxed off. The light rolling and stripes created after using the cylinder mower give the quality of finish which is desirable. For lower standard hockey pitches which form part of large playing fields, gang mowers could be used, although where resources are available the use of large cylinder mowers is infinitely preferable.

Soccer pitches are found to perform best in terms of both play and wear if mown at a winter playing height of 25-38 mm (1-1 1/2"), perhaps commencing the playing season at the higher end to protect a grass cover going into the wetter months. For Rugby where a cushioned surface is preferred and trueness of ball bounce is not so important then 75 mm (3") of grass growth is ideal, although fast running backs may prefer less grass. The turf may be topped at these heights as necessary during the winter, should any grass growth occur during warmer periods of weather. Tractor-mounted gang mowers are most frequently employed on multiple pitch sites for speed of cutting. Where presentation matters, a ride-on triple machine can provide a good appearance and relative speed but the same pedestrian machine as used on the hockey pitch will give the best quality finish. Obviously, multiple pitch sites holding different sports pose mowing difficulties in that different cutting heights must be employed. This either means employing a number of cutting units or changing the cutting level *in situ*.

There will be further variety to mowing pitches related to post renovation as seedlings establish. In this situation the young grass should be allowed to grow up to 50-63 mm (2-2$^1/_2$") before topping, with the initial cuts best made with a rotary mower, gradually taking the cut down to the conventional summer level as the sward thickens. Through the summer there can also be problems with heading ryegrass the stalks of which will be flattened by the roller on a cylinder machine. Topping with a rotary will be necessary to tidy up. There is also the problem of cutting around posts through the playing season and a strimmer is probably the most effective tool for this job. During the close season posts should be removed to ease mowing and also to prevent unwanted casual play in seeded goal mouths, a particular headache for pitches under local authority care.

Mowing faults
The following faults may be encountered:

[1] Scalping : cutting height set too low for the contours of the area being mown. Not generally a problem on winter pitches which have good levels or at most smooth undulations, but can occur is the cutting unit is incorrectly set or if there are problems in establishing sand slits, or drainage backfill is lying too proud and the cutting units are jumping. On sports grounds scalping is most often seen at the head of banks, which form the perimeter to the site when gang mowers cut along at an angle.

[2] Ribbing : grass being mown is too long for machine setting or machine is badly adjusted. This fault usually indicates inadequate cutting frequency – which has the added drawback of piles of long cuttings being left over the pitch.

[3] Wash boarding : continuous mowing in one direction. May result in surface undulations.

[4] Chewing : machine not cutting cleanly with the bottom blade or cylinder blunt or not correctly adjusted. Often seen during hot, dry summers on ryegrass when this species becomes excessively tough and difficult to cut cleanly. When chewing occurs the turf will take on a whitish hue and if viewed closely you can see white fibrous strands at the chewed edge of the grass blade.

[5] Uneven cutting : machine cutting at different heights at each end of the cylinder or bottom blade bent or damaged. Beware of gang units with different settings to each head. This can also happen when cutting large multiple sites or moving from one site to another. It is always wise to check the setting of the cutting units regularly through a days work, not only the height of cut but also the setting of cylinder to fixed sole plate.

SPIKERS AND SUB-AERATORS
Aeration of soils through the employment of spikers and sub aerators is required in order to:

[1] improve surface drainage;
[2] improve soil air supply;
[3] improve root growth;
[4] relieve compaction;

and indirectly to:

[5] improve soil structure;

[6] increase drought resistance;
[7] assist breakdown of fibre or thatch.

Aeration is essential on all types of sports turf particularly where wear is concentrated, e.g. soccer goal mouths, or where rolling is carried out, e.g. hockey pitches. Treatment is best carried out when the soil is moist to allow maximum tine penetration. For winter games the benefits of appropriate aeration are basically in promoting a dry playing surface of high wearability.

Aeration equipment
[1] Hand tools : although laborious, hand forking done properly still gives best results. Only workable in limited problem areas on a winter pitch. A basic hand fork will prove of value to maintain a playable surface in goal mouths although hollow tines which remove a core of soil can be particularly useful where compaction is severe and if sand is to be worked into a wet area. Other hand propelled devices are of limited value to professional users.

[2] Self-propelled revolving drum aerators : moderate working speed and can accept slit, solid, hollow or spoon tines. Effective as a back-up to more efficient overall aeration treatment specific to goal mouths or other heavily played parts of a pitch, or for use when ground conditions are unsuited to tractor work.

[3] Self-propelled punch-action aerators : slow working speed but ensure good tine penetration. Especially useful for hollow tining.

[4] Self-propelled mini mole plough : compaction can be relieved to a depth of 175 mm (7").

[5] Tractor implements : drum principle aerator, punch-action and mole plough type.

[6] Specialist turf maintenance systems include a variety of aerating attachments mainly based on drum principle. Working depth up to 200 mm (8").

[7] "Heavy duty" equipment for relieving deep-seated compaction, i.e. the Verti-Drain with a working depth of up to 400 mm (16").

[8] Specialist machinery using compressed air to relieve compaction, e.g. the Robin Dagger or; pressurised water, i.e. the Toro HydroJect.

The effects of play require constant attention to alleviate compaction and the ills which it fosters; impeded drainage, thatch, stagnation and poor root development. An open, well aerated, free-draining growing medium is of paramount importance in sports turf management and a package of aeration treatments is the major basic maintenance technique to help achieve these criteria. There are two basic forms of aeration equipment commonly employed on winter pitches, a conventional programme involves winter slitting backed up by the occasional intensive treatment , usually Verti-Draining, to relieve severe ailments. There are a great many other techniques available to the groundsman and he must be aware of the most suitable technique to deal effectively with any particular problem.

Slit tine aeration
Slit tining is the most frequent aeration treatment carried out on sports turf in this country as it introduces air into the soil profile whilst causing minimal surface disturbance. Primarily it is an autumn/winter task as slit marks can 'gape' if they dry out through the spring and summer months. Slit tines are described under a variety of terms; knife tines, diamond tine, chisel tines and root pruners. The nomenclature relates to the shape of the tine or its action. For winter pitches slitting through the playing season may be all the aeration required although chisels or root pruners may be safe to use during the summer, provided efficient irrigation is available. However, do not over water merely to facilitate the use of shallow slits rather than safer alternative forms of tine. Slit tines are available on the complete range of aeration implements. The working depth varies from 75-

PLATE 81. A drum-type aerator with knife-shaped tiners, the Sisis TDS tractor-mounted machine. (Courtesy Sisis Equipment [Macclesfield] Ltd.)

PLATE 82. A McConnel drum-type outfield slitter with broad triangular tines. (Courtesy McConnel Ltd., Ludlow.)

150 mm (3-6") on pedestrian units, down as far as 300 mm (12") on the larger tractor drawn aerators. Many tractor-mounted units have pressure frames or are controlled by downward pressure from the tractors hydraulics to give variable depth of penetration and to facilitate full depth when needed. The maxim that you should always slit as deeply as possible is inaccurate. Always aerating at the same depth will create panning at that depth, obviously less of a problem at 300 than 75 mm but a problem nonetheless.

Frequency of slitting must relate to the quality of soil to be worked and the needs of each specific site. Anything from weekly to monthly treatments could be appropriate, working along the same direction in any one slitting season as cutting across previous slit marks could promote serious disturbance to the playing surface, if not immediately then certainly through dry summers. Slitting can be over done, so frequent that marks are too close and promote unevenness, a situation exacerbated during frosty spells, or on heavy saturated soils when taking any machinery over the ground will cause more damage than the operation will do good. Starting a slitting programme for the first time can be disruptive although after a few passes lifting should be kept to a minimum. The initial damage is usually due to very poor rooting – a direct consequence of no, or very limited, aeration work in the past. Units drawn behind compact tractors for relatively small areas, say one or two pitches, often have a pressure roller following the slitter to smooth down any slight lifting. Slitters without such a roller can leave tufts of grass on removal of the slit from the ground which, unless smoothed down, can be cut off when next mowing producing small gaps in the turf cover.

There is evidence to suggest that slitting can reduce playing quality in certain circumstances. Where grass cover is being lost, e.g. in a goal mouth, ongoing slitting can increase the rate of defoliation by destabilising the surface. A similar situation can evolve on sand pitches but here we believe the grinding action of the slit tine through the sand may cause root shearing and thereby destabilisation at the surface. Care must therefore be taken with slitting treatments, postponing on all but well grassed areas on soil based pitches and perhaps looking to alternative means of compaction relief on sand constructions. Punch action chisel tines are a possible alternative.

Verti-Drain

The Verti-Drain was first introduced from Holland in 1982 and its use is now well established throughout the British Isles. The Verti-Drain is a specialised unit primarily designed to deal with deep-seated compaction which conventional aerators cannot reach. The operating principle is similar to hand forking where deep aeration of the soil profile is combined with breaking up of the compacted layers. Verti-Draining followed by top dressing also provides the opportunity to create vertical drainage channels which have a lasting effect.

There are currently five types of Verti-Drain available which are commonly referred to as the Pedestrian and the tractor-mounted Popular, Greens and Sports Ground machines (two available widths). The Pedestrian, Popular and Greens units are predominantly employed on fine turf areas, the Sports Ground machine on winter games pitches. The availability of a variety of solid tine sizes, working depth to a maximum of 400 mm (16"), tine spacing and overall working width, enables a wide range of problem situations in different sports to be tackled. The Sports Ground Verti-Drain (2 or 2.5 m width) fitted with 25 mm (1") tines is normally specified for winter games pitches for maximum working depth, drainage hole size, fissuring capability and preparation for top dressing. The other models may be employed if ground conditions are not too severe, the narrower Popular and Greens units more manoeuvrable in tight stadia. Even the Pedestrian machine can have a role in local follow up work to the tractor-mounted ones in goal mouths or other worn or wet parts of the pitch to prevent compaction developing or to treat an area not suited to tractor work. Hollow tines are available to carry out a deeper soil exchange which cannot be achieved by the use of more conventional equipment, but the primary value from Verti-Draining is heave, and this is only attainable with solid tines. Many contractors now hire out the above units with an operator, although an increasing number of Verti-Drains are being purchased by local authorities who want freedom to choose the timing of operation and have the need to use it on a regular basis on a number of areas.

Despite technical advances in other aeration methods, Verti-Draining remains the most valuable form of deep-seated compaction relief. Verti-Draining can create disruption where rooting is poorly developed, often the exact condition where maximum benefit may be obtained. For an initial operational setting the machine properly should minimise damage; employing a pressure roller behind the tines, working short of the maximum possible depth, using worn tines and minimal, if any, lift. It should be safe to work more deeply with greater heave during subsequent passes. Of utmost importance to achieve an even lift is regulation of travelling speed, advised at 0.25-0.65 mph, otherwise surface rippling will occur – a condition difficult to remedy. The operator should be aware of any shallow pipe drainage or irrigation supply pipes, the path of which can usefully be highlighted with a line marker prior to Verti-Draining if the work is completed during the close season to give time for the marks to be cut out. Worn tines will reduce the effectiveness of the unit and bent or wrongly aligned blocks of tines will invariably result in surface damage. Altering the angle at which the tines enter the soil decreases or increases the lifting effect of the unit and ensuring perpendicular penetration and removal of tines is essential to not only achieve optimum performance but also minimal surface damage.

The timing and frequency of Verti-Draining will depend on the nature of the site, soil condition and degree of compaction. As with other forms of aeration, the best result with the Verti-Drain occurs when the soil is no more than moist. A dry soil will hinder deep tine penetration and often result in tearing of the turf. To offset this condition, the application of an approved wetting agent can help to moisten the turf prior to the arrival of the Verti-Drain on site. Verti-Draining a wet soil will inevitably lead to smearing down the sides of tine holes and reduced fissuring of the soil.. Since play during the winter months on very wet soil surfaces inevitably causes very rapid loss of grass and the churning of the exposed soil surface into a quagmire, a prerequisite is that any compaction of the soil should be alleviated through the summer months prior to the beginning of the playing season. Shallow compaction can be controlled with occasional spiking at monthly intervals through the summer but deep-seated compaction requires penetration and breaking up of the soil to greater depth. Verti-Draining or deep slitting in late summer/early autumn when soil conditions are just moist can provide the necessary degree of deep disturbance and provide free passage of water to the underlying soil. Timing of the treatment becomes ever more critical as the soil to site becomes heavier and if Verti-Draining is delayed to October/November a wet clay soil is likely to create a smeared tine hole which will hold water and reduce effective drainage, the hole closing over rapidly at the surface under play. For such a site an operation in late summer-early autumn when the soil is just moist is essential to achieve fissuring and must be followed by top dressing to retain porosity at the surface. Remember too that recovery from the treatment will proceed much faster if completed when there is still vigorous growth. Late summer/autumn treatment on most sites is best, giving the greatest likelihood of suitable soil conditions for effective fissuring, improving drainage for the impending winter playing season.

Spring Verti-Draining may promote stronger root extension and relieve winter compaction but poses greater dangers, weather and ground conditions being more uncertain and increasing the likelihood of surface disruption before the last few, and possibly most important, matches of the season. Leaving Verti-Draining until after the end of the season, including the operation as part of renovation procedure may make sense but prove impractical if the season goes on until late May and ground conditions are baked. A dappled appearance from seeding can result in the months following Verti-Draining, stronger rooting and top growth through tine holes providing a positive visual advertisement for aeration, if disruptive to appearance in the short-term.

If a pitch is prone to deep-seated compaction then treatment at the start and end of a playing season may be recommended. Great care has to be taken if Verti-Draining is undertaken whilst play continues (particularly on hockey pitches) to avoid disruption to levels, although if too great a care is taken you may not be getting the best from the operation.

The Verti-Drain will cope successfully with a limited number of small stones in the soil profile but areas with significant stone content and rock near to the surface should be avoided. If the Verti-Drain does create surface upheaval, renovation work on localised areas of damage must be organised in advance and completed quickly and efficiently, removing debris which has been brought to the surface and making good levels with sandy compost or equivalent.

As well as relieving deep-seated compaction, Verti-Draining also provides an opportunity to give distinct, long-lasting vertical drainage channels between the surface and (hopefully) freer draining layers below, i.e. a drainage carpet or free-draining subsoil. These channels often act as a by-pass through more heavily compacted and destructured soil, allowing better movement of air and nutrients. Improved root growth and natural break-down of thatch through bacterial action follow as a result of the above work. To maintain this connection it is therefore important to top dress (most commonly with sand) either just before or just after Verti-Draining. However, on larger areas cost may well restrict the extent and amount of top dressing applied. On hockey pitches a light rolling may be given just to settle the surface before top dressing takes place.

The most commonly applied material is sand. For sand top dressing, a good quality medium/ fine lime-free material with a narrow particle size distribution range is recommended, although a similarly specified medium/coarse sand may be preferred on thatchy hockey pitches with deep-seated compaction in the soil profile. It is vital that as much sand as possible is worked down tine holes to make the connection between the surface and sub-base as well as avoiding a layering effect further down the profile in years to come (i.e. a sand root break). Apply a dry sand to a dry surface and work in immediately – this makes the above desired aim much easier to achieve. Larger diameter solid tines or hollow tining further aid the working in of sand.

The amount of sand to be applied will vary from approximately 60 tonnes on hockey pitches to 100 tonnes on other winter games pitches. It is important that the sand is applied uniformly to the whole pitch. There are distinct advantages of carrying out sanding prior to Verti-Draining, namely:

[a] The sand will stabilise the surface for the tractor fitted with the Verti-Drain if the surface is at all wet. The tines then punch some sand down the holes.

[b] The problem of heavy sand-spreading equipment recompacting the soil after compaction has been relieved by the Verti-Drain is avoided.

[c] Sand can be immediately worked into the surface whilst the tine holes are still open and receptive.

A programme of slit tining with occasional Verti-Draining, if site conditions dictate the need for more intensive work, will be sufficient for the majority of pitches. There are always exceptions to the rule and a wide variety of aeration implements has been designed to deal with virtually every imaginable situation.

Solid and hollow tine aeration

These are two operations which form part of the basics of an aeration programme on fine turf, golf greens and bowling greens, but are rarely encountered on winter pitches. However, the implementation of these techniques can have a most beneficial effect in specific situations and with the increase in sanding of pitches may become the primary answer to routine aeration.

With the danger of slit marks destabilising poorly grassed or sand based surfaces, but with the continued need to limit compaction through the main playing season, solid tining may provide a safe alternative. There may also be a requirement for summer aeration to assist penetration of irrigation, particularly on crowned pitches. Solid tines produce round holes which will not gape when they dry as do slit marks. The primary purpose for solid tining through the drier months is to reduce the degree of compaction built-up through the playing season and from continued use of other maintenance machines, e.g. mowers, and also to retain a permeable turf surface receptive to watering. As the objectives for solid tining mainly relate to the top 100 mm (4") of the soil profile, most solid tining tools can work through this depth. The desired hole spacing would be around 50 mm (2") centres. The frequency of treatment will be dependent on the intensity of wear and/or the degree of drought and may vary from fortnightly to monthly operations. Where solid tining is being used specifically to open the turf surface to permit free percolation of irrigation water, then it is often timed to precede an application of wetting agent.

Hand forking is a form of deeper solid tining and of particular value to goal mouths and centre circles on winter pitches during the playing season to help retain ground cover in these well worn areas. Intensive hand forking is the ideal precursor to sand dressings to maintain a firm, dry surface through ground prone to becoming muddy.

The possibility that solid tining might increase compaction has been suggested, the soil being squeezed in between the tines. This may have some factual basis but the need to solid tine for the reasons already outlined outweighs any minor firming of the topsoil, which can be overcome by other aeration techniques. Drum and punch action solid tiners are used, penetration is cleaner and deeper with those implements utilising a hydraulic ram system. There is the danger of weak-rooted turf rolling up like a carpet with the drum units.

A recent innovation is a machine with vibrating solid tines where studded discs rotate on a flexing axle to relieve compaction in the top few inches. A consequence of the tines' action is more movement of the soil and a larger hole. Disturbance to the surface is greater than from conventional aerators and must be followed by sand dressing or some other form of smoothing operation. This technique has limited potential during the playing season although prior to heavy sanding of goal mouths it may have value, surface renovation at the end of the playing season being seen as its main role.

Hollow tining is a means of thatch removal, soil exchange and relief of compaction near the surface, although there are now machines capable of working effectively to 150 mm (6"). The advent of ride-on and tractor-mounted equipment has extended the benefit of hollow tining to winter pitches. New pitch construction projects have brought about a further outlet for hollow tining where pitches have been turfed, importing soil foreign to that used for the growing medium. This can lead to capping and longer-term root break, so hollow tining is often employed in the first couple of years after laying to exchange the soil imported with the turf for a dressing compatible with the growing medium. Sand pitches are also prone to organic build up and hollow tining, followed by sanding, can maintain percolation rates. Disturbance from hollow tining can be minimised if removing thatch or foreign soil imported with turf which lie less than 50 mm (2") from the turf base by using mini-tines, as there is little point to taking out cores to greater depth, removing good top dressing applied through past years in the process. Mini-tines are also useful for overseeding and more frequent treatment, including summer work, if thatch or other surface impediments pose a real problem. For very thatchy turf and soil exchange, the best tines to use are those which remove the greatest volume of soil in a single pass. With ever increasing advice as to the benefits of heavy sand dressings to soil based winter pitches, hollow tining may play a greater role in pitch aeration programmes than in the past. There will be a point of diminishing returns where a similar material is being removed as is applied in the subsequent dressing. The most time-consuming and disruptive element of hollow tining is removal of cores. Hollow corers on a closed drum collect cores as the job proceeds and there are conveyor belt systems to harvest cores. It may be possible to break up the cores and work them back in if soil exchange is unnecessary or only partially required. Such a process must be completed in dry conditions.

The same sand dressings, as recommended following Verti-Draining, will be appropriate for hollow tining. The choice of top dressing after hollow tining or leaving tine holes open will depend, to a great extent, on timing and the primary purpose of treatment. If late in the autumn, say, when grass growth has declined to an insignificant level, top dressing will promote smothering and disease and tine holes are best left open, this situation will only apply to hockey pitches. Where thatch removal is the main reason for hollow tining, on pitches which have a sandy growing medium, it can be useful to leave the holes open to facilitate greater air movement through the turf base, provided the ground is not too soft. If contemplating leaving tine holes open then care must be exercised in selecting tine width and spacing to minimise disruption to the playing surface.

PLATE 83. The Twose Turf Conditioner is a vibrating mole plough. (Courtesy Twose of Tiverton Ltd.)

PLATE 84. The Sisis Quadraplay allows surface slitting, raking, rolling or brushing in any combination. (Courtesy Sisis Equipment [Macclesfield] Ltd.)

Mole plough and vibrating mole plough

The cheapest means of introducing drainage channels is through the employment of a mole plough, basically a bullet on the end of a vertical share. A mini mole plough is generally used for turf systems although there are agricultural implements with larger bullets. The agricultural types work at a greater depth but with a greater likelihood of disturbance. Although deeper channelling may initially promote an enhanced drainage capability there is little point working much beyond the depth of follow up slitting treatments, which must connect closely to the mole channel. The combination of Verti-Draining and deep mole ploughing may prove effective.

Mole ploughs are drawn through the soil, preferably uphill, hauling directly by tractor (wheeled or track laying) or by cable and winch. Their value is limited by soil type. Soil should be free of stones, boulders and sand pockets and should contain sufficient clay to prevent 'cave-ins'. Land must have a sufficient, even fall along the mole run, ideally 1:100 and a minimum 1:200. Moles placed at constant depth of 450–610 mm (18–24"), of bore 50–75 mm (2–3") and at 2.0–4.5 m (6–15') centres. For effective results the maximum length of run should be no more than 180 m (200 yds). Moles must be run into an open ditch (outfalls protected, e.g. by inserting a few lengths of pipe) or well-laid piped main, preferably 10 m (11 yds) from the edge of the field. The piped main should be at least 50 mm (2") below mole channels and the trench backfilled with suitable aggregate. Useful life of a mole system can be up to ten years or so, dependent on the nature of soil and the depth of the runs.

Carrying out intensive aeration over a shallow rooted turf or a site with a limited depth of topsoil poses great difficulties. Hollow tining will remove some of the valuable topsoil and Verti-Draining may prove too disruptive. The use of a vibrating mole plough could be the answer with a working depth limited to 125-175 mm (5-7"). Where severe compaction precludes other aeration options the mole plough can be a useful precursor to future Verti-Draining. A combination of the two operations can have value on heavy soils where the mole plough, applied a month or so after Verti-Draining, assists channelling of surface water away, although this does require a consistent fall across the ground so treated. In combination with hollow tining, mole a month after hollow tining; the secondary operation can facilitate more effective compaction relief and promote even migration of sandy dressings. There are a variety of machines available for this type of aeration work. (Select carefully if employing on top quality hockey pitches to limit disruption.) A pressure roller following the tine is a must to prevent lifting of the turf. The plough leaves a continuous slit along its run and it is best employed late autumn to early winter when surface healing will be more rapid. Insert and withdraw the unit at least a metre beyond the pitch, as it is at the start and end of each run where the dangers of ripping and more severe levels disturbance are greatest. As with the conventional form of mole plough, the unit should be drawn across the back-fill over a drain or perimeter ditch which will act as a positive outlet for channelled water.

Compressed-air

The air-exhaust of such units expel air under pressure at 45 cm to 1 m (18" to 3' 3") depth, more deeply than other aerators and has proved beneficial for treating wet ground or dry patch, although mostly restricted to local treatment as the operation is relatively slow. Depth of treatment can be varied but it is wise to remain below 250 mm (10") as the shallower the operation, the greater the danger of disturbance from the unpredictability of the pressure flow release at the surface. Solid or hollow tining is often recommended prior to use, the perforated surface acts as a release valve for the surge of air and negates any danger to turf tearing, root shearing and uneven settlement. This method is not an option where the tine penetrates into a gravel carpet or naturally free-draining substrate as the air is dissipated through the greater pore space of the stone. Where moisture is retained in the top few inches and the soil is dry below (often seen on pitches in a wet autumn following a dry summer) this type of aerator may be effective in promoting freer water movement to a depth without smearing the surface, as might happen with Verti-Draining. The technique has application to areas of intensive compaction (i.e. goal mouths) through the playing season to prevent waterlogging. A pedestrian operated tool may be worth purchasing if the pitch is suited to its mode of operation, as it can be used frequently through most weather and soil conditions. Backfilling the tine hole, funnelling in coarse sand or fine grit can provide a more persistent drainage channel than merely relying on fissuring. The pedestrian and larger tractor-mounted units can relieve compaction in areas of high wear concentration where a Verti-Drain or hollow tiner would bounce along. As such the compressed-air unit is a valuable precursor to other forms of aeration. Research has looked into the possibility of injecting fungicide through the probe of a compressed-air device and has proved of value in regulating fairy ring activity, although the effect may only last a single growing season.

Drills
A slow operation mostly restricted for use in treating severe compaction and can be employed year-round as surface disruption is minimal, although the action of the drill leaves a pile of soil at the turf surface, so the operation is best done in dry conditions if the soil is to be lifted or worked back in cleanly. Of value in aerating poor constructions if it is possible to work down to an underlying drainage layer, by-passing the impermeable rootzone material above. Semi-permanent drainage channels can be formed if backfilled with coarse sand or fine grit. This technique has value as a precursor to fairy ring control or wetting agent application.

High pressure water injection
Perhaps the most innovative approach to aeration developed in recent years. The primary applications for this technique are for treating dry ground, black layer in sand constructions and to facilitate aeration with minimal disturbance. The obvious benefit to managers of pitches will be enhanced results of renovation through dry summers, without disturbing the surface or rooting seedlings where there is a hose connection point to site but no facility for automatic watering. Other situations where water jet aeration may aid grass growth would be working through sand pitches prone to black layer and pitches with under soil heating close to the surface, which cannot safely be aerated by other means. The operation leaves pin holes at the surface but water disperses below ground to produce a fan effect. As a consequence, compaction relief tends to be short-lived after each treatment. The system has been employed as an aeration tool although there must be doubts as to the effectiveness of improving drainage rates, using water to dry a wet soil seems nonsensical and is unlikely to work unless the jets are breaking through water-retentive layers into an underlying drainage carpet. Be wary of too frequent use which may promote loss of soil structure through migration of fines and it may be best restricting use to 2-3 operations per year and advisable to combine water injection with hollow tining or Verti-Draining. The hose to the unit does deposit clippings and this leaves a bit of a mess which has to be cleared with a mowing pass once the surface has dried.

To summarise therefore, adequate aeration is needed to combat the damaging effects of heavy play and to enhance drainage rates of naturally slow draining soils. Treatments for specific circumstances must be seen as part of an aeration programme which will still incorporate conventional forms. Deciding which tool to use and when is the secret to healthy turf and maintenance of quality playing surfaces. There is no substitute to regular attention to aeration; occasional exhaustive treatments may relieve compaction which has built up over time but the benefits are relatively short lived and is unlikely to sustain healthy growing conditions between treatments.

BRUSHING
This should be a regular operation carried out to disperse dew and scatter worm casts, providing an invaluable preliminary to mowing and preparation of a surface for play. In addition to dispersing moisture, brushing helps to stand up the grass before mowing. A simple tractor-mounted brush is suitable although powered sweepers can produce a more effective treatment and serve other purposes, such as litter collection, leaf sweeping in autumn and the production of attractive striping when there is inadequate growth for doing so by cutting. Simple drag brushes can be used to work in top dressing – without the collection hopper the powered brushes can also be used for this purpose .

LINE MARKERS AND MARKING COMPOUNDS
In sports turf management the final presentation of the playing surface is of great importance and can be improved, or alternatively marred, by the standard of marking out operations. Uniform and

positive line marking is not only pleasing in appearance but it is essential to all participants and spectators in order that the rules of the game can be correctly interpreted. (The line marking requirements for each individual sport are covered in the first section of this volume.)

There are a variety of marking materials available for machine application which can be used on many different surfaces. Clearly, the persistency of materials varies and some are better suited to hard surfaces than to turf. In general, an ideal marking material should be waterproof, quick-drying, not easily rubbed off or liable to flake or powder. It should also meet health and safety requirements.

Line marking materials available

[1] Whiting. Whiting is composed of finely powdered chalk and has been particularly popular in the past. It can be applied either wet or dry but is not very persistent in either form. The limy nature of the material can also encourage weeds, worms and disease.

[2] Proprietary marking solutions. These are often semi-permanent which compensates for their higher cost. The solutions can be used on both grass and hard surfaces and are sometimes mixed with whiting. Various colours are available.

[3] Proprietary dry line materials. Dry aggregate combined with a binder compound adheres on contact with moist surfaces. The resulting line is fairly persistent, being water-repellent and not easily kicked off. Consequently, it is particularly useful in wet, muddy conditions but will also mark dry surfaces. Coloured aggregate is available.

[4] Emulsion paint. Again, this is a temporary marking used mainly on hard, porous surfaces.

[5] Tape. Permanent plastic tape held down by metal studs or nails can be used on hard, porous surfaces such as tennis courts. Self-anchoring plastic strips are also available.

[6] Sawdust. Sawdust is still used occasionally, although care should be taken not to apply too broad a line.

[7] Thread. Thread is used for marking out rinks on flat bowling greens and can be used to provide temporary boundaries on multiple playing fields.

[8] Road line paints. Road line paints are often bitumen-based and provide a permanent marking for hard surfaces.

[9] Hydrated lime (calcium hydroxide) and creosote. These two materials cannot now be recommended by the STRI due to the possible risk of injury to pitch users.

Machinery available

Careful consideration must be given to the type of line marking machine acquired in order that it suits both the material used and the ground conditions likely to be encountered. A variety of marking machines are available which may be generally categorised according to working principles and type of surface which they can mark. These categories include:

[1] Wheel to wheel transfer. Fluid is transferred from a wheel rotating in the tank on to a front wheel marker. This type of machinery is suitable for grass surfaces.

[2] Wheel and gravity feed. Fluid is transferred from the tank via a rotating wheel to a chute. The fluid is then gravity-fed down the chute to an absorbent marker wheel. Suitable for all surfaces.

[3] Belt feed. A moving belt system provides a continuous supply of marking material. Suitable for most surfaces.

[4] Gravity feed. Liquid contained inclined towards single front wheel and marking compound fed by gravity through a filter to absorbent marking roller. With this principle marking roller can be off-set to allow working close to obstructions. Suitable for all surfaces.

[5] Pressure pump. A wheel-driven pump forces marking fluid directly through a jet and on to the surface. Width of line can be varied with different jets. Suitable for all surfaces with the added benefit that marking is unaffected by ground conditions.

[6] Dry line markers. Dry material is gravity-fed from a container. A shutter allows line width to be adjusted.

[7] Aerosol. Normally used on permanent surfaces but may be useful to "top up" line markings, particularly on centre and penalty spots etc.

Immediately after use, marking machines must be cleaned thoroughly to avoid marking material hardening in the tank and interfering with future operations. There are combination line marker/sprayers available. Even greater care is required with these to ensure that chemical residue is thoroughly washed out to avoid a carry over to the next operation.

Surface preparations
Surface preparation prior to marking out is all-important in improving the efficiency and persistency of the marking material, particularly on turfed areas. When marking out on turf, the grass should not be too long and where mowing is necessary, the clippings should be removed, at least in the vicinity of the line marking. When marking out playing areas with a slightly longer grass cover, e.g. Rugby pitches, it can be useful to mow the grass shorter just along the lines which are to be marked out, perhaps with a 12" pedestrian mower.

Generally, wet marking produces best results on a dry surface but the dry line materials work better on wet grass. Dry weather conditions are desirable for either method. Prepare the marking solution carefully to ensure it is not lumpy. Lumps could cause application problems, particularly where pressure jet machines are to be used. Regular stirring may also be necessary to keep the material in suspension.

Herbicides have sometimes been mixed with liquid line-marking materials, but this has never been formally sanctioned and is now illegal unless the mixture is specifically approved. Apart from anything else, chemical reactions might occur between herbicides and line-marking material (especially lime) and herbicides might also be deactivated by mixture with particulate materials, whether liquid or solid. There is also the opposite possibility, that the herbicide might remain active in the line-marking slurry in a way it would not if drying on grass or soil. The only possibility therefore is for distinct and separate operations, provided that the reinforcement is not going to lead to the 'etching out' of deep lines which would infringe the rules of the various games, e.g. the prohibition for Association Football of 'a V-shaped rut'. Possible procedures have to be acceptable in several respects. Firstly, there must be no risk of player contact with, or accidental transfer of, active herbicide. Secondly, application techniques must avoid the possible reaction of herbicide with line-marking material or with unlined steel surfaces in line-marking equipment, if herbicide application through such equipment is approved: application of herbicide through a line-marker would of course make it a pedestrian-controlled 'hand-operated applicator', from the point of view of operator certification. Thirdly, there must be no herbicide contamination of tapes, lines etc. used for initial marking-out.

There are two alternative marking-out procedures which could meet these requirements, A and B below and an appropriate remarking procedure (C). For all of these paraquat is envisaged as the most suitable herbicide, although not necessarily the exclusive choice if others, e.g. glyphosate, are judged acceptable.

A : herbicide first, then marking-out
A1. Mark out initially with herbicide, in complete or partial lines, using an approved application method (dribble bar, sprayer, 'weed wiper' technique, aerosol, or clean line-marking equipment). The herbicide rate should be the manufacturer's recommended rate for maximum effect on mature plants with the chosen equipment. If there is a recommendation for watering can application, that would be the one to follow for use in clean line-marking equipment. Special care is needed in this

PLATES 85 and 86. The Starliner (dry – left) and Malvern (wet – right) line marking machines from Fleet (Line Markers) Ltd. of Malvern, Worcestershire. (Courtesy Fleet Ltd.)

PLATE 87. The Sisis LM/234 Truline marker is a wet marker available with 51, 76 and 102 mm belt widths. (Courtesy Sisis Equipment [Macclesfield] Ltd.)

case to avoid contamination of strings etc., especially if these are to be used again: it is recommended to make lines parallel to, but a short distance from, any strings which are laid down. A colorant (e.g. monastral blue) may be approved for use with the herbicide to show where it has been applied. Take care not to walk on treated lines.

A2. When herbicide is dry on grass leaves, marking-out with any proprietary material can be done, although it may be best to wait a day or so until herbicide effects begin to show.

B: marking-out first, then herbicide application
B1. Mark out with appropriate line-marking material.

B2. As soon as convenient, but in good drying conditions, herbicide may be applied to reinforce the marking, by methods and at rates outlined in A1 above.

C: remarking and additional line reinforcement
C1. Lines can be remarked at any time.

C2. If a further herbicide reinforcement of the lines is needed during the playing season, it depends on the line-marking material previously used and its persistence, whether or not paraquat can be used. If non-lime materials have been used, there should be no problem in using paraquat, but it would be prudent to obtain advice from the suppliers of the line-marking material and the herbicide.

The layout of pitches involves marking straight lines, exact angles and full or part circles. This cannot be done by eye to any degree of accuracy and pegging out pitches using string to act as a guide for the marker should be the first operation once the surface is fully prepared.

[1] Marking out rectangles.
Whenever possible the layout of pitches should be drawn on a scale plan before attempting to set out the lines on the turf. Firstly the four corners should be fixed. The 3:4:5 triangle principle can be used to determine right angles as set out below:-

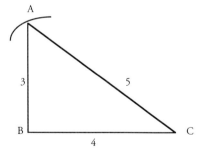

[a] Fix line BC at 4 m with pegs at each end.

[b] Guess right angle at B and measure 3 m from B to A but place 3 or 4 pegs on a short arc at A.

[c] From C measure 5 m to A and put in final peg at the point where this line AC cuts the arc formed by the provisional pegs at A.

The angle at B is now a right angle.

The centre spot may be determined by the intersection of diagonals. If the diagonals are of equal length this confirms that the rectangle has been formed correctly. Strings are essential when marking out for the first time and should be used subsequently, especially for broken lines as for Rugby so that the lines remain straight.

The corners of pitches may be indicated permanently by installing sockets or pegs.

[2] Marking out circles and semi-circles.
A length of cord attached to a peg will describe a circle or part thereof at a radius as determined by the length of the cord. The cord may be simply attached to the line marker. For large circles or the

semi-circles of a running track, wire may be more appropriate. If re-marking is anticipated then the centres of the circles should be fixed as permanently as possible.

SCARIFIERS AND HARROWS

Scarification is not an operation which is commonly carried out on winter games pitches because, for the majority, the major benefits from the treatment are carried out through play or unnecessary due to the nature of the grasses employed. However, the range of scarification tools carry out a variety of jobs and all have a place within the overview of winter pitch management.

Scarification is an important treatment in the maintenance of turf, especially turf composed of finer-leaved species. Scarification may be of particular value to better quality hockey pitches, but all winter pitches will benefit from some form of this work. The basic aim of scarification is to produce a sward with an erect growth habit and to remove creeping, straggly or coarse growth of grasses and weeds. In addition, scarification may do much to limit the production of excess organic matter in the turf and the accumulation of fibrous material at the turf base, more specific to grass species which rapidly develop fibre, i.e. bent, fescue, smooth-stalked meadow-grass and annual meadow-grass. Shaded pitches, often a problem on enclosed stadia, will benefit from occasional scarification treatment to "aerate" top growth. The appearance and playing qualities of a turf surface may be enhanced if such work is done at the appropriate frequency and with a suitable degree of severity.

The control of lateral grass growth is as important as mowing for the sake of turf vigour, playing quality and presentation. The deleterious effects of such growth are many and varied. Procumbent grass stems have an adverse effect on the smoothness and pace of the playing surface, in extreme cases producing a definite grain or nap. Bentgrasses, smooth-stalked meadow-grass, annual meadow-grass and perennial ryegrass are prone to flattened leaf growth, far more than fescue and this can be a major impediment to providing a uniform playing and visually attractive surface. Often the poor quality of a surface provided by a mixed sward encourages closer mowing and the rapid loss of the desirable species. Grasses producing seed and distinct patches of coarse grass also detract from playing quality and a visually uniform turf, yet can be regulated with an appropriate scarification programme. If not lifted by mechanical means, lateral stems and other plant parts will bed down at the turf base, evolving into thatch with all the problems that entails. Should too great a depth of thatch develop the turf can be prone to water retention, the ground affected by differential drying patterns. Such a situation can produce unpredictable bounce characteristics. Surface moisture encourages shallow rooting and a drought-prone turf, together with the promotion of annual meadow-grass, at the expense of bent and fescue. The presence of a fibre layer restricts penetration of moisture and consequently recovery enabling moss invasion which then competes with emerging grass seedlings. A ryegrass turf is usually not prone to fibre build-up, but such coarse grass species create the greatest nuisance where present in distinct tufts on pitches dominated by a tight knit turf composed of finer species, i.e. bent and fescue. Many a blasphemous outburst has been heard when a hockey player finds the ball jumping up at him after hitting a prominent patch of ryegrass.

For pitches dominated by the finer grass species, scarification as a precursor to top dressing application will increase the rate of absorption of the material. Avoid scarifying for at least four to five days after top dressing or fertiliser application, as much of the material will be lifted. More than one pass during a treatment may prove of value, although consecutive runs must be carried out at an oblique angle and the total number of passes during any single treatment regulated by the potential for recovery, a couple usually being the maximum. As part of the process of preparing ground for overseeding, 3-4 passes may be undertaken. Occasionally careful summer scarification can be contemplated if thatch poses a serious problem. Such a necessity usually indicates underlying problems, often related to compaction and drainage difficulties. Wet summers, excessive irrigation and over feeding promote thatch, so the development and presence of dense thatch requires a wider perspective for control involving other aspects of maintenance, particularly aeration, top dressing and limiting fertiliser application and irrigation.

Scarification physically lifts accumulated thatch. Being a relatively destructive treatment it is important to time scarification to coincide with vigorous growth in order to promote recovery, generally restricting to the autumn and spring. Scarification reels can be set to work lightly to work through top growth or deeply to cut into compressed thatch, although working deeper than 3 mm or so may seriously thin turf cover. The severity of scarification treatment requires careful judgement and the need for very harsh treatment should be avoided by carrying out moderately vigorous treatments at sufficient frequency. Scarification treatment should be suspended when growth is slow as in periods of dry weather. However, after a drought and just as rain returns, such treatment may do much to aid water penetration and thus assist recovery. The pattern of operation with regular scarifying is similar to mowing, aiming to vary the direction of cut as much as possible and to complete the exercise when the turf is dry for a better finish. Always scarify in straight lines as turning a curve with the units in operation will promote severe scuffing. Sharp, pointed tines should be employed as worn, rounded ones will prove ineffective or necessitate setting the blades dangerously low. It may be necessary to renew the cutting reel annually.

The machinery available to complete the variety of scarification duties can be extremely basic or highly mechanised. The choice of equipment will determine the intensity of treatment and quality of finish. A short toothed flexible grassland chain harrow or simple harrow made from stiff thorn branches, bound to a spar of wood or by binding a roll of chestnut palings with barbed wire, may suffice. Harrows with a single draw bar are effective and their performance can be enhanced by attaching weights to the trailing edge. There are harrows completely enclosed in a frame and may provide a more uniform finish to level ground. For the majority of work on a pitch the harrow should be used smooth side down as the teeth can rip into the turf leaving a poorer surface. Tractor drawn rake attachments can be used but a follow up pass with a mower is essential to cut off the material that is raised. Top quality playing surfaces will benefit from a scarification programme using powered reel type scarifiers. The reels are typically spring steel blades rigidly mounted on an axle but some machines have flail tines whilst others also accept wire tines and heavy duty blades. On pitches, scarification has to be completed with tractor-mounted units and the debris lifted by a sweeper. Combination sweeper/scarifiers are available and do a good job but are slow, as regular emptying is necessary and such combinations do not follow contoured ground as well as floating head units on hydraulically driven tractor-mounted scarifiers or detachable scarifying heads to gang mowers.

Efficient removal of scarification debris is clearly essential if the operation is to be effective. For extensive areas like winter pitches boxes on the scarifier for debris collection are not practical, thorough sweeping, including the use of powered sweepers is the only option for a truly clean finish. Another method for cleaning up is to make a pass with the mower set at the usual cutting height. Rotary mowers with clipping collection can also be used to good effect.

TRACTORS
The conventional tractor for sports ground maintenance, essentially mowing and slitting, is a 2-wheel drive model of 35-40 horse power. If the site is level, reasonably free-draining and has adequate access then such a tractor may well be suited. However, purchasing a higher specification of tractor may be money well spent. Selection of a suitable tractor will depend to a large extent on its intended range of functions. Therefore, certain features may be considered to be of greater importance than others.

Four-wheel drive is highly desirable as this feature will improve traction as well as offering the benefits of a smoother ride and better balance on any ground contours in either muddy or wet conditions. Indeed, four-wheel drive is a prerequisite when using implements which require downward pressure – exerted through a double-acting back ram – to operate efficiently, as this will reduce traction through the rear wheels.

Manual transmission with shuttle or synchro-mesh gearing provides as many as 16 forward and 16 reverse gears, giving a large number of speeds within a defined range, so that the pace of the tractor can be precisely tailored to the implement being employed, e.g. spraying, where a constant exact

PLATE 88. The Amazone Groundkeeper combines the functions of flail mower, scarifier and debris collector. (Courtesy Four Seasons Publicity, Banbury.)

PLATE 89. The Kubota 40 hp L3250 is typical of today's generation of general purpose tractors for sports ground usage. (Courtesy Kubota [UK] Ltd., Thame, Oxfordshire.)

forward speed is required for an even coverage. At very low "creep" speeds trenching and operations like Verti-Draining are facilitated.

Hydrostatic transmission usually has two or more hydrostatic ranges. Forward and reverse speeds are infinitely controlled by the use of foot pedals, which make it very versatile in confined or intricate operations, especially where power take-off speeds are not to alter with the forward speed of the tractor.

Hydraulic take-off via a double activity spool valve is essential for the operation of implements which have pressure rams, e.g. mowers and aerators, or even a front end loading bucket, whilst a "live" two speed power take-off is a prerequisite for the operation of many implements.

Safety should not be neglected in the interests of economy and a roll bar must by law be fitted to a tractor, to reduce the risk of the operator being injured in the case of an accident.

There is a vast range of tractors on the market. Choose one with a proven track record at stated horse power, compatible for use on turf, not agriculture. Tyres are perhaps the most obvious visual difference; use low ground pressure tyres with relatively smooth tread for turf situations, as cleated agricultural tyres will cause serious deterioration in playing quality when employed on soft ground.

For sites with limited access or single pitch venues where a range of smaller power tools are appropriate then a mid-range of 24-30 hp or compact tractor of 16-20 hp could be a better option. Compact tractors were originally developed to meet the requirements for a small, economical-to-run power unit on Japanese farms which only average 1.6 hectares. UK distributors soon realised the potential for compact tractors in a wide range of applications, particularly on amenity turf areas such as parks, sports grounds and golf courses. Nearly all compact tractors are still manufactured in Japan and include the now household names of Iseki, Kubota, Hinomoto and Yanmar, together with those machines which masquerade under Anglo-Saxon names such as Ford or Massey Ferguson. Even the American made John Deere has a Japanese engine.

One of the major advantages of the compact tractor is its extreme versatility. To complement the extensive range of attachments which have been specifically designed for use with compact tractors it is possible to fit implements from other maintenance systems. For example, the Sisis Hydromain implements can be attached directly to the tractor 3-point linkage or adapted for use with a compact tractor by means of a special mounting frame which allows downward pressure to be applied to the implements through the hydraulic system. In addition, the tractor must be fitted with an auxiliary spool valve of the doubt-acting type.

Local authorities, schools and sports grounds have realised the advantages of a compact, multi-purpose "prime-mover" for the installation of drains, earth moving operations, general turf maintenance and the transport of equipment between sites. The high power to weight ratio means that a set of three gangs can be towed with relative ease (or driven off the tractor's PTO) yet can still be used on the "vulnerable" wet surfaces with safety due to advances in low ground pressure tyre technology. The more powerful compact tractors can pull up to five gang units, although it is important not to over-burden the compact tractor as this will result in a reduction of its effective working life span. High ground clearance of the compact tractors enables mid-mounted rotary mowers to be fitted or the option of front or rear mounting of a range of flail or rotary mowers for specific models. Fully mounted, hydrostatic-driven mowers have also been developed for sports grounds and other formal grass areas where a higher quality finish is required. This offers the advantage of a purpose-built, self-propelled machine with the bonus of out of season availability of the "prime-mover" for other work.

Routine turf maintenance operations such as spiking, scarifying, spraying and top dressing can easily be accomplished by attachment of the appropriate implement. The compact tractor can easily exert sufficient pulling power for carrying out such operations as mini mole ploughing. In addition, modern compact tractors have the necessary hydraulic "muscle" to operate loaders, excavators and similar equipment. Therefore, drainage work can be accomplished and ditches cleared without the need to hire suitable equipment. Various cultivation operations can be carried out both quickly and efficiently. A special advantage of the compact tractor is that it can accomplish the functions above in areas which may be inaccessible to standard machines, whilst minimising turf wear and damage to the underlying soil structure on peripheral areas or the main traffic routes to and from the site of work.

Direct comparison with integrated maintenance systems such as those produced by Cushman and Sisis or even the larger types of tractor is tempting, although impractical since the role of the compact tractor overlaps into each of these two categories, as well as performing specific functions of its own.

Larger tractors, in both horse power and size, take up considerably more room in the shed and cannot manoeuvre or negotiate narrow paths with the same ease as compact tractors. However, they are particularly useful workhorses for carrying out operations such as routine mowing or deep spiking. Therefore, a compact tractor should not be seen as a replacement for the larger tractor but as a complementary unit.

An important consideration which favours the compact tractor is the reduced running costs when compared with their "big brothers". In particular, the new breed of highly efficient diesel engines give much improved fuel economy and reduce maintenance costs when fitted to compact tractors.

In summary, compact tractors have the capability of performing a vast range of difficult jobs in combination with a formidable array of compatible implements. This versatility, combined with economy, has been the major factor responsible for establishing a "niche" for compact tractors on sports grounds. The conventional 35-40 hp remains the work horse for the majority of winter pitch maintenance where the tractor's basic function is to pull the gang mower and slitter.

ROLLERS

The main requirements of hockey or polo surfaces are that they should be firm, fast and true so that when a ball is hit it does not readily rise in the air but runs freely on the ground. Surface levels are therefore much more critical for hockey compared with other winter pitches, such as soccer and Rugby. Many hockey pitches are located on cricket outfields and this greatly increases the pressure on the groundsman maintaining them when the break between the summer and winter playing seasons is generally very short. Rolling is often considered as a short-term answer to poor levels but there are serious consequences to inappropriate action. Regular heavy rolling destructures soil, reducing pore space and increasing moisture content through impaired drainage. Repeated heavy rolling treatments should be avoided as these will smear the surface and cause considerable compaction in the soil profile. With time, excessive heavy rolling will impede drainage and lead to waterlogging with resultant match cancellations. Grass cover then suffers as roots are starved of air and are unable to penetrate through the compacted soil. Domination of the weed grass, annual meadow-grass, is often an indication of over-rolling as this species is best adapted to conditions favouring shallow roots. The lack of anchorage provided by shallow roots results in large pieces of turf being kicked or divoted out during play and do not provide a good stud hold – a situation to be avoided on any pitch. Furthermore, such a condition will produce a spongy, fibrous turf which holds water and is prone to moss ingress. Any form of rolling should always be avoided when the ground is very wet as this is when compression of the soil structure will be at its greatest and smearing of worm casts at its height.

On the other hand, the demands of the sport may make occasional rolling necessary to help reinstate the surface but this must be carried out with discretion. Winter games pitches sometimes need a light roll after play in frosty weather merely to smooth the surface. Rolling should not be done on a dirty turf (e.g. wormy) before switching or brushing. Soil conditions affect results. Heavy soils bind more easily than sandy ones and similarly moist soil is more susceptible to consolidation and compaction than dry. A hockey pitch receiving minimum maintenance and which is mown with gang mowers can benefit from an annual roll in the spring. Any further rolling should be carried out with extreme care and must be coupled with spiking operations to relieve compaction.

A wide range of hand-operated, self-propelled, ride-on, tractor-mounted or trailed types are available to meet various requirements. The effect of a roller is dependent on its diameter and width as well as its weight. For winter pitches the wide tractor-mounted or trailed will be most appropriate. Weight of roller is important, although sheer weight means little in terms of compacting effect. Other factors must be taken into consideration to determine how the weight is spread over the turf, ground pressure being the figure to find. A formula to determine this is useful to compare the compacting effect of available rollers, the "rolling factor" calculated as follows:

$$\text{Rolling factor} \quad = \quad \frac{\text{gross weight or load [kg]}}{\text{width [cm] x diameter [cm] of rolls}}$$

A guideline for application to pitches is to aim for a maximum rolling factor of 0.03. Choose the roller carefully to provide a smoothing action and not compaction.

The wide cylinder mower used on better quality pitches also serves as a roller and may itself retain a smooth surface without additional rolling operations.

The alternatives to rolling rely on smoothing the surface with a light raking action, thereby causing minimal compaction. Chain harrows, a combination unit comprising rake, tractor-mounted spring tine rake or sweeper-scarifier could all do the job.

SAND DRESSERS

Sand dressings for winter pitches are being promoted more and more as an essential element in promoting drier surfaces, which can lead to fewer cancelled matches. Sand slit and sand construction pitches require sand dressing of up to 100 tonnes per annum. Ideally, 45 tonnes would be applied in spring, 45 tonnes in summer leaving 10 tonnes for playing season usage. During Verti-Draining a pitch can accept 60-100 tonnes of sand. Quantities of this magnitude are difficult to apply by hand although some persevere with men shovelling sand off the back of a tractor-drawn trailer. This technique is extremely time consuming and labour intensive with no guarantee of an even spread. The quantity of sand involved and frequency of treatment can make provision of a suitable dressing machine cost-effective in certain situations.

All large dressers are gravity fed and as a consequence many do not deal too well with wet material. When looking at the alternatives available this must be a major consideration and some form of agitator to "stir" the sand to keep it moving evenly through the spreader is required. The basic forms of dresser rely on a spinning disk, vibrating floor or conveyor belt mechanism to distribute the sand. A brush to the rear of the dresser gives more even flow and coverage from the vibrating floor and belt machines. Capacity of hopper varies from 0.6 cubic metres to handle 80 tonnes a day, up to 2.64 cubic metres and this has an obvious bearing on the speed of the operation, particularly if a number of pitches are to be dressed on any one site. Spreading with these machines is a fairly speedy operation – stopping to fill tends to delay. A further tractor with front loader could well be necessary. Temper the desire for maximum load of sand held in the hopper with ease of loading, ground pressure exerted from the fuller laden unit and the suitability of tractors on site to operate the unit. Further thought must be given to the nature of distribution and an adjustable off-load is preferable, ideally from a dusting of sand to application of an 18 mm thick layer in a single pass. There are smaller dressing units, from those attachments for compact tractors and turf maintenance system power units to pedestrian operated dressers, these may be perfectly adequate if only dressing goal mouths and centre circle, or even revert to throwing the sand off a trailer.

RENOVATION EQUIPMENT

Following each fixture, an examination of the pitch should be carried out and any necessary repairs made. These should involve replacing divots and carefully forking up any deep scars to help restore a smooth and uniform playing surface. This is a tremendously time-consuming task – just look at the number of groundstaff and ball boys replacing divots during the half-time break at professional soccer matches. There are a number of combination tools which can complete such work in a single pass, combining a slitter with a rake, brush and light pressure roller.

As soon as the winter playing season comes to an end thorough renovation work should proceed immediately, particularly on those pitches which are used as part of a cricket outfield during the summer. (For polo grounds and some Gaelic games pitches, autumn renovation may be required after a summer playing season.) Planning ahead is a most important priority as it is essential to have everything ready when it is needed so that the work is not held up and precious time lost. Materials such as fertilisers, seed, weedkiller and sand should have been ordered and have arrived before the last match of the season.

Generally, the scale of restoration work on hockey pitches is smaller than that of other winter pitches, such as soccer. It is important to thoroughly open up the surface of the pitch by overall spiking, preferably using a tractor-mounted unit. Several passes should be made in different directions across the pitch so that the surface is thoroughly perforated. Very worn and compacted areas should be hand fork cultivated, working the soil to a depth of at least 100 mm (4"). A smooth, level and evenly consolidated but not over-compacted seed bed tilth should then be formed by alternate hand raking and heeling. Any localised low areas which have developed could be made up using a sandy soil or appropriate sand/soil mixture, lightly cultivating the soil before-hand so that the added material keys into the surface.

Usually, larger areas require renovation at the end of a winter's play and tractor-mounted equipment is needed. Very basic, but effective seed bed preparation can be completed with a short toothed grassland harrow, initial passes with teeth penetrating to produce a suitable tilth and then smoothed with the reverse side. Alternatively, a scarifier can produce a tilth or the entire process done with a purpose-built overseeder. There are a variety of overseeders working on three basic principles. Some perform deep scarification as the means of bedding seed just off the soil surface (for good results 3 or 4 operating directions are necessary). Preparation of a seed bed tilth via shallow solid tine spiking is another means. The final principle is derived straight from agriculture, slot seeding where a groove is cut into which seed is deposited and a pressure roller then reseals the slot – for even establishment 3 or 4 passes are also required from this type of tool.

SOD CUTTING
Pedestrian and tractor mounted sod cutters allow sod to be cut accurately and thinly. With care there may be little turf wasted. On winter pitches a sod cutter may be needed if quick repairs are required during the playing season, either to overcome excessive wear or vandalism or if the close season is short and turfing is the only means of restoring a grass cover to parts of the pitch for the start of the playing season. With many professional stadia being used through the summer to host other events, e.g. rock concerts, the ability to patch damaged ground is becoming increasingly important.

WATER MOPS
Postponement of fixtures due to waterlogging is a nuisance at any level of winter games but can be a very expensive matter for professional clubs as a result of lost revenue. There is a potential benefit for the employment of implements which can remove surface water to first class fixtures immediately preceded by a downpour. The simplest form of "water mop" is the Squeegee, basically a foam roller or rubber strip on the end of a brush handle. More sophisticated motorised machines work to the same principle, both pedestrian-operated and ride-on rollers. A machine using suction based on the hover craft principle has also proved highly successful in quickly removing surface water, although as with the other tools there must be a suitable outlet to take the excess away from playing areas.

Damage can be done to turf through the use of such machinery. Grass may be bruised or even pulled out by heavy handed pushing of a squeegee or motorised sponge roller, similarly intensive and/or frequent use of the suction unit could produce similar turf deterioration. Using machines to physically remove surface water is no substitute to proper construction, good drainage or a sensible aeration programme.

MACHINERY INVENTORY

In order to maintain a pitch a minimum machinery range might include a tractor with gang mower and slitter. There is obviously a tremendous jump from the poor sports club to Premier Division football clubs and a corresponding increase in the expectation of performance standards from the pitch, if not always from the players! This has to be matched by the machinery available to look after the pitch, which may well include the following inventory.

The quality of cut needed to present the pitch for match day requires a 90 cm width cylinder mower (6-8 bladed) with trailing seat. If the groundsman is responsible for numerous training pitches as well, a set of trailed 3 gang or ride-on triple mowers will also be necessary. When growth is slow to non-existent the use of a narrow width sweeper can enhance presentation and lift debris.

A line marker is an obvious requirement. However, which type is best will vary according to weather conditions particularly now that soccer is almost a year round sport. The provision of a dry and wet line marker would be sensible.

A compact or mid-range tractor may be the best option as power unit for routine maintenance work. The options available to some tractors for tight turning circle with minimal scuffing are certainly worth considering. A tractor of up to 30 hp should be capable of completing the maintenance programme for a football pitch. Low pressure turf tyres are a must.

Winter play necessitates the promotion of a dry surface so an outfield slitter is essential. In addition to a unit to work behind the tractor, a pedestrian operated aerator is useful for supplementary work in goal mouths and centre circles. Infrequent intensive aeration, such as Verti-Draining, is one for the contractor.

For League grounds with sandy constructions and/or slit drainage schemes a tractor mounted sand dresser is useful. The type of construction will also determine the nature of the irrigation employed, sand constructions requiring an automatic system. On soil based pitches a manually operated sprinkler will usually suffice, able to cover renovated goal mouths and centre circle at the end of the playing season.

When play concludes overseeding is an operation which must be completed speedily as the close season is short. A suitable overseeder is an option although the specialist equipment available through contractors may prove more effective. Following end of season renovation a rotary mower will be required to carry out initial topping of seedling grasses.

A tractor-mounted or pedestrian operated fertiliser spreader is a basic tool.

The enclosed nature of football stadia can encourage meadow-grass and thatch production. High seeding rates employed at the end of the season to, sometimes mistakenly, ensure a dense cover for the start of the next playing year can add to a soft and lush turf. Employment of a scarifier at appropriate times of growth will have value. These conditions can promote disease. Weeds and worms can also prove a nuisance so Clubs should have access to a sprayer.

Other implements which have a place in the groundsman's shed would include a brush, rake, fork and spade for running repairs and lightweight roller for use after seeding.

Local authorities, or private contractors working to maintain a number of multiple sports sites may have a fairly basic range of equipment but will need a number of each item. Short-term hire is a suitable source of machines for specialised work, particularly the Verti-Drain, sand dressers and renovation equipment employed annually at the end of a playing season.

CARE OF EQUIPMENT

Equipment must be properly stored and adequately serviced if it is to be efficient and ready for use whenever needed. Close attention should be paid to the information books and leaflets supplied by the manufacturers and these should be kept for future reference. This will help to ensure that the correct maintenance procedures are adopted. Additional points which can be overlooked include:

[1] Proper equipment and facilities for cleaning should be provided. As machines are cleaned a check can be carried out for loose nuts and bolts and for signs of wear. Machines should be cleaned after each day's use, or more often through the day if performance is hampered by clinging grass cuttings, mud, etc.

[2] Keep a log book of machinery maintenance, usage, fuel consumption etc. This may provide a guide for budgeting purposes as well as highlighting the reasons for renewal or replacement.

[3] Machinery should be stored separately from fertilisers and other corrosive materials. If possible machines should be placed on planks of wood rather than directly on to a concrete floor over winter.

[4] Regular oil changes where appropriate will ensure that engines operate efficiently and give long service.

[5] General lubrication of moving parts and cutting surfaces in line with manufacturer's recommendations will ensure that equipment gives maximum useful life.

[6] Any equipment which holds water should be thoroughly drained prior to storage for the winter in order to avoid the risk of frost damage.

[7] Regular observation on the condition of cutting edges on mowers and tines on aeration equipment ensures the most effective work from such tools.

PLATE 90. The Hoverdry Type 101 (Sports) Series M101/S/BS is an unusual device for clearing surface water. First produced in April 1987, the Patented machine removes 60 gall. of water per minute and has seen use in local authority and professional soccer circles. (Courtesy Hoverdry Ltd., London.)

Section 7
FERTILISER FOR PITCHES
By D.M. Lawson

REQUIREMENTS OF THE GRASS PLANT

Turfgrasses, like all higher plants, need to obtain certain factors from their surroundings in order to achieve proper, healthy growth. Leaves need light, carbon dioxide from the atmosphere, along with water in order to photosynthesise, whereby the plant manufactures sugars in the leaves. Oxygen from the atmosphere is also required by the leaves, as well as the roots, for respiration.

The soil supplies a number of extremely important factors for plant growth. Firstly, physical support for the roots – in turfgrasses this is obviously vital. Secondly, a supply of water for the plant to take up via the root system and thirdly, the ability to conduct oxygen from the atmosphere to the roots as well as allow waste gases to escape into the atmosphere. Finally, the soil maintains a reserve of essential nutrients for plants. Examples of these are: nitrogen, phosphorus, potassium, sulphur and calcium.

Many of these requirements cannot be significantly influenced by the groundsman. For instance, the amount of light the grass receives will depend largely on its physical location and weather conditions. However, the supply of oxygen to roots can be aided by aeration, as described in Section 6. The amounts of essential nutrients supplied by the soil will depend on the geological formation on which it was formed, its cultivation history and local climate. The groundsman can greatly influence the amounts of nutrients which the turf actually receives through the application of fertilisers.

By far the most important nutrient derived from the soil is nitrogen.

NITROGEN (N)

Nitrogen is needed in plants in order to form proteins, including enzymes, but many other compounds, such as chlorophyll, also contain nitrogen. In turfgrasses the content of N is about 2–4% of the dry weight, but this will vary according to time of year, species, stage of growth and fertiliser application. If the grass does not obtain sufficient amounts of nitrogen, overall growth rate is diminished, the leaf blade turns yellow and the turf may eventually die off. In the grass species used for winter games pitches, lack of nitrogen will lessen the ability of the turf to recover from play. On the other hand, if the turfgrasses take up excessive amounts of nitrogen then leaves become soft and intolerant to wear and root development is poor.

Most of the soil's nitrogen is held within the organic matter; generally the greater amount of organic matter present, the greater are the reserves of nitrogen. However, such organic N is not immediately available for uptake by the turfgrasses as it must first be converted to soluble forms which can be taken in through the roots. The conversion to soluble forms is carried out by soil microorganisms; in particular, bacteria. The process (known as mineralisation) is highly dependent on the soil temperature and moisture conditions, so that mineralisation takes place most actively in the autumn when soils are still warm, but moist from autumnal rainfall.

The first product of mineralisation is ammonium (NH_4^+) which can be absorbed by the roots. During relatively cool, spring temperatures there may be some accumulation of NH_4 in the soil, but as soil temperatures increase in summer the NH_4^+ is quickly converted to nitrate (NO_3^+) by bacteria. This is the form which is most readily taken up by the turfgrasses.

In one year approximately 2% of the soil nitrogen is mineralised to plant-available forms. For an intensively used playing field this supply of nitrogen is inadequate for the provision of a dense turf cover with good wear recovery characteristics. Therefore, fertiliser N must be applied in order to supplement the soil's own supply.

POTASSIUM (K)

Potassium does not form part of the plant's solid structure in the way that nitrogen does, but it is needed for the biochemical pathways which produce carbohydrates and proteins. In addition, it has an important role to play in the control of water retention within the plant leaf. In turfgrasses the normal concentration of potassium in the leaf is about 2% of the dry weight, but this can fluctuate greatly as plants can take up "luxury" amounts of K if there are large amounts available in the soil. On the other hand, a substantial proportion of leaf potassium can be leached out by rainfall. If insufficient amounts of potassium are present in the grass it will be less tolerant of drought conditions.

In the soil potassium is present within the mineral matter; the sand, silt and clay material. This potassium is "locked up" and so not available for plants. However, a proportion is released to provide a reserve which can be exploited by the roots. Many soils naturally contain significant reserves of plant-available K, particularly where there is a large amount of clay material present. On sandy soils there is little retention of K and indeed, significant amounts may be leached out of the rootzone by rain water. Soil testing can show whether or not there is an adequate concentration of potassium for turf growth.

PHOSPHORUS (P)

Phosphorus comprises about 0.3% of leaf dry weight in turfgrasses. It is involved with energy transport and storage in the plant cells and is also part of the nucleic acid molecules which carry genetic information during cell division. It is particularly important that seedling turfgrasses receive an adequate supply of P in order to prevent inadequate root development. Apart from its effect on root growth, P deficiency has a deleterious effect on overall growth, the first symptom of which is an overall blue colouration in the leaf.

In soils, phosphorus is present in both the organic matter and mineral fraction. Like nitrogen, microbial breakdown of the organic matter releases soluble, plant-available P in the form of phosphate ($H_2PO_4^-$ or HPO_4^{2-}) which can be taken up by the roots. There is also an important source of P held on the surfaces of the soil clays where oxides of iron and aluminium bind phosphate; with great strength in acidic soils. In alkaline soils, phosphate forms relatively insoluble compounds with calcium. Therefore, soil phosphate is at its greatest availability to turf in soils which are neither acid or alkaline, i.e. neutral soils. Soil testing can indicate whether or not there is enough phosphorus present for turf growth.

CALCIUM (Ca)

Calcium is needed to maintain the integrity of plant cell structure and is also needed for the process of cell division. It is particularly important in the development of a strong, healthy root system. Turfgrass leaves normally contain about 0.5% calcium as a proportion of their dry weight. Deficiency will lead to a reddish discolouration of the leaf and restriction in root development.

Most soils contain concentrations of Ca far in excess of that required by turfgrasses. Only in acid, sandy soils is there a likelihood of deficiency. Alkaline soils contain large amounts of calcium in the form of calcium carbonate. Soil tests can show the concentration of plant-available Ca.

MAGNESIUM (Mg)

In the grass leaf, magnesium comprises about 0.2% of the dry weight and it performs a number of roles within the plant. It is required by enzymes associated with photosynthesis; is involved with protein production and forms part of the chlorophyll molecule which absorbs sunlight and gives the leaf its green colour. Visual symptoms of deficiency are a reddish discolouration followed by yellowing of leaves.

Like calcium, most soils contain adequate amounts of Mg for turf and low concentrations will only be encountered on acid, sandy soils. Again soil testing can show whether or not there is enough available Mg for turf growth.

SULPHUR (S)

Sulphur is present within plant protein and makes up about 0.1% of leaf dry weight. Deficiency will lead to an overall reduction in growth and yellowing of leaves.

The soil organic matter contains significant reserves of sulphur and it is only on soils with a low organic content that sulphur deficiency is likely to be encountered.

MICRONUTRIENTS

In addition to the major plant nutrients described above, plants must obtain trace quantities of other elements. These are the micronutrients and individually, they are present in the grass leaf at between 0.0001% and 0.02% of dry weight. These micronutrients are chlorine (C1), iron (Fe), manganese (Mn), boron (B), zinc (Zn), copper (Cu) and molybdenum (Mo).

Those micronutrients which are metals are necessary for enzyme activation, whereas boron forms part of the plant cell wall. Deficiency in these elements is generally unlikely to occur in turfgrasses. However, on highly alkaline soils the uptake of iron, manganese, copper and zinc may be restricted. Soil tests are useful in assessing micronutrient availability.

AVAILABILITY OF NUTRIENTS

Soils vary in their inherent nutrient content, but there are other factors which will influence the rate at which individual nutrients are taken up by the turfgrasses. The effect of soil temperature on nitrogen availability has already been mentioned. Inevitably, soil temperature will have an effect on other nutrients, for instance, phosphate absorption by roots is reduced in cold soil conditions. Some nutrients interfere with the uptake of other nutrients, for instance, high concentrations of potassium will reduce the uptake of magnesium. However, one of the most important factors in determining nutrient availability is the acidity or alkalinity of the soil, i.e. its pH value. This will be dealt with next.

SOIL pH

The acidity or alkalinity of a system is defined in terms of its pH value. This is a measure of the hydrogen ion concentration; the greater the hydrogen ion concentration the greater is the acidity. The pH value is a negative logarithmic measurement of the hydrogen ion concentration and so high concentrations (i.e. high acidity) gives a low pH value. High pH values are indicative of alkaline conditions where the hydrogen ion concentration is relatively low.

Measurement of soil pH is actually a measure of the effect which the soil material has on the pH of the soil water (or "soil solution") and where the value lies between 6 and 7 the soil is neither acid nor alkaline; it is said to be neutral. Below 6 the soil would be categorised as mildly acidic; below 5 as acid. Most soils do not fall much below 4 in pH. Soils with values above 7 are categorised as alkaline and rarely are values obtained above 8.2 in temperate climates (see Plate 91). Because pH is measured on a logarithmic scale the actual values do not always make apparent the true difference in acidity or alkalinity. For instance, a soil with pH of 5.0 is ten times more acid than one with a value of 6.0. A soil with a pH of 4.0 is ten times more acid than one with a value of 5.0 and one hundred times more acid than one with a value of 6.0.

Changes in a soil's pH value are brought about by a number of factors. Firstly, percolation of rain water through soil causes some acidification due to natural acidity. Fertiliser application can have a major effect on the soil pH, the form of fertiliser, nitrogen being particularly important. Ammonium nitrogen is extremely acidifying; urea nitrogen is moderately acidifying and the nitrate form actually produces alkalinity in soil. The rate at which the pH value changes is determined by the buffering capacity of the soil. This is its ability to resist acidification or alkalification. The greater the proportions of clay and organic matter the greater is the buffering capacity, so that in very sandy soils pH may change rapidly.

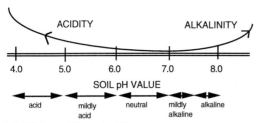

PLATE 91. The soil pH scale.

The high pH values of alkaline soils are due to the presence of limestone or chalk. Such soils are resistant to reduction in pH as the limestone or chalk must dissolve out of the rootzone before the pH will fall below 7.0.

Soil pH is not directly of importance to the turfgrass; it is the effect on the availability of nutrients to the grass which is vital. For most nutrients the major effect of pH is to change their solubility in the soil. For others, such as nitrogen, the effect of pH is on the soil microbes which release nitrogen to the turf from organic matter.

Most nutrients are at their greatest availability when soil pH is within the neutral range (6.0 to 7.0). For this reason the soils of winter games pitches should show a neutral pH value as leaf growth will be at its most vigorous. In addition, root growth is more extensive at neutral pH.

Amending soil pH
On rootzones dominated by soil the pH value should be measured every 4-5 years. On sand dominated rootzones pH tends to decrease very rapidly and so the value should be measured every 1-2 years.

Where pH is found to be below 6.0 lime should be applied in the form of ground limestone or ground chalk. The amount of lime to be applied will depend on the physical nature of the soil as well as its pH value. As an approximate guide:

clay soil pH 5.0 : apply 2.8 t/ha
clay soil pH 5.5 : apply 2.1 t/ha
sandy soil pH 5.0 : apply 2.1 t/ha
sandy soil pH 5.5 : apply 1.4 t/ha

FERTILISER MATERIALS
Of the mineral nutrients detailed previously, soil nitrogen, potassium and, to a lesser extent, phosphorus have to be supplemented for turf cultivation. In soils of very sandy texture magnesium and micronutrients may also require application.

Straight fertilisers are those which contain only one plant nutrient whereas compound fertilisers contain at least two in combined form. In the United Kingdom the nutrient analysis of fertilisers is given as per cent N for nitrogen content, P_2O_5 (phosphorus pentoxide) for phosphorus content and K_2O (potassium oxide) for potassium content. Thus, a fertiliser with an analysis of 10:15:10 contains 10% N, 15% P_2O_5 and 10% K_2O. If magnesium is present, then its content is usually expressed in terms of MgO (magnesium oxide). The nutrient content of proprietary fertilisers is also expressed in terms of the pure element, i.e. N, P, K and Mg. To convert P to P_2O_5 multiply by 2.29; K to K_2O multiply by 1.20 and Mg to MgO multiply by 1.66. The degree of phosphorus solubility is indicated by the proportions soluble in water and in citrate solution.

The following sections describe the materials commonly used in fertiliser for turf. Many of them can be obtained and applied alone (or 'straight'), but on winter games pitches proprietary compound fertilisers are normally used. These are made up of a mixture of materials.

NITROGEN FERTILISERS

The nitrogen sources used as fertiliser on turf can be categorised into soluble inorganic materials, organic compounds derived from animals or plants and synthetic slow release forms.

Inorganic N sources

These materials are all highly soluble, quick acting fertilisers which provide a flush of growth soon after application. Their effects on growth normally last 4-5 weeks after application.

Ammonium sulphate; $(NH_4)_2 SO_4$. Contains 21% N
This is a highly acidifying nitrogen source, commonly used within proprietary fertilisers for turf.

Ammonium nitrate; $NH_4 NO_3$. Contains 35% N
This is a quick acting material as it supplies nitrate-N direct to the grass root. It has a smaller acidifying effect than ammonium sulphate.

Ammonium nitrate is normally produced in granular form. It is also obtainable with calcium carbonate (lime) incorporated into the granules (21-28% N), e.g. "Nitrochalk". It is also used as a liquid fertiliser.

Pure ammonium nitrate is a potential fire and explosive hazard and it must be stored with care; as directed by the manufacturer.

Sodium nitrate; $Na NO_3$. Contains 16% N
This material is usually sold in granular form. Because all the nitrogen is in the nitrate form, it is a very quick acting fertiliser. Because no ammonium is present it has little or no acidifying effect.

Potassium nitrate; KNO_3. Contains 13% N
Another material which is a soluble source of nitrate nitrogen. It also contains a high concentration of potassium (46% K_2O; 38% K).

Urea; $(NH_2)_2 CO$. Contains 46% N
Urea is obtained as a white crystalline material which is very soluble in water and it is commonly used for liquid fertiliser products. In the soil it is quickly converted to ammonium carbonate, with the ammonium then being converted to nitrate. Urea application does not cause so much acidification of soil as ammonium sulphate due to the neutralising effect of the carbonate. There may be a loss of gaseous ammonia (NH_3) when urea is applied to the soil surface, especially if the soil is sandy. However, this may be compensated by the low cost of the product. Because of the ammonia release and concomitant toxicity, urea-containing fertilisers are inappropriate for use on germinating seed and seedlings.

Others
Besides the inorganic N sources mentioned above, other nitrogen compounds may be incorporated into proprietary granular fertilisers according to commercial convenience. These include calcium nitrate, ammonium phosphate and calcium ammonium nitrate.

Organic N sources derived from animals and plants

Organic fertilisers are those materials derived from previously living sources. They are generally more expensive than inorganic types and are not commonly used on winter games pitches.

Dried blood; Contains 10-14% N
Dried blood is quickly mineralised to ammonium by soil micro-organisms and under warm conditions it can break down so quickly that it produces a growth response similar to that of ammonium sulphate. However, it is non-acidifying in the soil due to the production of carbonate.

Hoof and horn meal; Contains 13% N
This has a lower mineralisation rate than dried blood and so provides a more long lasting growth

response. The more finely ground the meal the quicker is its break down in the soil. Like dried blood it is non-acidifying.

Others
Materials such as fish meal, rape meal, meat and bone meal all have a significant nitrogen content (5-10% N). They also contain significant amounts of phosphorus and so are useful where a phosphorus-containing mix is required. They are also non-acidifying.

Slow release N sources
Some of the natural organic sources have noticeable long-term nitrogen release characteristics, but their properties tend to be rather unpredictable. For this reason, synthetic nitrogen fertilisers have been produced which provide a more predictable prolonged release of plant-available nitrogen. There are three main groups of these available for use on turf:-

[1] Synthetic organic nitrogen compounds.
[2] Inorganic fertilisers treated to decrease their solubility.
[3] Products containing nitrification inhibitors.

The principal advantages likely to be gained from the use of slow release products is the fewer number of applications required in comparison to the more conventional fertiliser materials, along with a more even rate of growth.

[1] Synthetic organic nitrogen compounds
These products' slow release properties depend largely on the fact that they are only slightly soluble in water.

Isobutylidene diurea; (IBDU). Contains 32% N
When applied to soil, IBDU is broken down by micro-organisms to soluble urea; the rate of breakdown increasing with soil temperature and moisture and with decreasing fertiliser granule size. The urea is then converted to ammonium carbonate. Little or no soil acidification is caused by IBDU application.

During winter when microbial activity is at a minimum, there is still some release of plant-available nitrogen from IBDU in order to enhance turf growth. This results from a purely chemical degradation of the material. In addition, an autumn application of IBDU has been shown to produce a carry-over effect to the following spring, providing an early greening-up of the turf.

Commercial fertilisers containing IBDU are now widely available. Such products may contain almost all of their nitrogen as IBDU or in combination with soluble inorganic sources. If within a compound fertiliser, then the other nutrients are present in conventional inorganic forms.

Methylene urea; Contains approximately 40% N
Commonly known as ureaform, this is the oldest of the synthetic organic materials used as fertiliser. It actually is comprised of a range of chemical compounds which vary in their solubility in water and rate of urea release in the soil through decomposition by microorganisms. The factors controlling decomposition are similar to those of IBDU, but the more soluble portion of ureaform tends to break down very quickly in the soil, whereas the less soluble portions tend to break down so slowly that they have little fertilising property. Thus, approximately 10% of the nitrogen in ureaform has no value as a fertiliser. Like IBDU, ureaform produces a spring carry-over effect.

[2] Inorganic fertilisers with restricted solubility
Magnesium ammonium phosphate; $Mg\,NH_4\,PO_4$. Contains 10% N
The chemical nature of this material causes it to be only very slightly soluble in water. The release of nitrogen (as ammonium-N) is due to chemical reactions and is not so dependent on soil temperature as with the synthetic organic compounds.

Resin coated fertiliser; Various analyses
In these products, soluble nitrogen carriers are coated with resin, through which they gradually diffuse into the soil solution. A range of products is available containing various ratios of nitrogen, phosphorus and potassium . One major advantage of these materials over other slow release fertilisers is that all of the major plant nutrients, not just nitrogen, can be gradually released to the grass. The release rate increases at higher temperatures. Many resin coated fertilisers are unsuitable for surface application to turf because of their large prill size.

Sulphur coated urea; (SCU). Contains 32% N
By coating urea with elemental sulphur its solubility in the soil is greatly reduced. The urea gradually enters the soil solution by diffusion through the sulphur coating or by decomposition of the coating. As the temperature increases, the release rate increases. The sulphur coating is converted to sulphate (SO_4^{2-}) by soil bacteria with resulting production of acidity. Large prill-size SCU is unsuitable for turf because of pick-up by machinery and damage to the coating causing severe turf scorching.

[3] Addition of nitrification inhibitors.
It was noted earlier that the nitrification process through which ammonium-N is converted to nitrate-N depends on the action of soil bacteria. If the activity of these bacteria could be restricted, then only small quantities of nitrate would be available over a more prolonged period; the ammonium (NH_4^+) being held on the negative exchange sites on clay minerals and organic matter. A few chemicals have been shown to inhibit nitrification by bacteria, two of the most commonly used being dicyandiamide and nitrapyrin. Proprietary turf fertilisers are available which contain conventional soluble nitrogen sources along with dicyandiamide, 'Didin'. Didin itself acts as a synthetic organic slow release nitrogen fertiliser.

POTASSIUM FERTILISERS
All sources of potassium commonly used for fertilizer are inorganic and highly soluble in water.

Potassium chloride; KCl. Contains 60% K_2O (50% K)
The chloride salt of potassium is the most common source of potassium for commercial granular compound fertilisers. It is still often referred to by its traditional name of muriate of potash.

Potassium sulphate; K_2SO_4. Contains 50% K_2O (42% K)
For the purpose of mixing straight fertilizers, potassium sulphate is preferable as, unlike potassium chloride, it causes little problem with setting in damp conditions. However, it is more expensive than the chloride. In trials no differences have been observed between the effects of applying the sulphate or chloride.

Others
Two other impure potassium sources are sometimes used for fertiliser mixes: potash salts (30% K_2O; 25% K) and Kainit (14% K_2O; 12% K). They attract moisture and so tend to cake. In addition, they contain a large proportion of sodium chloride (common salt) and so regular use could be damaging to soil structure.

PHOSPHORUS FERTILISERS
Inorganic and natural organic forms of phosphorus are both used in fertilisers for turf. In both cases phosphorus is present as the phosphate (PO_4^{3-}) molecule, although the inorganic phosphates tend to be more soluble thus providing a quicker plant uptake of phosphate from these types. However, even with the more soluble sources, the phosphate not used by the turfgrass is eventually transformed to relatively insoluble compounds in the soil. In acidic soils these compounds are phosphates of aluminium and iron, whereas in alkaline soils insoluble calcium phosphates are formed.

Inorganic P sources
Superphosphate; Contains 19% P_2O_5 (8% P)
This is a widely used source of water soluble phosphate, which is present in the form of mono-

calcium phosphate. It also contains a large proportion of calcium sulphate (gypsum). Both powder and granular types are produced. The powder form has a tendency to cake in damp conditions.

Triple superphosphate; Contains 47% P_2O_5 (21% P)
This has a higher phosphate content than ordinary superphosphate as a result of its lower calcium sulphate content. It contains soluble mono-calcium phosphate and so reacts in the soil in a similar way to ordinary superphosphate.

Ammonium phosphate; Contains 50% P_2O_5 (22% P)
This is not readily available for use on its own, but is used as part of high analysis compound fertilisers. It contains approximately 11% N. The phosphate present is water soluble and so is often used as the phosphate source in liquid fertilisers.

Organic P sources
Organic phosphorus fertilisers are based on preparations of bones. The phosphorus is present as the highly insoluble tri-calcium phosphate and so is only slowly available to the grass root. In acid soils its availability is increased.

Bone meal; Contains 22% P_2O_5 (10% P)
This is produced from crushed, degreased bones. Along with phosphorus it supplies nitrogen to turf (4% N). It is often used as a conditioner in order to stop caking of powder fertiliser mixtures in damp conditions.

Steamed bone flour; Contains 28% P_2O_5 (12% P)
Steamed bone flour is similar in composition and effect to bone meal, but most of its nitrogen has been removed (<1% N). It is also used as a conditioner for fertiliser mixes.

MAGNESIUM FERTILISERS
The two most commonly used sources of magnesium for fertiliser are Kieserite, $Mg\ SO_4 . H_2O$ (27% MgO; 16% Mg) and Epsom salts $Mg\ SO_4 . 7H_2O$ (17% MgO; 10% Mg). If there is a requirement for magnesium on an acid soil to which lime is being added, dolomitic limestone can be used. This contains 17-18% MgO; 10-11% Mg.

MICRONUTRIENT FERTILISERS
Some proprietary compound fertilisers contain micronutrients (or trace elements) along with the major plant nutrients. There are also available products which contain micronutrients in powder form, in solution and fused within glass frits which release the elements slowly into the soil solution. Organic nitrogen sources and seaweed meals also contain a significant micronutrient content.

LIQUID FERTILISER PRODUCTS
Liquid fertilisers are derived from highly soluble inorganic materials such as urea, ammonium nitrate and potassium nitrate. They are available in a wide range of nutrient content and when sprayed onto plants a proportion of the nutrients is taken up by the leaf itself. On amenity turf they are useful for the even application of small amounts of fertiliser nutrient, but because of cost they are not commonly used on sports pitches.

A number of liquid products are derived from seaweed extracts and/or farm slurry. These in themselves supply little or no nutrients when applied to turf. For any fertiliser value to be obtained inorganic nutrients, such as those described above, have to be added.

CALCULATING APPLICATION RATES
The basis for calculating fertiliser application rates is the quantity of individual nutrient per unit of area. This is normally expressed as kilogram nutrient per hectare (10,000 metre^2) or kg/ha of nutrient. For relatively small areas such as golf greens it is more appropriate to calculate in terms of grams nutrient per square metre (g/m^2 of nutrient). The application rate in kg/ha can be converted

to g/m^2 by dividing by 10; $1 g/m^2 = 10 kg/ha$. These metric measurements can be converted to Imperial through the following conversion factors:

$$125 kg/ha = 1 cwt/acre$$
$$35 g/m^2 = 1 oz/yd^2$$

If, for example, it is desired to apply 40 kg/ha N; 20 kg/ha P_2O_5 and 20 kg/ha K_2O then the application rate of fertiliser can be found from:

$$\frac{100}{x} \quad x \quad 40 kg/ha \ N \qquad where \ x = \% \ N \ content \ of \ product$$

$$\frac{100}{y} \quad x \quad 20 kg/ha \ P_2O_5 \quad where \ y = \% \ P_2O_5 \ content \ of \ product$$

$$\frac{100}{z} \quad x \quad 20 kg/ha \ K_2O \quad where \ z = \% \ K_2O \ content \ of \ product$$

From a compound fertiliser a nutrient ratio of $2N:1P_2O_5:1 K_2O$ would be appropriate, e.g. 20:10:10 (i.e. 20% N:10% P_2O_5:10% K_2O). The application rate of the 20:10:10 product would be:

$$\frac{100}{20} \ x \ 40 kg/ha \ N = 200 kg/ha \ of \ product.$$

Generally, lower amounts of nutrients are obtainable from liquid fertiliser products compared to solids due to the danger of leaf scorching from concentrated solutions. However, the amounts which are applied can be calculated as in the following example:-

A liquid product contains 15% N, i.e. 15 g of N per 100 ml of liquid. Applied undiluted this would cause severe scorching of the turfgrasses. Therefore it is diluted by adding (at least) 2 volumes of water to 1 volume of fertiliser. The diluted material now contains 5 g of N per 100 ml and is then applied at 60 litres per 1000 m^2, i.e. 60 mls per m^2.

Thus, $\frac{5 g N}{100 ml} \ x \ 60 ml = 3.0 \ g/m^2 \ N$ is applied (30 kg/ha N).

COMPARING COSTS

In the first example given above a compound fertiliser with nutrient analysis 20:10:10 was used. However, the same proportions of N, P and K could have been supplied by fertilisers with nutrient ratios of 12:6:6, 14:7:7 and 22:11:11. In order to choose between them, it is useful to compare the cost of applying nutrients from the alternatives. The following example demonstrates the method of calculation:

Comparing   [a]   12:6:6   at £5.00 per 25 kg bag
          [b]   20:10:10   at £7.00 per 25 kg bag

The calculation need only be based on the nitrogen contents of the products.

[1] Application rate - 40 kg/ha N

Require   [a]   12:6:6   at $\frac{100}{12} \ x \ 40 = 333 kg/ha$ product.

        [b]   20:10:10   at $\frac{100}{20} \ x \ 40 = 200 kg/ha$ product.

[2] Cost to achieve the application rate of 40 kg/ha N from 25 kg bags.

[a]   12:6:6   - $\frac{333}{25}$ x £5.00 = £66.60

[b]   20:10:10   - $\frac{200}{25}$ x £7.00 = £56.00

Therefore, the cost of applying nutrients from the 20:10:10 product is lower.

When purchasing fertilisers, significant discounts can be made by buying in bulk. In addition, prices may vary considerably between suppliers.

STORING FERTILISERS
Fertilisers must always be stored under cover. Materials which are not packed in plastic bags should be kept very dry and cool. Even fertiliser sealed in polythene bags should be off the floor, on pallets, to avoid condensation spoiling the product. As fertiliser bags are heavy, they should be stored in such a way as to avoid awkward lifting; the most convenient arrangement being criss-cross stacking to about six bags height.

FERTILISER PROGRAMMES
The aim of fertiliser application, along with other maintenance practices, is to produce a dense, vigorous turf which is tolerant of wear; not prone to diseases; contains few weeds (including unwanted grass species); withstands adverse weather conditions; and is aesthetically pleasing. The most influential mineral nutrient in achieving these aims is nitrogen as it has the greatest effect on the growth rate of the grass plant. However, a balanced uptake of all the plant nutrients is required as a deficiency in only one nutrient will be deleterious to growth. The majority of soils contain adequate concentrations of calcium, magnesium, sulphur and the micronutrients for turfgrasses. Only nitrogen, potassium and, to a lesser extent, phosphorus are likely to be deficient and so have to be supplemented by fertiliser application.

The actual amounts of nitrogen, phosphorus and potassium required by turf varies according to the species of turfgrass, whether established turf or seedling grasses are being treated; the physical nature of the soil; its nutrient status (fertility); and whether or not mower clippings are returned.

GRASS SPECIES
The turf of soccer pitches and Rugby pitches are composed of broad-leaved grasses such as perennial ryegrass and smooth-stalked meadow-grass. These hard-wearing species have a higher nutrient requirement than fescues or bents. However, hockey pitches often contain these latter species so that fertiliser application has to be adjusted accordingly.

PHYSICAL NATURE OF SOIL
A soil of very sandy texture has little inherent nutrient reserves. This is particularly true if it also has a low organic matter content. An extreme instance of this is the all-sand rootzone constructions used for some winter games pitches. In addition to their low nutrient status, they are unable to retain soluble nutrients derived from fertilisers. Potassium, ammonium and nitrate are either immediately taken up by the turf or quickly leached through the rootzone and lost in the drainage water. In loam soils the clay fraction withholds the potassium and ammonium against quick and excessive uptake by the grass, as well as leaching.

NUTRIENT STATUS OF SOIL AND SOIL TESTING
The nutrient status of soils and their ability to supply nutrients to plants can be measured by chemical analysis. This is particularly true for phosphorus, potassium, magnesium and the micronutrients copper, zinc, boron and manganese. At present there is no reliable analytical test to predict the concentration of plant-available nitrogen in outdoor soils. This is because many factors

control the amount of plant-available nitrogen, in particular the rate at which soil organic matter is mineralised. Unfortunately, such a process could not be predicted by routine soil analysis. Thus, the groundsman observes the nitrogen status of the soil indirectly, through the rate of grass growth and depth of coloration.

In testing soils for phosphate, potassium, magnesium or micronutrient concentrations, sub-samples should be obtained at random over the whole pitch to a depth of 10 cm. These sub-samples should then be bulked together to form one soil sample. Analysis of the sample for nutrient content is normally carried out by extracting the soil with a solution which removes the nutrient fraction that is potentially plant-available. The nutrient content of the extracting solution is then analysed chemically.

It should be noted that the amount of plant nutrient removed from the soil depends on the nature of the extracting solution used. It is important that this is known when interpreting analytical results. Proper interpretation of results, with regard to fertiliser application, must also take into account particular local site conditions.

There are portable soil test kits available which are useful in providing an immediate on-site guide to soil nutrient concentrations.

REMOVAL OR RETURN OF GRASS CLIPPINGS

Grass clippings contain a significant amount of nitrogen, phosphorus and potassium, equivalent to approximately 3% N; 0.7% P_2O_5; 2% K_2O in dry leaf material. Thus, allowing clippings to fly returns some nutrients to the soil.

On top-class football and hockey pitches clippings are removed. In all these situations plant nutrients are being withdrawn from the soil-plant system so that reserves have to be supplemented through fertilising.

SEED BEDS AND TURFING

Developing seedlings and newly laid turf both have particular nutrient requirements. In both cases phosphate is required in the fertiliser treatments to aid rooting of the seedlings and the extension of roots from turf sods. Relatively high potassium levels in the soil also promotes disease resistance during the early growth of seedlings and reduces drought susceptibility.

Established swards of seedling grasses require a higher nitrogen application rate than mature turf in order to promote vigorous growth.

TIMING OF FERTILISER APPLICATIONS

With soluble inorganic types of fertiliser there is little point in giving dressings when there is little or no grass growth. The turf manager has to decide when spring growth is commencing as the soil and air temperatures increase. Soluble fertiliser should not be applied when soil or air temperatures are below 5°C. It is generally accepted that the first spring fertiliser dressing is particularly important as it helps grass recover from winter wear and quickly improves the turf appearance for the summer. During the growing season applications should take place every four to six weeks.

On heavily used professional football pitches, light dressings of compound granular fertilisers in late autumn (late September to mid-October) and early spring (mid-March), when minimal growth is taking place, have proved worthwhile in helping the turf recover from play.

The use of synthetic slow release fertilisers means that application times need not be restricted to periods of active growth. This results from the low solubility and diminished leaching liability of these products. Therefore, fertiliser could be applied from December to February so that as mild periods are encountered during winter just enough nitrogen is available to enhance plant growth and turf appearance without promoting disease. In addition, enough nitrogen will remain present in the soil to give vigorous spring growth. These advantages are not obtained from products containing nitrification inhibitors. With all slow release fertiliser products, the frequency of application during the summer months is lessened; normally dressings need only be applied every seven to eight weeks.

RECOMMENDED FERTILISER PROGRAMMES
It is possible only to provide general guidance on the amounts of fertiliser to apply in various situations.

In the following sections annual nutrient rates are suggested. From these, the amounts of the appropriate fertiliser required can be calculated from the nutrient analysis of compound fertiliser. The phosphate and potassium rates suggested may not be required every year and soil analysis can be used to judge if applications are necessary.

FOOTBALL AND RUGBY PITCHES (AND MOST OTHER GAMES EXCEPT HOCKEY)
The quality of the turf depends on the requirements of the user. In general, on local council sports fields grass clippings are returned so that the fertiliser requirement is lower. These situations contrast with high class football and rugby pitches where clippings are boxed off in order to provide a firm surface.

Annual nutrient application:

Moderate quality turf; clippings returned - N : 80-100 kg/ha
$\qquad\qquad\qquad\qquad\qquad\qquad$ P_2O_5 : 20-50 kg/ha *
$\qquad\qquad\qquad\qquad\qquad\qquad$ K_2O : 20-50 kg/ha *

High class; clippings removed - N : 160-200 kg/ha
$\qquad\qquad\qquad\qquad\qquad\qquad$ P_2O_5 : 80-100 kg/ha *
$\qquad\qquad\qquad\qquad\qquad\qquad$ K_2O : 80-100 kg/ha *
$\qquad\qquad\qquad\qquad\qquad\qquad$ * depending on soil analysis

Applications on moderate quality turf would be split into two dressings, one in spring and the other in late summer just prior to the onset of the playing season. For summer games such as polo, such timing would also be appropriate, giving the spring dressing to promote growth for the playing period and a late summer application to aid renovation. Any phosphate and potassium dressings would be applied in spring for winter games, especially if reseeding is being carried out, supplemented by late summer nitrogen to boost growth for the playing season.

On high class winter games pitches, four or five dressings would be applied. The first would be in March, the second at the end of the playing season, one or two during summer with one being two weeks before the start of the playing season, and a final one in late September to mid-October. Half of the phosphate and/or potassium annual application would be given at the end of the playing season, before renovation work, and the second half in the autumn in order to promote hardy growth in the turfgrasses.

Ordinary granular fertilisers are generally acceptable for use on perennial ryegrass dominated turf. Granular ammonium nitrate can be used in nitrogen- only dressings and compound granular products where phosphate and/or potassium are to be applied with the nitrogen. Fertilisers are available with nutrient ratios of suitable analysis for the recommended nutrient applications given above. Where the N content is above 20% in a granular fertiliser a speckling effect is likely to be obtained because of localised high soil N concentrations. Mini-crumb or mini-granular compound fertilisers can also be used on winter games pitches. Their smaller size and relatively low N analysis provides a more even distribution than the ordinary granular types.

Slow release nitrogen fertilisers may be found advantageous on high class winter games pitches, especially on very sandy or sand only constructions. With these products the annual nitrogen rate would be split into three dressings; one in mid-May, the second at the end of August and the third in late October. This last dressing will encourage growth during mild winter weather and in the following spring. Materials based on nitrification inhibitors will not produce the spring carry-over effect so that the first dressing should be in March with the second in early May and third in early October.

On sports pitches of high sand or pure sand construction the annual nitrogen application rate should be increased to 250 kg/ha N. If ordinary soluble granular fertilisers are used, then the number of dressings should be increased to six or seven per year. Slow release fertilisers may be particularly advantageous on such construction types and the recommendations given above for their use would be appropriate.

The magnesium content of sand rootzones is likely to become low and, if so, an application of Kieserite to provide 20 kg/ha MgO or Epsom salts should be given between two dressings, one in spring and one in late summer. Alternatively, a granular or mini-granular fertiliser containing magnesium can be used.

HOCKEY PITCHES AND LACROSSE
Where hockey or lacrosse is played on natural turf, the best surface is provided by a fescue-bent-perennial ryegrass sward.

Annual nutrient application:
Clippings returned -   N : 40-50 kg/ha
                               P_2O_5 : 0
                               K_2O : 0

Clippings removed -   N : 80-200 kg/ha
                               P_2O_5 : 20 kg/ha*
                               K_2O : 60-150 kg/ha*
                               * depending on soil analysis

The annual nitrogen application should be applied in two or three dressings per year; in spring and late summer, before the end of August. A third dressing would be applied in mid-summer.

SEED BEDS AND TURF BEDS
In order to promote healthy root growth and disease resistance, it is important that phosphate and potassium are well supplied to newly laid turves and seedling grasses.

Nutrient applications:
Seed Beds   -   N : 40-80 kg/ha
                                    P_2O_5 : 60-120 kg/ha *
                                    K_2O : 40-80 kg/ha *

Turf beds: Spring   -   N : 40-80 kg/ha
                                    P_2O_5 : 60-120 kg/ha*
                                    K_2O : 40-80 kg/ha *

Turf beds: Autumn   -   N : 10-30 kg/ha
                                    P_2O_5 : 60-120 kg/ha*
                                    K_2O : 40-80 kg/ha*
                                    * depending on soil analysis
                     (divide by 10 to convert kg/ha to g/m^2)

The higher end of the nutrient ranges for phosphate and potassium should be employed when soil concentrations of the nutrients are low. For seed beds and spring turfing a granular fertiliser of nutrient ratio 2 N : 3 P_2O_5 : 2 K_2O would be ideal (e.g. 10:15:10). However, turfing is usually carried out in autumn and it is important that a low nitrogen fertiliser is used during this period in order to reduce the possibility of disease from weak, lush growth. Slow release nitrogen fertilisers are particularly suitable for seed and turf beds as they reduce the leaching losses encountered from ordinary soluble fertilisers.

NEWLY SEEDED AREAS

In the first full growing season after seedling establishment grasses must obtain a generous nitrogen supply in order to produce a well knit, mature turf.

Annual nutrient application - N : 160-200 kg/ha
P$_2$O$_5$: 80-100 kg/ha*
K$_2$O : 80-100 kg/ha*
* depending on soil analysis
(divide by 10 to convert kg/ha to g/m^2)

The above rates would be given within four or five dressings during the year. It is unlikely that phosphate would be required if used in the seed bed fertiliser, but potassium application may be necessary if the soil is of a very sandy nature.

FERTILISER DISTRIBUTION

Because an even rate of growth on an area of turf is desirable, it must be a prime aim in fertiliser application to distribute the material as evenly as possible. As well as causing problems in mowing, inconsistent distribution may damage turf due to scorching on sections where excess fertiliser has been applied.

The best time for fertiliser application is during a dry interlude in showery weather conditions. In this way dressings are well washed into the soil. If no rain falls, then the material should be well watered in, especially on fine turf which is particularly susceptible to fertiliser scorch.

It is important that no solid fertiliser is left exposed on the surface prior to play. These materials may cause some skin irritation to players, especially on cuts or abrasions. Therefore fertiliser application during the playing season should be carried out during showery weather.

GRANULAR, CRUMB OR PELLETED FORMS

Compound fertilisers normally consist of materials which have been physically compressed into small crumbs or fairly large granules, with a size range of 2-5 mm. Agricultural granular products are commonly applied to playing fields where any localised scorching effects are disguised by the long grass cover.

PLATE 92. Belt--fed box-type fertiliser spreaders have been in use for many years. This Sisis model dates from 1961 but machines working on the same principle may still be encountered today.

PLATE 93. Pedestrian operated spinner-type fertiliser distributor from T. Parker & Sons. Hopper capacity is 90 lb.

PLATE 94. Tractor drawn spinner type distributor from BS of Italy. Tractor mounted models are also available, driven from the PTO.

DISTRIBUTORS

The majority of turf managers use mechanical spreaders. Although there are a wide range of types, distributors can be classed in three main categories:

[a] Belt or force-fed types - pedestrian operated, tractor-drawn or mounted.

[b] Spinner types - pedestrian operated, trailed, tractor mounted or truck mounted.

[c] Oscillating nozzle types - generally trailed or tractor mounted.

On site calibration of distributors before use is essential as the calibration marks on machines can be considered only as guides. In order to obtain a more accurate setting, the loaded distributor is passed at working speed over an area on which trays or a large sheet have been placed. The amount falling on to each tray or the sheet is then weighed. Because weather conditions and storage can affect the physical nature of materials, the rate of application at a particular distributor setting may vary, even when using the same fertiliser.

When applying fertiliser with a belt spreader the quantity should be split in two and two runs made over the whole area; the second run being at right angles to the first (see Plate 95). Spinner and oscillating type distributors tend to apply more material in the middle of the spread. To avoid a striped growth pattern developing the width of coverage achieved by the unit should be measured when set to apply at half the required rate. Guide lines or marker posts should then be used to ensure that each successive pass is set at half the width covered by the spinner (see Plate 96).

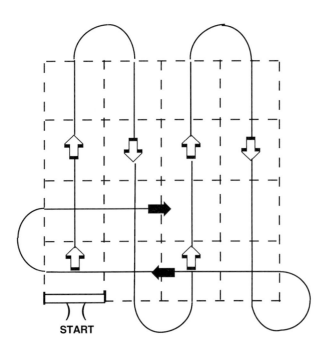

START

PLATE 95. Using a linear type distributor.

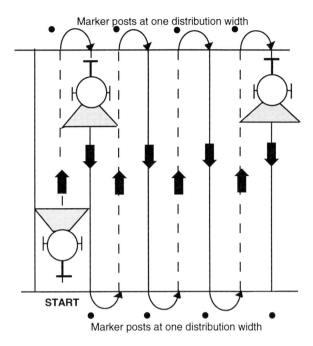

Marker posts at one distribution width

START

Marker posts at one distribution width

PLATE 96 Using a spinner type distributor.

APPLICATION OF LIQUID FERTILISERS

Although solid fertilisers are generally preferable to liquid forms for use on turf, liquid forms provide a convenient way of giving a quick green-up prior to a match without leaving fertiliser granules on the turf surface.

Spraying from vehicle-mounted or walk-over sprayers gives an even distribution. The liquid is applied in a single run using marker posts to ensure that there are no overlaps or gaps between passes.

Section 8

WEEDS, PESTS AND DISEASES
By N.R.W. Squires

Essentially, the maintenance work described in this section is not adopted on a routine basis, but rather as individual operations carried out to deal with specific problems as these may arise. However, on winter sports pitches weeds are often such a regular occurrence that treatment may be required as a matter of course in most years. Pests and diseases occur less frequently on winter sports pitches, but may require urgent treatment on occasion. As with other areas of sports turf, the adoption of good, overall turf management practices will help to ensure a dense cover of vigorously growing grass, which is less susceptible to invasion by weeds and pests or attack by disease.

Before discussing the control of individual problems, it is necessary to discuss the broad framework of the regulations regarding the use of the chemicals which it may be necessary to use.

PESTICIDE LEGISLATION
A pesticide is any substance which is used for destroying or controlling a pest and the definition thus includes herbicides, fungicides, insecticides, moss killers and earthworm killers. Plant growth regulators are also classed as pesticides, but fertilisers, soil conditioners and wetting agents are not since no pest control is involved. All pesticides are potentially dangerous to some degree to the operator applying the pesticide, the user of the turf and to the environment generally. Therefore, the legislation which governs pesticide use is designed to regulate the procedures and products so that adequate protection is provided and allows safe use of pesticides whilst also providing a satisfactory function. The main applicable legislation is provided by the following two acts:

Heath and Safety at Work Act 1974 which places general obligations on the employer to provide training and safety equipment; the employee is obliged to use the safety equipment provided. Regulations have been produced by the Health & Safety Executive, to control the risks in the work place arising from substances hazardous to health which may include pesticides. These regulations are the Control of Substances Hazardous to Health Regulations (COSHH).

Food and Environment Protection Act 1985 (FEPA) has as its aim "to protect the health of human beings, creatures and plants, to safeguard the environment and to secure safe efficient and humane methods of controlling pests". FEPA is implemented by the Control of Pesticides Regulations 1986 (COPR), so that only products which have been approved by government ministers on grounds of safety and efficacy may be used. Users must comply with the conditions of the approval, whilst additionally taking reasonable care to ensure safe use. 'Reasonable care' is defined in Codes of Practice for the appropriate area of use, which for our purposes is the Code of Practice for the Use of Approved Pesticides in Amenity and Industrial Areas.

The Code of Practice is much like the Highway Code in that "failure on the part of any person to follow the guidance given in the Code will not render the person liable to proceedings of any kind; but such failure will be admissible in evidence in any criminal proceedings brought under the 1985 Act".

Thus, it is strongly recommended that any person intending to use pesticides should obtain and study the Code of Practice for the Use of Approved Pesticides in Amenity and Industrial Areas. Furthermore, very useful information on the selection and use of pesticides is contained in the *Amenity Handbook* produced by the British Agrochemical Association, which also lists those pesticide products which are approved for use in amenity areas.

Other Acts which may well be relevant in addition include:

The Control of Pollution Act 1974 which precludes the deposition of controlled wastes (from commercial, local authority and industrial premises) on land except under licence.

The Water Act 1989 under which it is an offence to allow any poisonous, noxious or polluting matter to enter any controlled waters (rivers, lakes, canals, estuaries, coastal waters and underground waters) without a *Consent to Discharge* issued by the National Rivers Authority.

Finally, it is strongly recommended that all users of pesticides should receive appropriate and adequate training to ensure that they are competent to apply any pesticide treatment safely and effectively. Indeed, many users will be required by law to undergo training and certification which is by means of examination. Training is given by local agricultural and horticultural colleges, whilst examination is undertaken by the National Proficiency Tests Council.

The potential turfgrasses have been described in Section 5. Weed control in swards of these species means the elimination of broad-leaved species, rushes and also of undesirable grasses. The last named may include cocksfoot (*Dactylis glomerata*) or Yorkshire fog (*Holcus lanatus*), which are seldom considered acceptable in fine turf, and annual meadow-grass (*Poa annua*), which is best considered a pernicious weed in turf and not an essential turfgrass.

A weed can simply be defined as "a plant growing out of place". Turf for winter sports pitches should consist of a very limited number of desirable grass species and all other plants are weeds. Weeds may spoil the appearance and playing surface of the sward, compete with the desired turfgrasses for nutrients and water and may harbour diseases and insect pests.

CHEMICAL WEED CONTROL

The term "weedkiller" is best restricted to proprietary products, sold under trade names. The active ingredients in these products are described as "herbicides". For example, three different proprietary products or weed killers "x", "y" and "z", might have in common the same active ingredient (ai) or herbicide, for example mecoprop. Some weed killers contain two or more active ingredients.

The proportion of active ingredient varies between products. Thus if two firms sell weed killers with the same active ingredient, firm A may formulate its product with 20% ai whilst firm B formulates its product with 30% ai. In a situation where, for example, the greenkeeper is recommended to use 2 kg/ha of the active ingredient, he could apply the 2 kg ai by using 10 litres of A's product per hectare but would only need to use 6.7 litre/ha of the more concentrated product of B. (For some herbicides, the active ingredient is expressed as "acid equivalent" or "ae". Although the two terms are not the same, they have a similar meaning for the layman, both being used to distinguish the active herbicide from the "carrier" in a proprietary product.)

All recommendations in this book, as in other independent advisory publications, are in terms of ai. and ae. Manufacturers, however, give rates in terms of product, but also specify the % ai or ae of their product on the label or in leaflets, so that rates can be compared with independent recommendations.

Remember that under legislation it is only permissible to use approved products and that the conditions and restrictions on the label must be strictly observed. Approved products are listed in the current BAA *Amenity Handbook*.

Always follow manufacturers label instructions carefully. All herbicides are potentially dangerous to the user. Always be careful in measuring out and mixing concentrated herbicides: avoid inhaling the spray: and store and dispose of containers carefully. If appropriate, use gloves, protective clothing and face mask. Above all, read everything on the label before opening the container. This is now a legal requirement and all pesticide users should therefore be familiar with the Food and Environment Protection Act (1985), Part 3: and the Control of Pesticides Regulations (1986).

DISCOURAGING WEED INVASION

With the range of herbicides now available, most broad-leaved weeds of turf are fairly easily controlled. The same applies to rushes and mosses. The use of chemicals, however, is only one method of weed control in turf, and all weed control measures are only one part of good general management aimed at maintaining a first-class turf.

Playing under wet conditions may result in a scarred weak surface, providing conditions under which annual meadow-grass for example may thrive. Although such treatment generally cannot be avoided if turf is to fulfil its purpose, it may sometimes be possible to minimise damage and, at least, preparations can be made to deal with a foreseeable weed problem. Height of cut affects weed population. Allowing grass to grow very long and then shaving it right down will encourage weeds by weakening the grass. In fact any treatment which weakens the grass will encourage weeds; for example, careless fertiliser application can kill grass and leave bare patches which then fill up with weeds. A plentiful earthworm population results in a large number of casts; each of these smothers grass and provides a seed bed for weeds. For this and other reasons it pays to limit earthworm number. Earthworms thrive where there is lime: therefore do not use it unnecessarily. The wise use of lime and sensible fertiliser treatment have a considerable effect on the number of weeds in turf. "Alkaline-type" fertilisers and organic fertilisers encourage both earthworms and weeds. Sulphate of ammonia and sulphate of iron tend to discourage weeds and keep them out.

Weeds may indeed serve a useful purpose by indicating turf faults or mis-management, focusing attention for example on excessive alkalinity, bad drainage or lack of nutrients. When this happens, it is essential to pay attention to the underlying fault. Unless this is corrected, no amount of chemical weed treatment will be effective; but if the fault is corrected, the weed will probably disappear without chemical treatment, simply because conditions are no longer favouring it.

Hand-weeding at an early stage is often the cheapest and simplest method of weed control albeit only really feasible on small areas and the only really reliable one at present for grass weeds, though it must be done efficiently, cutting weeds out at root level rather than just pulling up leaves.

Weeds are distributed in the various ways listed below, as seed or as plant fragments (especially pieces of rhizome of underground stem).

[i]   Wind.

[ii]   Flooding.

[iii] Birds and animals.

[iv]   From weed infested banks or surrounding lawns.

[v]   Contaminants in grass seed.

[vi]   Weed-infested, unsterilised compost or other top dressing.

[vii] Equipment (particularly mowers) and shoes.

[viii] Use of poor quality turf.

These sources of contamination should be constantly borne in mind by the groundsman, especially those which are under his control and particularly the last three.

WEED CONTROL BEFORE ESTABLISHING NEW TURF AREAS

Before sowing a new area make sure the seed bed is clean. Prevention of weed establishment is much better than control, both for the turf and for the groundsman. All methods of weed distribution noted above are potential sources of problems, and bare soil is particularly likely to be colonised.

To kill off a heavy infestation of weeds before any construction work starts, use non-residual herbicides (e.g. paraquat or glyphosate).

To obtain a clean seed bed by fallowing, a whole year is needed for a thorough job, unless land has been kept unusually clean in its previous use. Many weeds have two germination periods, spring and early autumn, and a short fallow in early summer, for example, will not affect the species best adapted to germinate when the turfgrass is sown in early autumn. Nevertheless any fallowing is better than none. Weeds must obviously not be allowed to set seed. Cultivate at fairly frequent intervals to induce more germination and use paraquat or glyphosate to kill weed seedlings. These herbicides do not persist in the soil, so sowing can be done almost at once after spraying (recommended interval – three days).

To deal with persistent rhizomatous weeds, chop rhizome fragments small in the initial cultivation and then exhaust them by repeated cultivations whenever shoots show one or two leaves, and by the use of glyphosate (which, unlike paraquat, is translocated throughout the plant). More persistent residual herbicides can be used but require specialised techniques and knowledge, and must be given time to become inactive.

Soil fumigation with methyl bromide is quicker than fallowing and can be very effective but it is costly, needs professional operators and may possibly cause future problems by killing beneficial soil organisms. Dazomet is a cheaper, safer but less efficient alternative.

Whatever cleaning operations are adopted – fallowing with cultivations and herbicides or sterilisation with methyl bromide – it is particularly important to avoid new weed contamination during the period between the end of the cleaning operations and sowing.

Where new areas are to be established from sod, weed seeds in the soil can be more safely ignored than when sowing seed, but rhizomes of any troublesome weeds should be destroyed.

WEED CONTROL IN NEWLY-ESTABLISHED TURF
Do not be over-anxious about small amounts of broad-leaved weeds at early stages. Some may be killed when mowing starts, and the turf if best left to grow without herbicide check or hand-weeding damage if possible. Herbicides can, however, be used to kill or check the seedlings of broad-leaved weeds among grass seedlings once they have reached a certain stage: details are given in [i] and [ii] below.

Do not spray if the sward seems weak or is under any environmental stress. Grass sown in spring may be fit to spray two months later if growing conditions have been good: grass sown in late summer or autumn should not be sprayed until the following spring.

New laid sod should not be sprayed until it is well established and growing normally.

No herbicide can at present be recommended against grass weeds but hand-weeding may be worthwhile.

[i] Ioxynil on seedling turf
Seedlings of all normal turf species except crested dogstail will tolerate ioxynil at the recommended rate when they have two expanded leaves. Ioxynil must not be used through hand held applicators.

[ii] Other herbicides on seedling turf
Low strength application of some herbicides can be made to:

[a] strong-growing species such as perennial ryegrass, creeping red fescue or timothy, when they have at least two or three expanded leaves.

[b] fine grasses (e.g. Chewings fescue and bents), after the sward is satisfactorily established and regular mowing has begun under normal good management.

The herbicides which can be used at low-strength rates for young grass are as follows:

MCPA	)	
2,4-D amine	)	Can be used on young grass at application rates lower than
2,4-D ester	)	those recommended for mature turf. See product labels for
mecoprop	)	application rates which must be followed.
dicamba (only in mixture)	)	

If worn areas are being renovated, grass seed may safely be sown about a week after the use of 2,4-D but not for several weeks after using MCPA or mecoprop. If sowing has to be done sooner, use a higher seed rate than normal to allow for the persistence of the chemical and its effect on the germinating seed.

[iii] Isoxaben on seedling turf

Isoxaben is a residual herbicide applied to the soil, which provides control of a range of germinating broad-leaved weed seedlings in newly sown or reseeded areas of turf, when applied shortly after the seeding operation. It finds particular use against knotgrass, which is so often a common and persistent weed of compact areas of winter sports pitches, such as goal mouth areas. Isoxaben is a useful treatment for use during spring renovation of winter sports pitches, where there is known to be a potential problem from germination of weed seedlings, but it provides no control of existing weed plants.

USE OF HERBICIDES TO CONTROL BROAD-LEAVED WEEDS IN ESTABLISHED TURF

Once turf is well established, herbicides for controlling broad-leaved weeds can be used at the normal rates as shown on the product label. Most manufacturers also provide detailed information on the weeds controlled by their products, and a list of weeds and their reactions, closely similar to that in the table here, is given in the *Weed Control Handbook Volume 2*.

MCPA	=	MCPA salt	)	
2,4-D	=	2,4-D amine and ester	)	
Mecoprop	=	mecoprop salt	)	
Mixture	=	2,4-D	)	See product labels for definitive instructions as to
		plus one of the following:		application rates
		[a] mecoprop	)	
		[b] dicamba	)	

A herbicide mixture widely used on turf is a 1 : 2 mixture of 2,4-D and mecoprop at rates appropriate to the particular formulation produced by the manufacturer. The three columns below show how the two elements of this broad-spectrum mixture complement each other, each controlling some important weeds but not others:

2,4-D	2,4-D or mecoprop	mecoprop
bulbous buttercup	cat's ear	mouse-ear chickweed
creeping buttercup	heath bedstraw	pearlwort
daisy	plantains	self-heal
dandelion		white clover
hawkbits		

MCPA is used instead of 2,4-D in some herbicide mixtures. It has broadly the same effectiveness as 2,4-D to which it is similar chemically: MCPA is better against mouse-ear chickweed and white clover, but possibly worse against daisy.

A herbicide mixture containing fluroxypyr and mecoprop-p has particular use against some difficult to control weeds such as slender speedwell, yellow suckling clover, yarrow and white clover as well as controlling many common weeds. It also has the advantage that it can be used in the spring on young turf, provided two months have elapsed between sowing and application.

Dicamba may also be valuable in a mixture for its action on a few specific weeds, including *Polygonum* species.

All the herbicides mentioned above are growth-regulator herbicides. After being taken into plants, chiefly through the leaves and also to a small extent through the roots, they act to destroy susceptible species, upsetting normal processes and distorting growth. Effects can be seen in twisting of leaves and freak growth within a day or two of application, but weeds may not die for four to eight weeks. Resistant species either take in less (e.g. because of angle and type of leaf, which partly accounts for selectivity between grasses and broad-leaved species) or avoid the poisoning effect in various ways.

Other herbicides act primarily by contact. Ioxynil is one such. It is valuable against broad-leaved weeds in turf, either by itself or, more importantly, in combination with other herbicides to make a useful broad-spectrum mixture. This has special value for some problem weeds, e.g. speedwells if applied in early spring before the speedwell flower heads form.

Calcined sulphate of iron is a slightly different type of material. It is often included in fertiliser mixtures for turf. It helps to keep weeds out of clean turf and to reduce their numbers in weedy turf. A lawn sand consisting of 1 part calcined sulphate of iron, 3 parts sulphate of ammonia and 20 parts (by weight) sand or compost at 140 g/m² (4 oz/sq yd) will help to discourage many weeds, including some like parsley piert and speedwells which are difficult to control with other materials. Sulphate of iron is also used against moss (see later section on moss).

COMMON WEEDS AND THEIR SUSCEPTIBILITY TO HERBICIDES

The first requirement for successful weed control is the correct identification of the weed or weeds occurring on a particular pitch. It is outside the scope of this present volume to provide instruction which would allow the identification of all the weeds likely to be found in sports turf. An inspection of the pitch in company with an experienced groundsman or other expert is probably the best way in which the amateur can learn weed identification, but a Flora of the British Isles (with colour illustrations) can be helpful. As with the grasses, however, the appearance of a weed can be rather different when it is growing naturally than it is in close-mown turf. However, broad-leaved weeds are at least easier to tell one from the other than the grasses.

In the following weed list, only those weeds which are commonly encountered in sports turf are included - it is by no means a comprehensive list of British weeds. The four columns to the right of the weed name show the susceptibility or resistance of the mature weed species to the main herbicides. Abbreviations are as follows:

S	= susceptible, i.e. consistently killed by one application
MS	= moderately susceptible: one application usually kills but second sometimes needed
MR	= moderately resistant: two or three applications usually needed for adequate control
R	= resistant: no useful effect
–	= information lacking

"Mixture" = either 2,4-D or MCPA in mixture with mecoprop or dicamba or mecoprop + dicamba

Common Name	Botanical Name	Susceptibility			
		MCPA	2,4-D	Mecoprop	"Mixture"
Creeping buttercup	*Ranunculus repens*	S	S	MR	S
Bulbous buttercup	*Ranunculus bulbosus*	MS	MS	MR	MS
Lesser celandine	*Ranunculus ficaria*	MS	MR	MR	MR
Common mouse-ear chickweed	*Cerastium fontanum*	MS	MR	S	S
Common chickweed	*Stellaria media*	MS	MS	S	S
Procumbent pearlwort	*Sagina procumbens*	MR	MR	S	S
Blinks	*Montia fontana*	-	-	-	MR
Dove's-foot crane's-bill	*Geranium molle*	R	R	MR	MR
Sea stork's-bill	*Erodium maritimum*	MS	MS	-	MS

Common Name	Botanical Name	Susceptibility			
		MCPA	2,4-D	Mecoprop	"Mixture"
Common stork's-bill	*Erodium cicutarium*	MS	MS	MS	MS
Black medick	*Medicago lupulina*	R	R	MS	MS
Suckling clover	*Trifolium dubium*	R	R	MR	MR-MS
White clover	*Trifolium repens*	MR	R	MS	MS
Common birdsfoot trefoil	*Lotus corniculatus*	R	R	MR	MR
Silverweed	*Potentilla anserina*	MR-MS	MR-MS	MR-MS	MR-MS
Creeping cinquefoil	*Potentilla reptans*	MR-MS	MR-MS	MR-MS	MR-MS
Parsley-piert	*Aphanes arvensis*	R	R	MR-MS	MR-MS
Marsh pennywort	*Hydrocotyle vulgaris*	MS	MS	MR	-
Knotgrass	*Polygonum aviculare*	R*	R*	R*	S**
Sheep's sorrel	*Rumex acetosella*	MS	MS	R	M
Common sorrel	*Rumex acetosa*	MS	MS	R	MS
Curled dock	*Rumex crispus*	MS	MS	MR	MS
Mind-your-own-business	*Soleirolia soleirolii*	R	R	MR	MR
Germander speedwell	*Veronica chamaedrys*	R	R	MR	MR
Thyme-leaved speedwell	*Veronica serpyllifolia*	R	R	MR	MR
Slender speedwell	*Veronica filiformis*	R	R	MR	MR
Selfheal	*Prunella vulgaris*	MR	MR	MS	MS
Greater plantain	*Plantago major*	S	S	S	S
Hoary plantain	*Plantago media*	S	S	S	S
Ribwort plantain	*Plantago lanceolata*	S	S	S	S
Sea plantain	*Plantago maritima*	S	S	MS	S
Buck's-horn plantain (starweed)	*Plantago coronopus*	S	S	S	S
Field madder	*Sherardia arvensis*	R	-	MS	MS
Lady's bedstraw	*Galium verum*	MR?	MR?	-	MR?
Heath bedstraw	*Galium saxatile*	MS	MS	MS	MS
Common ragwort	*Senecio jacobaea*	MS	MS	-	MS
Daisy	*Bellis perennis*	MR	MS	MR	MS
Yarrow	*Achillea millefolium*	MR	MR	MR-MS	MR-MS
Cotula (button weed)	*Cotula coronopifolia*	R?	R?	R?	R?
Dwarf thistle	*Cirsium acaule*	MS	MS	MR	MS
Cat's ear	*Hypochaeris radicata*	MS	MS	MS	MS
Autumn hawkbit	*Leontodon autumnalis*	MS	MS	R	MS
Rough hawkbit	*Leontodon hispidus*	MR	MS	MR	MS
Mouse-ear hawkweed	*Hieracium pilosella*	S	S	S	S
Smooth hawk's-beard	*Crepis capillaris*	MS	MS	MS	MS
Dandelion	*Taraxacum officinale*	MS	MS	MR	MS
Toadrush	*Juncus bufonius*	R	R	MR	MS
Field woodrush	*Luzula campestris*	R	R	MR	MR

* seedlings MR ** dicamba mixtures

THE APPLICATION OF SELECTIVE WEED KILLERS TO TURF

Selective weed killers are generally formulated as liquids for application by sprayer or by watering can.

There is a wide range of spraying equipment available. For treating comparatively small areas if weed problems are localised, a knapsack sprayer may be adequate but even better are "knapsacks on wheels" or other pedestrian equipment. A horizontal boom with several nozzles is essential if even coverage is to be achieved. However, on winter sports pitches the areas to be treated are very often considerable and most spray treatments will be most easily accomplished using a tractor mounted or trailed boom sprayer.

The technical specification, safety features and performance of suitable tractor boom sprayers have been improved greatly in recent years and a modern sprayer is essential for accurate and safe application of pesticides. If the cost of purchase of a suitable sprayer is too much for an individual club for the limited use necessary, then possibly a joint co-operative purchase with one or more other local clubs may be possible. Alternatively if there is lack of both funds and expertise within the club then it may well be sensible to hand over all spraying work to a suitable experienced professional, i.e. a specialist spray contractor.

Safe and effective application of weed killers requires accurate and uniform spray coverage of the turf, which in turn requires accurate calibration of the sprayer and correct selection of nozzle type and size, operating pressure and speed of movement over the ground. This subject is beyond the scope of this book, but is fully covered by a series of publications from BCPC, i.e. *Hand-operated Sprayers Handbook, Boom Sprayers Handbook, Nozzle Selection Handbook.*

Additionally, accurate application must avoid overlaps and missed strips so that use of markers is essential. Grass is resistant to recommended rates but not to over-application. A very skilled and knowledgeable operator may be able to make successful spot treatments with a hand sprayer or watering-can but scorch is the most common result. Aerosol cans or weed-sticks are a safer method of spot treatment but the risk of grass scorch is by no means eliminated.

Selective weed killers based on growth-regulator herbicides may be applied at any time from spring to early autumn when there is growth occurring, but late spring applications usually give most satisfactory results. The best conditions are fine, warm weather when the soil is moist and growth is vigorous. If overseeding has been carried out on pitches in the spring as part of the end of season renovation programme, then spraying for weed control may have to be delayed until seedling grasses have reached a suitable stage of development to allow safe spraying. In an early spring with good growth it may be possible to carry out a spray treatment before any renovation work is started, but the effects of the treatment may be less than would be hoped for. Late autumn treatment or treatment during drought may damage turf. Heavy rain shortly after application may reduce effectiveness. Wind gives risk of drift. Catching the right weather and growth conditions is the key to success. Make sure equipment is calibrated and in good condition in advance. Don't leave this until the last minute.

It is beneficial to give nitrogenous fertiliser, e.g. sulphate of ammonia at 17 g/m^2 ($^1/_2$ oz/sq yd) suitably bulked with carrier, 10-14 days before applying growth-regulator herbicides which act best when both weeds and grass are growing vigorously. Weed control work can thus be linked in with the normal spring fertiliser treatment.

Leave turf unmown for a period after spraying to allow intake of herbicide from foliage before it is mown off. An interval of 2-3 days is preferable, but at the very least leave one clear day before mowing.

Growth-regulator herbicides are very powerful and can affect susceptible plants even in minute doses. Risks are very real where plants other than grass and cereals are grown nearby. Do not treat areas of turf near valued plants in flower beds, etc. except on a calm day. If contamination of such plants is suspected, wash them down copiously with clean water. Clean out equipment thoroughly after use.

WEED GRASSES

It may be helpful to reiterate here that there are as yet no recommended selective herbicide treatments for coarse weed grass in turfgrass swards, however, there is approval for use of ethofumesate to control annual meadow-grass in ryegrass swards. Other herbicide treatments developed for agricultural grassland or grass seed crops are either unsafe or still untested for the conditions of intensive turf management and use.

PLATE 97. Rosette weeds such as this ribwort plantain (*Plantago lanceolata*) are common but relatively easy to control.

PLATE 98. Creeping weeds like white clover (*Trifolium repens*) are more difficult to eliminate. Clover is trouble-some as it can make winter games surfaces slippery and by releasing nitrogen, produces unsightly patches of dark green grass.

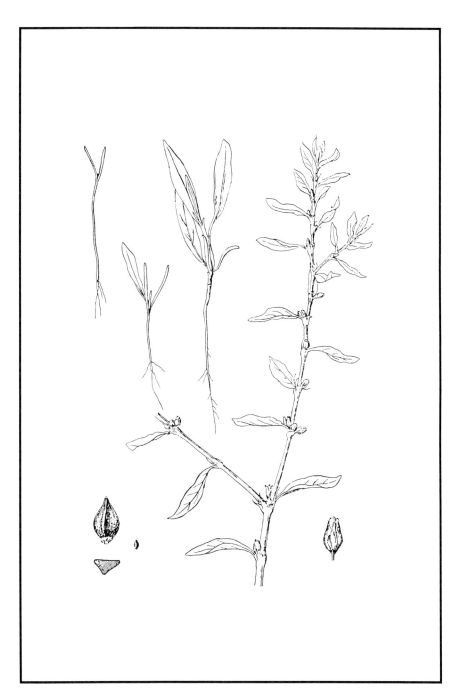

PLATE 99. Knotweed or knotgrass (*Polygonum aviculare*) is a common and very troublesome weed of winter games pitches. Three seedling stages are illustrated here, together with the adult plant - reddish stems and enlarged leaf nodes are characteristic. Isoxaben residual herbicide may be used to control germinating seedlings during spring renovation. Control of mature plants later in the season is complicated in practice by the need to avoid damage to newly sown grass establishing after spring renovation, but 2,4-D plus dicamba mixtures are effective in controlling the weed once the grass sward is fully established.

The best prescription for avoiding annual meadow-grass in turf is to prepare a clean seed bed, sow good cultivars of the required species and then manage the turf to favour them rather than the annual meadow-grass.

In the absence of herbicide treatments which can be recommended for turf, scattered plants of weed grasses are best dealt with by hand weeding (pulling or cutting out) young plants as soon as they are noticed. Always take care to remove the whole plant. Yorkshire fog is often a special problem. In newly-sown areas, remove young plants by hand. Once plants become well-established, they may be weakened by slashing by hand with a knife across the patch, coupled with raking during mowing, or by scarification or Verti-Grooming. The only certain treatment, however, is to cut plants out at the roots and, if necessary, replace the turf with new sod.

GROWTH RETARDANTS

In the turfgrass context, a growth retardant is a chemical which in some way reduces or slows down normal grass growth, thus reducing the need for mowing to maintain a neat and tidy turfgrass area, which is visually acceptable to the general public. When first marketed for amenity use, growth retardants were heralded as a panacea for the landscape manager, and even as a cure-all for the time-consuming and expensive process of grass cutting. However, despite certain advantages which may be gained from growth retardants, currently only a small proportion of amenity grassland is being managed chemically.

For large areas of grassland, for example, parks or golf fairways, gang mowing is often the easiest and most cost-effective way of restricting sward height. However, growth retardants have proved their worth in certain situations such as where the grass area in question contains many obstacles, for example such as graveyards. Small, isolated areas, for example around schools, hotels and hospitals, where mowing may be expensive and/or inconvenient are also suitable cases for growth retardant treatment. On low maintenance areas, such as roadside verges, growth retardants may be appropriate, as they are also for boundaries and steep banks, where mowing would be difficult or dangerous in practice. Also, growth retardants have a specialist use on erosion control areas where it is important to maintain a dense, uniform growth of deep rooted grass to resist soil erosion. Indeed, it is in these types of situations where growth retardants may be extremely cost effective. In comparative studies, reducing grass growth by spraying has been shown to be a quarter of the cost of maintenance using a rotary mower and one-fifth the cost of Flymo operation. Thus, the use of growth retardants will not be appropriate for main pitch areas, but may be appropriate to those areas of grass which surround the pitches and which may form a considerable part of a sports ground. However, where surface levels are smooth enough then gang mowing is likely to remain the primary means of control of grass growth.

The growth retardants currently available, are based on 3 active ingredients, namely maleic hydrazide, mefluidide and paclobutrazol. Maleic hydrazide works through foliar absorption, inhibiting plant cell division, thus producing a slower growing grass plant. Mefluidide, although distinct chemically from maleic hydrazide, also works via foliar absorption, and by slowing down leaf growth, but in addition it inhibits seed-head production of the grass sward. Paclobutrazol is effective in a completely different way, being root absorbed and it inhibits grass growth by preventing the production of the plant growth hormone gibberelic acid.

The growth retardation achieved by these chemicals may, in ideal situations, be considerable. In field trials conducted by the Sports Turf Research Institute maleic hydrazide, mefluidide and paclobutrazol reduced grass growth by up to 25%, 60% and 45% respectively, dependent on the grass species present. The duration of grass growth suppression also varies according to the chemical applied. Both maleic hydrazide and mefluidide are considered relatively quick acting with up to 8 weeks and 12 weeks suppression of grass growth achievable respectively. Generally, little or no effect of paclobutrazol is observed 10-15 days after application, but growth inhibition has been recorded up to 14 weeks thereafter and occasionally treatment effect is carried over to the following season. However, each growth retardant has differing effects according to the botanical composition of the sward. Maleic hydrazide tends to inhibit coarser grasses, leaving the finer species, in particular fescues, to thrive. Mefluide has long lasting effects on annual meadow-grass, bents, perennial ryegrass and crested dogs tail and in the shorter-term, will suppress the growth of fescue, Timothy and smooth-stalked meadow-grass. Paclobutrazol tends to have lesser effect on deep rooted, coarser grass species.

In situations where growth retardants are being considered, there is usually a range of grass species present, together with non-grass species, such as broad-leaf weeds. Whilst mowing trims all vegetation present instantly to the required height, growth retardants have varying effects, according to the botanical composition of the sward. Paclobutrazol is available only as a mixture with the herbicide dicamba to inhibit both grass and broad-leaf weeds. To achieve similar aims maleic hydrazide is available as a mixture with the herbicides dicamba and MCPA, although there are several maleic hydrazide only products. Currently mefluidide is not formulated together with a herbicide as this chemical does give some suppression of broad-leaf species, although in situations where broad-leaf weeds are a problem, they may be controlled by tank mixing with approved herbicide formulations. Certain growth retardants may also be tank mixed, paclobutrazol plus mefluidide or paclobutrazol plus maleic hydrazide are recommended where coarse grasses, such as cocksfoot, are dominant or in situations such as airfields where suppression of grass seed heads is important.

When using growth retardants it is critical to follow the manufacturers recommendations for use carefully to achieve acceptable results. With maleic hydrazide the application rate is critical as a small over application may lead to severe scorching, whilst if under applied effectiveness is markedly reduced. Consequently, when combined with climatic effects such as rain after application, growth retardation by maleic hydrazide may be unpredictable. In contrast, mefluidide is overall very reliable, providing it is used correctly. Mefluide should be applied when the grass is dry, ideally 8 hours elapsing before rainfall. Best results are obtained when mefluidide is applied in April-May when grass growth is strong. Mefluide tends to make the sward greener and more lush in appearance, although some discolouration may occur if applied in very dry conditions. Paclobutrazol has its greatest effect when applied in early spring (February-March) prior to onset of grass growth, or in August-September to reduce the autumn flush of growth. Paclobutrazol is relatively inactive in dry conditions, but acts reliably when soil moisture is high. Generally, paclobutrazol is leached slowly although heavy rain after application may negate effects.

Advantages	Disadvantages
Significant cost savings over conventional mowers for specific situations	Trained and qualified operators needed for application
Highly suited to difficult/dangerous areas to mow	Unsuitable for high quality, fine turf or large open areas
Drought resistance of sward may be improved	Do not give the high quality visual appearance of mowing
Season long control may be achieved from 2-3 applications	No single growth retardant available to suit all situations
Minimises yield of unwanted clippings produced by mowing	Some lack of predictability of the effects
May be integrated with mowing to produce the desired effect	

PLATE 100. The AM-TR-2-600 trailed sprayer has a 6 m boom and a 600 litre tank. Also available with 800 and 1500 litre capacity. (Courtesy Hardi Ltd., Hinkley.)

PLATE 101. The Hardi AML 200-300 tractor mounted sprayer has a 6 m boom and a tank capacity of 200 or 300 litres. (Courtesy Hardi Ltd., Hinkley.)

MOSSES, LICHENS & ALGAE
Mosses
Although not generally a serious problem in vigorous winter sports turf, occasionally moss may affect playing surfaces if turf management is unsatisfactory. However, the presence of moss is an indication of other underlying problems and direct control will seldom be successful unless the reason for moss presence is also addressed. Mosses belong to a division of the plant kingdom known as the *Bryophyta*. They are non-flowering plants which can be found growing in a wide variety of situations. Their growth is usually restricted to approximately 25 mm (1") in height, the main body of the plant consisting of slender stems which are soft, fleshy and covered with minute green or brown leaves. The roots, which are like slender filaments, are known as rhizoids and they serve the same function as roots in flowering plants, namely to absorb moisture and nutrients and to anchor the plant into the soil.

In the United Kingdom there are approximately 600 species of moss, but in the sports turf environment occurrence is confined to three main types.

[1] Fern or Feather type, usually of trailing appearance, e.g. *Hypnum* and *Eurhynchium* spp.
These mosses are present in many turf situations but are often overlooked. They are often associated with soft, fluffy, fibrous turf which is less intensively managed.

[2] Tufted or mat type, e.g. *Ceratodon purpureus*, *Bryum* spp.
These mosses tend to be particularly prevalent on acidic soils. *Ceratodon purpureus* is known as the so-called "Winter moss" that colonises the sward during the autumn when sward vigour declines and appears to die out in the spring when vigour returns. It forms a dense accumulation which tends to form a mat or cushion type effect, and the problem will get progressively worse unless checked.

[3] Upright type, e.g. *Polytrichum* spp.
Most commonly found on dry mounds and slopes, in fact any area which is prone to drying out. This type of moss is not usually very troublesome except in particularly acidic conditions.

They all have a life cycle that shows a typical alternation of generations, this simply means that the plants exhibit two distinct types of growth structure in their life cycle. Most species produce dust-like spores which are single celled. When these germinate they produce a fine filamentous structure (protonema) which quickly turns green and grows in different directions over the soil surface. The protonema is the first stage in the development of the moss plant as we know it.

When the moss is mature it produces special sexual reproductive organs, the male organs being called the antheridia, the female organs being called the archegonia. Once fertilisation takes place a new structure called the capsule is produced. Once ripe, this splits to release new spores which restart the life cycle once more.

The presence of moss is usually indicative of some basic underlying problem. Because most control measures are palliative, the moss will soon return and recolonise if the original prblem is not addressed. As a result, cultural control measures have to be considered in order to maintain a strong, healthy sward with which moss cannot compete.

The factors which favour moss colonisation include the following:

[1] A moist turf - poor drainage encourages the fern-like and tufted mosses.

[2] A very dry soil, e.g. over drains, on mounds and ridges - inadequate watering or over-drainage - encourages the upright type.

[3] Cutting too closely.

[4] Poor surface levels - scalping.

[5] A soft, spongy sward with a thick fibre layer.

[6] Low fertility, e.g. deficiencies of plant foods, lime, etc. or insufficient soil depth.

[7] Over-consolidation of the soil - compaction.

[8] Shade.

The cultural control of moss therefore depends on finding the underlying cause and then correcting the factor responsible.

Chemical control works well in the long-term only if it is combined with cultural control.

The traditional chemical for moss in turf is sulphate of iron, applied in the calcined form.

Sulphate of iron gives a fast kill and is cheap but is not long-lasting. It can be used alone bulked with a carrier such as sand, but often the more convenient liquid formulations of sulphate of iron are used nowadays.
Other mosskillers include:

Dichlorophen
This is the material now normally recommended. It is fairly quick acting and moderately persistent. It controls both the adult plant and the spores, so that the effect may last for several months depending on weather conditions.

LICHENS
A lichen is a symbiotic relationship (mutually beneficial) between an alga and a fungus. They are encouraged by similar conditions already described for mosses, when strong, healthy sward growth becomes compromised. They are rarely troublesome and are certainly not as significant a problem as moss.

Again, cultural control can be achieved by encouraging more vigorous grass growth, and if chemical control should be necessary then methods already described for moss control will be successful. They are rarely seen on the playing surface except in times of severe mismanagement.

ALGAE
Algae are microscopic plants that may appear on areas of bare ground often in the form of a green scum. Once a grass cover is achieved and the surface dries out, the algae usually disappear. Sometimes algae appear in the form of black or dark green jelly-like lumps during the autumn or the spring periods.

The significance of algae and the problems it can cause have become more apparent in recent times, with "squidge" now affecting many turf areas. This again appears in bare areas, particularly on banks and slopes, and looks like green frog-spawn. Because of its nature and occurrence, it can be particularly hazardous both to players and maintenance staff alike.

Good control of the problem can usually be achieved by light spiking and sanding to help dry out the surface. If, however, the problem persists, then treatment should involve the methods already described for mosses and lichens.

EARTHWORMS, INSECTS AND VERTEBRATE PESTS
EARTHWORMS
There are about 25 species of earthworm which are active in turfgrass in the UK. Only three main species, however, produce surface casts and it is the casts alone which are undesirable as far as turf management is concerned. Each earthworm is hermaphrodite, i.e. it has both male and female reproductive organs. However, cross-fertilisation between two individuals is still necessary.

Mating takes place on the surface at night at any season of the year, providing the weather is damp and mild. Eight to 16 eggs are produced in a cocoon and take from 4 to 20 weeks to hatch. The young worms resemble their parents except in size, and mature in 40 to 70 weeks.

Worms feed on dead and decaying plant or animal material found in the soil and are therefore more common on humus-rich soils. They are not active during frosty weather, when they burrow more deeply, or during drought when they similarly become dormant. It is in mild, moist weather, usually during spring and autumn that the earthworms are most active and when control is most effective, although irrigation does also increase their activity. Light sandy soils are not as prone to infestation as heavy soils - earthworms preferring moisture retentive soils where there is a higher percentage of organic matter.

Advantages of worms
There may be up to 1 million earthworms per hectare of sports turf. These have a very significant effect on the soil ecosystem and play an important role in the decomposition process and in modifying soil structure. Apart from the surface casting habit of a restricted number of species, earthworms are beneficial. Their tunnels alleviate soil compaction and provide beneficial aeration. Worms also secrete mucus to stabilise their burrow linings, thus aggregating soil particles and improving structure.

The eating habits of earthworms are also beneficial to turfgrass in that they eat living and dead plant material and also small soil fauna. Hence they are significant in breaking down thatch and fibre, and by breaking up organic matter they make soil nutrients available for plant growth.

Disadvantages of worms
It is only the indigestible waste material ejected by the earthworm on the surface as a cast which is a disadvantage in the sports turf management situation.

Worm casts are a problem because they are unsightly, because they interfere with the run of the ball and because they cause muddy conditions – sealing the surface and thus reducing surface drainage. The production of casts can bring dormant weed seeds to the surface and the casts themselves then provide an ideal site for weed seeds to establish. Furthermore, casts can also smother existing turfgrasses and the presence of worms may encourage moles.

In most turf management it is usually considered that the disadvantages of earthworm activity outweigh the advantages. However, potential control measures by chemical means on the large areas of winter sports pitches can incur a heavy cost penalty. Very often worms remain untreated or limited treatments are applied only to the worst affected areas. However, some degree of worm control can also be achieved by attention to general turf management.

Worm control can be achieved by managerial and/or chemical control.

Turf management practices which discourage earthworms
Through good turf management practices earthworm activity may be kept at a low level, thus minimising the need for chemical control.

Since worms feed readily on thatch, they can be discouraged by eliminating sub-surface thatch layers, which are an undesirable feature on most sports turf surfaces from other points of view as well. It is also true that allowing clippings to fly encourages earthworms as these provide them with a constant source of nutriment. From this point of view, it would be an advantage to box off clippings from all playing surfaces, although this may not be practical. However, boxing off clippings may be feasible on some high quality surfaces and excessively organic top dressings (again providing worms with a food supply) should be avoided.

Fortunately, worms do not like acidic conditions, probably because soil acids irritate sensitive skins. This is most useful as far as fine turf cultivation is concerned as acidic soil conditions also favour the desirable bent and fescue grasses.

Chemical control of earthworm casting
The chemical worm killers available fall into two groups, worm expellents and worm killers:

[1] Worm expellents
The now somewhat outdated use of expellents was widespread in the past. The operation brings worms to the surface without necessarily killing them and a messy sweeping-up operation is essential: otherwise a proportion of the worms may recover. Expellents have little long-term effect and treatment must be repeated at regular intervals. Three materials used to be employed – mowrah meal, rotenone and permanganate of potash. The last named is still available and it has been erroneously suggested that it is not covered by the current pesticide regulations, as it was said to expel earthworms without being fatal to them. Recent trials have, however, shown that up to 80% of a worm population can be killed by the use of this material and it must therefore be classed as a pesticide. Currently, it is not approved for use on turf and its employment cannot therefore be advocated.

[2] Worm killers
Worm expellents have now been superseded to a large extent by worm killers. Worm killers kill worms below the surface, avoiding the need for messy clearing up operations, and longer term control is possible. The worm killers available today fall into two groups.

[a] Non-selective
This type iof poroduct kills all species of worms indiscriminately.

[i] Carbaryl
Carbaryl is a contact insecticide and available in proprietary form as a wettable powder or flowable suspension. It should be applied during mild, damp weather in autumn or spring (autumn is preferable) when the worms are active near the surface. In the case of a severe infestation two applications, one in autumn and one in spring, give better control. Watering after application increases the efficiency of the material. Carbaryl kills worms below the surface and, therefore, no sweeping-up is required. The makers claim that 93% control of casting worms is achieved in 4 days. The duration of control is short; even the makers claim only one season's control.

[b] Selective worm killers
These materials are claimed to kill only surface-feeding, casting species, leaving unharmed earthworms which live deeper in the soil and which cause no damage to turf.

[i] Thiophanate-methyl + gamma-HCH
Applied to the surface, it kills worms which feed and cast on or near the surface. It should be applied when active casting can be seen, usually spring or autumn. The effect is not reduced by rain after treatment. Duration of control is about three months or so only. It is safe to use on all turf areas but take normal precautions in handling and storage.

[ii] Carbendazim
Available as a liquid, carbendazim is better known as a fungicide, effective against fusarium, dollar spot and red thread disease. It is said to kill harmful casting species only and should be applied to moist soil when worms are active. Do not mow immediately after treatment. Duration of control is short. Normal precautions applicable when handling chemicals should be observed.

INSECT PESTS OF TURF
Flies
Entomologists limit the term 'fly' to a particular group of insects. The true flies have only one pair of wings, compared with typical adult winged insects which have two pairs. Young stages of flies are without legs and move by expanding and contracting the body rather like an earthworm. Adult flies

are generally not harmful to turf. The larvae of several species, in particular the leatherjacket, may damage turf.

Leatherjackets (*Tipula* spp.)

Leatherjackets are the larvae of crane flies or 'daddy long-legs' (*Tipula* species). The adults are active and fly in August when they may be attracted to lights in houses. Eggs are laid in grassy places and the larvae hatch within ten days to feed either on plant tissues or decaying vegetable matter in the soil. Their feeding increases in the spring as they develop and grow. When they are fully grown the leatherjackets are about 30-40 mm long, grey-brown, legless and without obvious heads. Pupation occurs below ground but just before emergence the pupa pushes itself out of the soil.

Leatherjackets feed throughout the autumn and winter during mild weather, causing damage to established turf on golf fairways and to reseeded grass, especially later-sown turf. They feed particularly voraciously again in the spring.

Leatherjackets can attack young plants, biting off the stems at or just below ground level. The cut ends of the plants have frayed edges. Leaf tips may be eaten or even pulled below the soil surface. Leatherjackets are usually found near to the damaged plants or, if conditions are mild, close to the soil surface. Autumn-sown grass will usually show signs of damage by early April, although occasionally this will be seen in the autumn (November to December).

On heavily infested established turf areas bare patches appear where the plants have been destroyed. These may quickly be covered with weeds. However, in other cases the first signs are either straw-coloured areas of grass debris or pieces of fibrous turf torn up by birds. Often attacks remain undetected until the flush of spring growth reveals patches of greatly reduced vigour in the turf.

If poor, weak areas are seen in the early spring, with accompanied bird activity (usually rooks or starlings), leatherjacket damage should be suspected.

Where visible signs of damage are evident and where leatherjackets can be easily found, then chemical control measures are justified. Three chemicals chlorpyrifos, gamma-HCH and gamma-HCH/thiophanate methyl can be used for control of leatherjackets. In established turf it is usually more reliable to use a high volume spray.

Fever flies (*Dilophus*) and related species (*Bibio* spp.)

There are 22 species of British fever flies which lay eggs in turf from May to September, the breeding season being dependent on the species involved. The grubs are smaller than leatherjackets and have a distinct shiny brown head. They also tend to remain in definite colonies in small patches of turf, but their feeding habits and the kind of damage produced is similar to that resulting from leatherjackets. There are no current approvals for insecticides for control of fever flies.

Frit fly

Frit fly may occasionally do damage to turfgrass, particularly in newly sown or turfed areas, which have previously been used for growing cereals or grass ley. Frit fly larvae resembling small white maggots may be found within the stem, which soon withers and dies or sometimes may be distorted. Chlorpyrifos is approved for the control of frit fly in turf in the UK.

Chafers

The grubs of five species of chafer beetle are pests of local importance in Britain. The species which is most widespread and the most troublesome in grassland is the garden chafer (*Phyllopertha horticola*). The adult is about 9 mm long with a metallic-green head and thorax and reddish-brown wing-cases. The grubs are white and about 18 mm long when fully grown.

The life-cycle occupies one year. Adult beetles swarm during June and July, feeding on a variety of plants. Eggs are laid in the soil, usually in the same area where the beetles emerged. Thus, infested turf is regularly re-infested each summer, although the areas with obvious damage are often different each year. Grubs feed from the summer until late autumn.

Damage appears in September and October and the severity depends on the numbers of chafer larvae in the soil. Generally more than 50 per m² must be present before damage becomes obvious.

Usually poorly growing patches become obvious and these turn brown in dry weather. The grubs can be found immediately below the surface. Soil in these areas is often fine in texture and fluffy. This is due to the grubs actually ingesting soil as they feed on roots.

Severely damaged areas are usually sharply defined, and because the roots are severed, the turf can be rolled up like a carpet. Frequently, birds cause further damage to the turf as they rip up the grass whilst searching for the grubs. The chemical approved by MAFF for control is gamma-HCH.

Other insect pests
Very occasionally wire worms and millipedes may damage turf.

Insecticides for control of insect turf pests

PEST	INSECTICIDE		
	Chlorpyrifos	gamma-HCH	gamma-HCH/thiophanate-methyl
Chafer grubs	-	✓	-
Frit fly	✓	-	-
Leatherjackets	✓	✓	-
Wire worms	-	✓	✓

VERTEBRATE PESTS
Moles
There are five methods of control. The first two are the methods recommended by the Ministry of Agriculture, Fisheries and Food (MAFF).

[1] Trapping
Probably best dealt with by a professional mole trapper.

[2] Poisoning by baits
Very effective poison baits consist of worms treated with strychnine placed in the deeper main runs. This is a very dangerous poison: permits are available from MAFF issued strictly according to requirements and to professional users only.

[3] Gassing
A sodium cyanide product is available to professional pest control operatives only. This gives off hydrogen cyanide in contact with soil moisture. For non-professional use, there are mole smokes whilst engine exhaust gas is also quite effective, but both these methods are more effective in repelling or moving moles than killing them.

[4] Electronic
A device generating sonic vibration is claimed to clear an area up to about 1000 m².

[5] Removal of worms
Moles feed almost entirely on earthworms so worm killing can indirectly control moles.

Rabbits

Rabbits present in large numbers can cause significant damage, especially where the soil is light and sandy, they will enlarge by their scratching and burrowing any areas which have been damaged initially by play.

Trapping, gassing and shooting at night over lights are the most effective means of control, although the latter can be difficult where abundant cover is available. Repellents such as Stay Off, Dog Off, Hoppit or Scuttle may provide some short-term control and are ineffective after rainfall.

Birds

Birds, particularly starlings, rooks, jackdaws, gulls, etc., can damage turf seeking grubs like leatherjackets. The simplest method is to eradicate the primary cause of trouble by destroying the insect which the birds are looking for.

TURFGRASS DISEASES

Winter sports turf is not cut as closely as fine turf and hence is under less physiological stress, moreover, the main turfgrass species present is the vigorous perennial ryegrass. Hence, winter sports turf is not often affected to the same extent by turfgrass diseases as fine turf and the range of problem diseases is much more limited. The coverage presented here will be confined to the most commonly occurring problems, but for a full coverage of potential problems and fungicide treatments, one should consult *Turfgrass Pests and Diseases* by N A Baldwin (see Bibliography).

The best approach to potential disease problems is undoubtedly provided by adopting a good general strategy of winter sports turf management. This will both provide a good playing surface and will ensure a healthy and vigorous sward which is less susceptible to disease attack. It should always be the aim to prevent disease incidence rather than have to rely on the use of fungicides to control a disease problem, since the fungicide spray treatment will undoubtedly prove very expensive for the pitch area involved. Certainly if fungicides have to be used this should only be to treat an existing problem. The use of preventative spray treatments is to be discouraged because the fungicide will kill many beneficial organisms as well as any potential harmful ones. Also, the repeated exposure to a fungicide increases the risk of the selection of strains of the fungus which are resistant to the fungicide.

The following diseases are those most commonly occurring on winter sports pitches.

DISEASES OF SEEDLING TURF

Because of the intensive use of many winter sports pitches during the winter months, when soils are wet and there is little or no grass growth occurring, the level of sward damage at the end of the playing season is often severe. Consequently, overseeding may form a regular part of the end of season renovation programme. Often weather conditions at the time of renovation may be less than ideal with cold soil and germination and establishment may be slow and uneven. At this time therefore, seedling diseases may occur. Seedling diseases may be categorised as follows:

Seed rot, i.e. seed fails to germinate and rots in the soil.
Pre-emergence damping-off, i.e. seed germinates but fails to emerge.
Post-emergence damping-off, i.e. seedling emerges but fails to establish.

Causal fungi

Many fungi may attack seedlings. *Fusarium culmorum* (W.G. Smith)*, Microdochium nivale, Cladochytrium* spp., *Drechslera* spp., *Rhizoctonia* spp. and *Pythium* spp. may cause severe losses.

Importance

Common if conditions are suitable for disease development. May reduce establishment significantly.

Symptoms of seedling diseases

The symptoms of seed rot are a very thin stand. Seed which can be found shows no signs of germination and seed may be rotten and permeated with fungal mycelium.

The symptoms of pre-emergence damping-off are a thin and patchy stand. Initial roots and coleoptiles may be lesioned and rotting in the ground, i.e. the seed has germinated but failed to emerge.

The symptoms of post-emergence damping-off are patches of grass which are affected but large areas may be damaged rapidly. Coleoptile and/or seedling leaves appear and then collapse due to rotting at the base. The leaves of affected seedlings often turn red, purple or yellow in colour and seedling death often occurs.

Grasses and turf types affected
Seed rot and pre-emergence damping-off affect all turfgrass species. Post-emergence damping-off is most severe on bents, fescues and smooth-stalked meadow-grass.

Conditions which favour the disease
Very dry conditions favour seedling disease due to *Fusarium* spp. whilst wet conditions favour attacks by *Cladochytrium* spp. and *Pythium* spp. Both inadequate and excessive seedbed fertiliser favours seedling diseases. Early-spring or late-autumn sowings are often severely attacked especially when uneven sowings are made into a poorly prepared seedbed.

Integrated disease control
The seedbed should be generally well prepared, have good drainage, and appropriate pre-seeding seedbed fertiliser. Seed should be sown evenly and at the correct rate for the seed mixture used. Sowings should only be made in good growing conditions, i.e. not too early in the spring before the soil has had time to warm up or too late in the autumn in moist, cool or cold conditions.

Control of seedling diseases is very difficult to achieve in practice due to the many different fungi involved. In the past drenches or sprays of broad-spectrum fungicides have given some success, although as seedlings are very small, contact of the fungicide with leaf tissue is relatively small and consequently much chemical is wasted. Currently there are no UK approved fungicides for control of seedling diseases of amenity grass. Fungicide seed dressings based on a mixture of thiabendazole and metalaxyl are now available for control of seedling diseases.

RED THREAD

Other name	Corticium disease.
Causal fungus	*Laetisaria fuciformis* (formerly *Corticium fuciforme*).
Importance	Very common disease. Severe outbreaks may kill the grass but generally infected areas will recover from attack. Often occurs together as a disease complex with pink patch disease.
Season	During summer and autumn. May persist into winter if conditions remain mild.
Symptoms	Patches of damaged grass which often have a pink or red appearance. This is due partly to the presence of red needles which stick out from diseased leaves. These needles are the survival phase of the fungus. They may be straight or branched, brittle and up to 25 mm long. The size and shape of infected patches vary from 20-50 mm up to 350 mm in diameter. Commonly, unless the grass growth is poor and the attack serious the appearance is of a fairly superficial damage to the leaves, which die back from their tips. Such patches do not have a very distinct margin and live green leaves exist within them.
Grasses and turf	May be found on any type of turf. Red fescue (*Festuca rubra*) and perennial ryegrass (*Lolium perenne*) are the species most often affected but other species are attacked occasionally.

Conditions under which the disease is likely to occur	Low fertility, particularly insufficient nitrogen.
Integrated disease control	The disease can be prevented by the selection of cultivars which are less susceptible to the disease, especially if they are to be grown in low fertility situations. During summer, applications of nitrogenous fertiliser should be made if sufficient moisture is available. This will assist grass growth and reduce the severity of the disease. Treatment with fungicides is not generally considered worthwhile or cost-effective in winter sports pitches.

RUST

Rusts occasionally affect winter sports turf and especially perennial ryegrass during the summer months when the effects may become quite severe in suitable conditions. The grass blades will become covered by the orange/yellow pustules and the whole sward takes on a yellow appearance, whilst walking on affected swards can result in a yellow dusting of the shoes. Cultural treatment of swards is the only treatment since there are no approved fungicide treatments. Usually an application of nitrogen will help the sward to grow away from the problem, coupled with regular mowing to remove affected leaf blades.

TYPE 1 FAIRY RINGS

Causal fungus	Usually *Marasmius oreades*.
Importance	Fairly frequently seen on winter sports pitches especially hockey pitches and can be very long-lived, gradually increasing in size if no treatment is carried out.
Season	Symptoms most obvious during dry weather in the summer.
Symptoms	Type 1 rings are those that kill the grass or badly damage it. Two rings, arcs or ribbons of stimulated and darker green grass growth are seen. Between them there is a ring of bare ground. There are several ways in which *M. oreades* is able to kill the grass in this bare zone. The most important way is that the fungus creates extremely hydrophobic soil conditions, thus droughting plants out. Beneath the ring are large masses of white mycelium which have a characteristic musty smell. Small tan-coloured mushrooms may be seen in the outer ring any time between early summer and autumn.
Grasses and turf types affected	May occur in any type of turf.
Conditions that favour development	The conditions that favour the original establishment of rings are not understood fully but surface moisture may be important. Rings may be found on all soil types but are most noticeable on light sandy soils.
Integrated control	Several possible methods are available for the suppression of rings but complete eradication is difficult to achieve. An effective method of control is the laborious one of digging out most of the soil from an infected area and sterilising with formaldehyde any contaminated soil that remains. Digging out alone may be sufficient, if done thoroughly but the addition of a sterilisation agent increases the likelihood of success.
	The mycelium of *M. oreades* is very difficult to wet effectively. Consequently, fungicide solutions in water are easily repelled. To enable maximum concentration of fungicide to come into contact with the fungal mycelium wetting agents are needed.
	Three systemic fungicides, benodanil, oxycarboxin and triforine are effective against type 1 rings providing the following procedure is adhered to strictly.
	[1] Measure area to be treated and mark off with string. This must include turf within the ring and 0.5 m around the edge.

[2] Thoroughly spike the area with a hollow tine fork. This will assist the penetration of fungicide into the turf.

[3] Apply a solution of wetting agent to the area and leave to soak in for 1 hour.

[4] Apply either benodanil, oxycarboxin or triforine at the recommended rate and dilution using a watering can.

[5] Again water with wetting agent to assist penetration by fungicide. The most suitable time for this treatment is thought to be in the spring when the mycelium of the fungus is starting to grow actively. Often, to suppress the most aggressive rings, a second treatment is necessary during the autumn.

TYPE 2 FAIRY RINGS

Other names	None.
Causal fungi	*Agaricus, Lycoperdon* and *Scleroderma* spp.
Importance	Seen commonly on many turf areas. Cause little actual damage to the grass.
Season	Symptoms are usually most noticeable during the summer and autumn but the fungi are present all the year round.
Symptoms	Rings, arcs or ribbons of stimulated grass which is darker green and faster growing than that nearby. No actual damage is done to the grass. Occasionally fruiting bodies (toadstools, mushrooms or puff balls) are associated with the stimulated grass.
Grasses and turf types affected	Many types of turf may be affected. Most noticeable on hockey pitches.
Conditions that favour development	Not known. Symptoms are most marked when nitrogen is deficient.
Integrated control	No method of preventing type 2 rings is known. As the grass is not damaged rings are often tolerated but they can spoil the appearance of fine turf. As described for type 1 rings, it is possible to dig out type 2 rings but this is rarely thought worthwhile. During the growing season the symptoms can be disguised by giving extra nitrogen to the whole area. Applications of sulphate of iron will also mask the rings by generally darkening the area. Fungicides benodanil, triforine and oxycarboxin can be effective.

TYPE 3 FAIRY RINGS

Causal fungi	Many basidiomycetes, e.g. *Hygrophorus* spp., *Psilocybe* spp.
Importance	Very common. Usually no effect on the grass.
Season	The fungus is present all year round but the ring is seen only for a short period, often in autumn but depending on species sometimes in spring or early winter.
Symptoms	Fungal activity is indicated by a ring or sometimes a less distinct pattern of fruiting bodies (toadstools or puff-balls).
Grass and turf	Found in most types of turf but not seen usually on types affected by heavily worn areas.
Conditions that favour development	Not known.

Integrated control	Control is attempted rarely as there is no change to the grass. To prevent rings from spreading to other areas, fruiting bodies are sometimes picked by hand to stop the liberation of spores. If thought necessary, fruiting bodies may be suppressed by applying a fungicide. Benodanil, oxycarboxin and triforine are thought to be effective.

Note: As well as forming rings, fruiting bodies of Basidiomycete fungi may occur also on turf areas and be seen as solitary specimens arranged apparently in a ring or circular fashion. Some of these fungi may be true lawn fungi whilst others may be colonising buried debris such as twigs or tree roots. The "magic mushroom" (*Psilocybe*) is known to occur in this manner on a wide range of amenity turf surfaces. This can present problems due to members of the public trespassing to pick the mushrooms for their hallucinogenic effects. No chemical control method is available as yet but the fruiting bodies may be destroyed using a mower or a hand brush.

SUPERFICIAL FAIRY RINGS

Other names	Superficial basidiomycetes, thatch fungi.
Causal fungi	*Trechispora alnicola*. Possibly many non-sporing basidiomycetes involved. Very difficult to identify.
Importance	Common problem in fine turf which seems to be increasing. May also occur in hockey pitches.
Season	May be seen at any time of the year.
Symptoms	Intense fungal activity in the thatch layer of the turf, often invading grass sheath bases. Dense white mycelium is visible frequently and the thickness of the thatch layer may be reduced. Grass in infected areas is often greener than that on adjacent areas but may sometimes turn yellow or bleached. Various patterns are formed, including circular patches, complete rings, parts of rings and irregular narrow lines.
Grasses and turf types affected	Any type of turf may be affected. Particularly troublesome on fine turf areas where a deep thatch layer is present.
Conditions that favour development	The presence of a marked thatch layer. There is some evidence that the use of benzimidazole systemic fungicides may favour the fungi responsible also soil sterilisation, which may inhibit antagonistic fungi, has been implicated in this condition.
Integrated control	Reduce the thatch layer by turf management practices such as aeration and mechanical thatch removal. The fungicides triforine is approved for control of superficial fairy rings.

SECTION 9
END OF SEASON RENOVATION
By A. R. Cole

Whatever sport is being played, the natural grass surface will be subjected to wear and tear throughout the playing season. The degree of damage inflicted upon the turf will relate directly to the sport being played (compare hockey with Rugby) prevailing ground and weather conditions, alongside the frequency of use of the said pitch. It must always be remembered that we are dealing with a natural "product" in turf and the level of play a pitch can support will be related to soil type, drainage characteristics and level of maintenance the pitch receives. Renovation work falls into two distinct categories:

[a] After match repair, to restore the playing surface in advance of the next game, generally localised.

[b] End of season renovation, when the pitch will receive a full programme of maintenance not only to restore the playing surface, but an opportunity to improve the site too.

HOCKEY AND LACROSSE
The main requirements of a hockey surface are that it should be firm, fast and true to allow a struck ball to run freely across the surface with minimal deviation and rise. Surface levels are therefore critical for the game of hockey and one of the main reasons why the sport is now more commonly played (League hockey) on an artificial surface, where a perfect playing surface can be presented all year round. The requirements for a lacrosse pitch are similar to that of hockey where, on occasion, the ball will travel across the turf. In the main, however, the ball is played between players through the air, although the turf should be maintained at a height which will allow the ball to be "picked up" with case. With the declining use of hockey pitches for their designated purpose, many are being acquired by lacrosse clubs, providing a quality playing surface.

Following each fixture an examination of the pitch should be undertaken by the groundsman to assess the level of damage inflicted. The main objective is to maintain a smooth, level surface and in this respect, divots must be replaced and deep scars carefully forked up. Deeper scars should be levelled up with a suitable sandy soil and an appropriate seed mixture incorporated with the "divot mix". This time consuming operation is essential if a first class playing surface is to be preserved and failure to carry out the necessary after match repair can only result in a decline in surface quality.

One of the most important features of a winter games pitch is that it must support good drainage. Therefore, attention must be given to aeration to relieve compaction created by play and general maintenance operations to promote surface drainage through the upper profile. Aeration should form part of the groundsman's maintenance programme through the winter, but as part of his after match repair, consideration must also be given to localised areas which receive intensive wear, e.g. goal mouths. Invariably the turf becomes worn and the soil in the top few centimetres of the profile loses its structure. Supplementary hand forking is to be encouraged in these areas, together with a liberal top dressing of a lime-free, medium grade sand brushed well into the tine holes to help stabilise the heavily worn area. Supplies of a good quality sand should always be available to enable the groundsman to spot-treat wet areas, fill divots and generally preserve a good surface.

Many hockey and lacrosse pitches are sited on cricket outfields, where the quality of turf required for the different sports is very similar and there is no major alterations required to produce either surface. However, the busiest time for a groundsman, responsible for a dual use facility, is the short period between the end of the winter games season and the start of the cricket season. His task is made easier if a clear two weeks or more can be left before the start of the cricket season, but this is not always possible in practice. Poor ground and weather conditions during the vital change-over period may also hamper end of season repair and renovation which of course would be unforeseen.

Forward planning is the key to success; to have everything to hand when it is required so that work

PLATE 102. End of season repair by turfing on a Gaelic games pitch at Pairc nah Eireann (courtesy Warwickshire Gaelic Athletic Association).

PLATE 103. Self-travelling sprinklers are a useful method of minimising drought problems after spring reseeding or returfing where automatic pop-up systems are unavailable.

is not held up or precious time lost. Materials such as fertiliser, seed, weed killer and approved sand should have been ordered to arrive before the last match of the season, together with specialised renovation equipment if required.

Renovation work should start soon after the final game has been played to maximise the time available for the pitch to recover before it is brought back into play. Generally, the scale of restoration work is smaller than that of other winter games pitches, although obviously surface disruption would be increased during a wet playing season, on poorly drained soils or where the pitches receive a high level of usage.

ASSOCIATION FOOTBALL (SOCCER)

The playing characteristics are slightly different to that required for hockey, although the need for good drainage is still of paramount importance. Soccer requires a smooth surface over which a ball can roll, although not necessarily flat with many League soccer pitches being constructed with a camber to promote better surface drainage. Ball bounce is also important and the recent demise of artificial pitches for League use serves to illustrate the importance of a fair bounce and not "ping-pong" football.

Throughout the playing season surface disruption is to be expected following each game. As the season progresses replacing torn turf, divoting and forking up shallow surface scars will become more time consuming, but nonetheless time well spent to preserve a quality playing surface through the season. Be methodical in your approach when walking the pitch and a good guide would be to walk up and down the mower lines until the whole pitch is covered. If divots are replaced quickly they will root once again and far less obvious wear would result - in the professional game the groundstaff are often to be seen divoting the pitch at half-time for a televised game.

Unfortunately, we are not always fortunate enough to have the manpower or time available to conscientiously walk the pitch and repair the damage and in this situation consideration should be given to mechanical implements to speed up the operation. Machinery such as the Sisis Quadraplay has the facility for light raking and brushing (with a lute, shallow slitter and roller also available) and independently adjustable, to knock down major divots to restore a reasonable surface. The Quadra-groom (Sisis) also has the facility for deep slit tine aeration at the same time. Alternatively, a trailed tilther rake or the smooth side of a grassland chain harrow can also be regarded as useful tools.

Unlike hockey and lacrosse, the wear pattern on a soccer pitch is distributed between the two goals and the centre of the pitch in a diamond formation, with goal and central regions becoming particularly worn. When conditions become too wet for the use of heavy tractor mounted aeration equipment, the groundsman is encouraged to use a pedestrian aerator, such as the Pattisson SP spiker or the Sisis Auto-Outfield unit. The use of these machines should be confined to the more heavily used goal and central regions to keep the surface open. Wet or developing muddy areas should be deep hand forked (prising back on the tines) and working in a liberal dressing of a lime-free, medium grade sand to help dry and stabilise the surface.

Until recently, the idea of returfing a worn goal area or centre circle during the playing season has not been recommended, as the new turf does not have sufficient time to root and a stable surface has been lost. However, Inturf have developed a turf cutting system, called a TurfTile, where "blocks" of turf are cut 1 m² to a depth of 70 mm and a corresponding block removed from the pitch, which provides an instant repair and a more stable surface than that achieved through conventional means.

The technique was first tried at Wembley Stadium, where turf was transplanted from the margins of the pitch and the margin repaired with conventional turf. This ensures continuity of both colour and turf texture and soil compatibility. Turf tiles will inevitably remove a large quantity of soil, but this is replaced immediately to reduce any possibility of topsoil depletion. Custom grown turf is also available where the client supplies his own rootzone and the turf then purpose grown to a specification. Clubs who have already taken advantage of this system include Wembley Stadium, Manchester United, Norwich City and the whole pitch at Parc de Prince in July 1993.

PLATE 104. Equipment developed by Inturf of Pocklington, Yorkshire to transport large Turf Tiles, pictured at Wembley Stadium.

PLATE 105. Turf Tiles are 1 m² and 70 mm thick - final positioning by hand at Parc de Prince, France (both photographs courtesy of Inturf Ltd).

RUGBY FOOTBALL

Interactions between the ball and the surface are far less important for Rugby than they are for soccer, but of the utmost importance for hockey. The interaction between the player and the surface are more important for Rugby and football, where traction or grip enables a player (or players) to make movements without excessive slipping or falling when running or changing direction. Rugby is also a contact sport and there is a high degree of player contact with the surface. Hence, the grass cover is left "long" to offer some resistance, however, if left too long would cause player fatigue. Requirements for American football are obviously very similar.

Rugby pitches are the least demanding in respect of surface smoothness, not least due to the shape of the ball. A satisfactory surface can therefore be restored more easily using mechanical methods, e.g. tilther rake or smooth side of a grassland chain harrow, without the need to meticulously walk the pitch with a hand fork, which is required for soccer and hockey. Obviously in a professional situation the quality of surface and manpower available may be sufficient to justify restoration by hand. A change in the rules has reduced damage inflicted on the surface by the goal kicker, who is now encouraged to kick the ball from a small pile of sand or rubber ring, in preference to "digging up the turf" with his heel.

There is a less well defined wear pattern on a Rugby pitch, although the majority of wear is confined to scrummage areas, where two 'packs' of eight are pushing against one another to gain possession of the ball. Where play is stopped for an infringement at the line-out, a scrummage will be made 5 m in from the touch-line. Likewise, where the ball is carried over the goal line by the defending team, a scrummage will be awarded 5 m from the goal line. All other scrummages take place at the point of infringement. These areas can become devastated during a game and localised deep forking and sanding may be required to help stabilise the surface in advance of the next game.

In the past, dual use of a turf facility was generally confined to a cricket outfield used for the purpose of a winter game. More recently, however, an increasing number of League soccer grounds are becoming the permanent homes of Rugby League clubs. In this situation the surface is prepared primarily for the needs of the soccer team, which requires a closer height of cut than would be provided for Rugby and consequently, when Rugby is played surface disruption is more acute.

In many school grounds, limited space forces the dual use of cricket outfields for soccer, Rugby, hockey and lacrosse, the latter two we have already confirmed to be compatible, although out of necessity the former sports are often played. Considerable renovation is required over soccer and Rugby pitches before the start of the cricket season and it is likely that the quality of the outfield will be low during the early part of the season. The height of cut will also be maintained at a higher level than would be considered desirable for cricket – approximately 25 mm, instead of the usual 12 mm, to preserve the dominant ryegrass species in the sward.

GAELIC FOOTBALL, HURLING AND SHINTY

To a large extent, both Gaelic football and hurling are "summer games", the playing season stretching from 1 March until 30 November inclusive, but in practice the games are played throughout the year.

Unlike the other winter games, these sports are played through the main growing season (i.e. April-September), where growth can compensate for the wear and tear of play. Both games require a similar playing surface to that outlined for lacrosse and football. Divoting and after match repair must still be undertaken if a quality playing surface is to be retained, although in a dry summer irrigation must not be neglected if the repaired turf is to recover.

The end of the playing season corresponds with the start of the winter period, i.e. falling ground temperature, reduced grass growth, increased moisture in the profile, which renders renovation by seed very difficult. In the writer's experience, high levels of wear are characteristically found in the goal area and these are returfed on an annual basis. The provision of a turf nursery to carry out this annual task is therefore to be encouraged.

POLO

The needs of a polo field must take into consideration two major factors if the game is to be played to the highest standard. In the first instance, there is the ball/surface interaction (similar to hockey) where a smooth and true surface is required to enable a struck ball to travel across the field unhindered. Secondly, the surface must also provide a sound footing for the ponies, the action of the hoof and constantly changing direction inflicts considerable daage to the field. The game therefore has somewhat contrasting demands on the turf.

High goal polo is divided into six $7^1/2$ minute periods (or Chukkas) with an interval of 4 minutes between each period; low goal polo comprises four Chukkas, but overall each match will take up to an hour and a half to play. At the Guards Polo Club it is usual for two matches to be played per day. With this high level of usage, the need for after match repair is paramount if a quality surface is to be preserved and for "the big day" it is somewhat of a tradition that the crowd will help knock back the larger divots at half-time, more as a social event than groundsmanship!

At the end of a day's play the groundsman would concentrate his efforts on repairing the heavily worn tee and goal areas, which receive concentrated wear, forking up shallow surface scars, replacing torn turf and divots and relevelling deeper holes with a sand/soil mix (with a seed mixture included). Localised light top dressing may also be undertaken at this stage to restore surface levels. At Cirencester the Sisis Quadraplay has been used to good effect to restore the playing surface, with a considerable saving on manpower. Obviously, the most effective restoration is carried out by hand, although more labour-intensive. At the end of each game, following repair, the pitch may be lightly rolled to re-firm the surface. Care must be taken not to over-roll at this stage, which would affect the quality of the playing surface and if too hard, would be injurious to the ponies. With polo being a summer sport, turf recovery can be aided by irrigation during periods of prolonged, dry weather, although managed to avoid creating too soft a surface.

Whilst there is strong and persistent growth taking place at the end of the season, the field must be fully renovated to return a strong and healthy sward for the following season. Scarification may be undertaken in two forms, e.g. Veemo units, to raise any flat or procumbent growth, which may have developed during the summer and short toothed grassland chain harrows to lift any unwanted divots from the playing surface. All debris is then swept from the surface.

During the playing season topsoil compaction is inevitable (not just through play but also through rolling and general maintenance) which must be relieved. A tractor mounted deep slit tine aerator can be used for this purpose, making several passes in different directions to thoroughly perforate the turf. If deep seated compaction has set in, consideration may also be given to careful use of the Verti-Drain. Throughout the winter months aeration should be continued.

Top dressing is essential to restore surface levels using an approved 50:50 sand:soil mixture or approved medium grade sand at 12.5-25 tonnes/hectare, depending on surface wear. The dressing should be worked well into the base of the sward with a large drag mat to bring back surface levels. Overseeding of the whole field is completed with a recommended grass seed mixture (see Section 5 - Grasses for Winter Pitches) at 35 g/m², either broadcast or using a Contravator. In advance of overseeding, a fertiliser dressing will be applied subject to soil analyses confirming levels of pH, phosphate and potash.

SPRING RENOVATION

The spring renovation programme on winter games pitches requires plenty of forward planning, to ensure that all the appropriate machinery and materials are available to allow work to proceed as early as possible. Depending on the prevailing ground and weather conditions, renovation should get underway immediately the final fixture from the old season has been completed. This is important because a good recovery of turf is essential, so that the turf will be in a presentable and playable condition when play resumes in the following season. However, in many instances the length of the close season is being constantly reduced with more matches being played later on in the year and the demand for summer fixtures increases. Consequently, the remaining months can become extremely busy for the groundsman, who is confronted with renovating his winter pitches, often during unfavourable weather conditions, whilst at the same time carrying out other time-consuming operations on cricket, tennis and bowls areas.

Throughout the playing season the drainage characteristics of the pitch must be continually assessed and if wanting, provision must be made in advance to correct these deficiencies through the close season. On a League soccer pitch, with a maximum of only 12 weeks respite before the end of one season and the start of the next, if drainage is required the club should seek to rearrange the last few remaining fixtures of the season to be played away from home to extend the time available for drainage and subsequent renovation.

[1] AERATION

One of the first major operations to be carried out at the end of the playing season is compaction relief through aeration. In the majority of cases a tractor mounted unit, capable of penetrating the soil to a depth of 200-225 mm, is considered satisfactory. Four or five passes are made in different directions to thoroughly perforate the surface and relieve compaction within the upper profile. Aeration not only relieves topsoil compaction, but by getting air into the profile can help to promote deeper rooting, surface moisture penetration and encourage microbial breakdown of organic matter, which can be a problem where the finer bent and fescue grass species are employed, e.g. hockey. As you can see, multiple benefits are achieved through this single treatment.

Play and use of maintenance equipment during adverse weather conditions effectively seal the surface impeding water movement and allowing deep seated compaction to develop, especially where the grass cover is lost. Small, localised areas can be worked using a hand fork, particularly important during the playing season, but for an overall treatment Verti-Draining can be invaluable in alleviating the above conditions. To prolong the effect of the Verti-Drain treatment and improve surface levels, the application of a medium/fine sand is recommended, the amount varying from approximately 60 tonnes on a hockey pitch to 100 tonnes on other winter pitches. It is important that the sand is applied uniformly to the whole pitch, generally through a purpose built top dressing unit. There are distinct advantages to be gained from carrying out sanding prior to Verti-Draining, namely:

[a] The sand will stabilise the surface for the tractor fitted with the Verti-Drain if the surface is at all slippery.

[b] The tines can punch the sand down the holes.

[c[Sand will immediately find its way into the open tine holes and can be washed in whilst the holes are open and receptive.

Depending on the contractor used, preference may be given to Verti-Draining first followed by top dressing and working the sand in, to reduce abrasion and wearing of the tines through the sand. The Sports Ground Verti-Drain or Terraspike, fitted with 25 mm diameter tines, is normally specified for winter games pitches.

The Verti-Drain is not a cure-all for a drainage problem, but where compaction within the profile is restricting water movement the Verti-Drain can penetrate to a maximum of 400 mm, with sufficient heave to shatter the profile. If, however, the machine is used on wet, heavy clay, cracking and fissuring of the profile may not be achieved and in the worst scenario, the operation could make the pitch wetter. Ground conditions must therefore be taken into account before the Verti-Drain is used.

The use of a vibrating mole plough has proved useful on heavy, moist soils where the channel can be held intact for a number of years (a cheap method of temporary drainage), but compaction is also relieved through the action of the vibrating mole plough. The unit should be drawn at an angle of 20° across the maximum fall and the fall must be level to produce a drainage channel which will run

PLATE 106. In spite of sophisticated modern aeration machinery, there is still a very useful role for the hand fork, in this case the long-tined Aerdrain fork from Sisis Equipment (Macclesfield) Ltd.

PLATE 107. Pedestrian spikers such as the Sisis Outfield machine are particularly useful when ground conditions are too soft for the safe use of tractor mounted equipment.

freely to a positive drainage outlet. The operation may also be carried out in conjunction with a medium/fine sand top dressing to once again prolong the effect of this operation.

Other forms of specialised aeration equipment which may be deemed necessary in individual circumstances include units which base their action on compressed air or deep drilling. The former operation involves the insertion of one or more probes into the soil and forcing compressed air into the ground to relieve compaction. In theory, the air could follow the lines of least resistance before escaping and may not break up compacted soil, however, experience has shown positive benefits in highly compacted goal mouths and should not be discounted. Tractor-mounted drills are also available to relieve compaction to depth, although due to the nature of the treatment is confined to small areas only.

[2] CULTIVATION

On heavily used pitches, areas such as goal mouths and centre circles usually become very worn and compacted by the end of the season and some form of soil cultivation is required. For localised areas a hand fork can be used to break up the soil, working to a depth of 100-125 mm and a seed bed tilth produced by alternate raking and heeling. If level discrepancies are observed, additional medium/ fine sand should be incorporated to return a smooth, level surface.

When extensive areas of a pitch become devoid of grass, implements such as a tractor drawn disc harrow and tilther rakes could be used to work the soil, although harrows have become more or less superseded by the Contravator type overseeding units now available. Chain harrows and tilther rakes, alongside the more complex units such as the Sisis Quadraplay, still have a role to play in re-establishing a smooth surface through raking and brushing prior to overseeding.

Throughout the winter sand is commonly used in wet or developing muddy areas to help dry and stabilise the playing surface. The spring renovation period is an ideal time to improve local "wet spots" and restore surface levels through amelioration. Local areas can be made up with a sandy topsoil or suitable sand/soil mix, making sure that the ground is thoroughly cultivated before the new material is introduced to help it "key-in".

We have already confirmed the importance of sand in helping to stabilise the playing surface and prolong the effectiveness of deep aeration, but of equal importance is the preservation of a free-draining surface. Pitches which have been sand slit, sand banded or similar rely on the direct contact between the surface and the drainage layer to remove surface water quickly. If, following the installation of a slit drainage system the pitch is not top dressed with an approved sand, soil will become smeared across the drainage channels and reduce their efficiency due to soil "capping". Emphasis is also placed on using an approved sand for top dressing and not any old "builders sand" which happens to be cheap.

[3] FERTILISER

At a suitable opportunity during the renovation programme, a spring fertiliser dressing should be applied, preferably some 7-10 days in advance of overseeding. This will strengthen growth of the grass which remains as well as providing the necessary nutrients to promote seedling establishment. Where hockey is played on a predominantly bent/fescue sward the annual nutrient requirement for the turf is relatively small where clippings are removed, i.e. 40-50 kg N/ha/year, however, on a top class facility where clippings are removed, the requirement is increased to 80-200 kg N/ha/year (the upper figures where dwarf type perennial ryegrass is also included in the mixture). Phosphate and potash requirements are confirmed by soil analyses and grass composition.

Where perennial ryegrass is the dominant species, used for its hard wearing characteristics, a higher nutrient regime is required than fescue and bent turf. Where grass clippings are returned (multiple sports fields etc), the fertiliser requirement is low, e.g. 80-100 kg N/ha/year, with 20-50 kg/ha of P_2O_5 and K_2O, depending on soil analyses. For high class sport where clippings are boxed off to reduce organic matter deposition, the nutrient requirement is notably higher, e.g. 160-200 kg/N/ha/year with 80-100 kg/ha of P_2O_5 and K_2O. Applications would be split into two dressings for moderate quality turf, with four or five applied to turf of higher quality.

The nature of the underlying soil will also influence the fertiliser regime. A pitch on a very sandy soil has very little natural nutrient reserves and also a limited availability to hold on to nutrients. Consequently such pitches will need more fertilising than a pitch over a loam soil, where the clay fraction of the soil holds potassium and ammonium against leaching. In order to alleviate the problem of low nutrient-holding capacity, slow release products are worth considering for pitches on sand-based rootzones.

[4] OVERSEEDING

On completion of the soil cultivation works and once a firm, fine seed bed tilth has been formed, sowing of thin and bare areas should then proceed. This may involve broadcasting the seed by hand in the immediate goal mouth and centre circle areas only. If, however, large-scale overseeding is necessary, a suitable Contravator unit can be employed. The Contravator is most effectively used if several passes are made in different directions to avoid creating straight lines, usually sowing a total rate of 35 g/m². This would be supplemented by broadcasting the seed in the weakest areas to help produce a dense turf. Choice of the most appropriate grass species and currently recommended cultivars have been thoroughly discussed previously and should be referred to.

The time available for the seed to germinate and establish is often limited and therefore it is important that no checks in growth occur which could otherwise have been avoided. If, following the spring renovation programme, conditions become very dry it is essential that renovated sections of turf are kept adequately watered, to ensure full germination and establishment of the young grasses.

Germination and establishment can also be improved on small areas using a germination blanket, such as currently available products called 'Tildenent' or 'Grocover', which retain warmth and moisture whilst at the same time allowing the surface to "breathe", thereby reducing the risk of damping-off.

If the winter pitch also forms part of a cricket outfield, there may be a case for returfing the more heavily worn goal mouth areas. Much greater emphasis is then placed on adequate irrigation to prevent the turves shrinking and drying out.

[5] MOWING

Assuming that the subsequent weather conditions are favourable and adequate irrigation has been supplied, the ryegrass component of the sown mixture should begin to appear in about a week. When the young grass seedlings reach a height of approximately 60 mm the first cut should be made, removing no more than the top 20 mm. As a general guide with any cutting regime, you should never remove more than one-third of the available leaf with any single cut to avoid weakening the sward. The sward should be maintained at this height for the next few cuts before gradually reducing to the appropriate routine summer level. A controlled reduction in cutting height is called for to promote tillering and thickening of the sward to develop a hard wearing turf.

[6] SCARIFICATION

A sward composed predominantly of the finer-leaved bent and fescue species is especially prone to becoming soft as thatch builds up at the base of the sward. This material can be physically removed using a tractor mounted scarifier, making several passes over the pitch and collecting the subsequent arisings. A more crude method of scarification can be achieved using a grassland chain harrow or a tilther rake towed behind a tractor. Scarification also reduces the likelihood of perennial ryegrass developing a tufted growth habit and is best carried out in July/August, when strong and persistent growth is being produced to effect rapid turf recovery.

[7] REDUCING LOCALISED WEAR

The amount of wear and tear on hockey and football pitches can often be reduced by moving the position of the pitch, thereby moving the area of wear. On school playing fields or larger sports-grounds there is often room to do this.

PLATES 108 and 109. Surface seeding machines are widely used to overseed worn pitches. Several passes in varying directions should be made to ensure an even cover.

190

At the end of the playing season, goal posts and nets must be removed and the area roped off to discourage unauthorised play during the summer, when the renovated area needs time to establish. If there is space available off the pitch, erect a set of goal posts for practice to provide a kick-about-goal area. Alternatively it may be prudent to provide a set of goal posts.

[8] RENOVATION OF SAND CONSTRUCTIONS

The maintenance work required on a sand pitch is not too dissimilar to that on natural soil, however, greater skill is required in the management of fertiliser and water if a quality turf is to be produced.

For winter games, the idea of pure sand with its free-draining characteristics and air movement in the profile is very attractive. Unfortunately when the turf becomes worn and lost during the playing season, the surface becomes unstable and the playing quality of the surface is affected. Various materials are available for incorporation at the construction phase to stabilise the sand, e.g. Netlon, Fibreturf etc., although working and production of a seed bed is often more difficult.

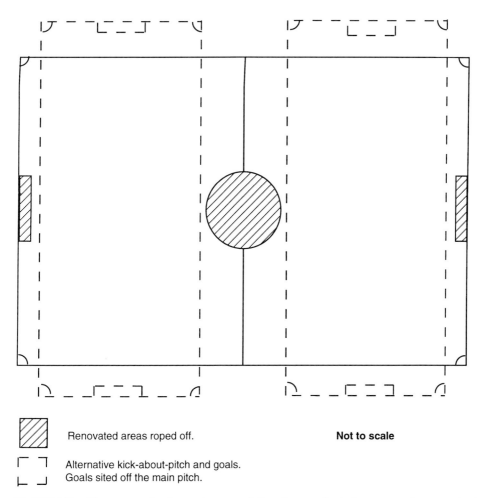

Renovated areas roped off.
Not to scale

Alternative kick-about-pitch and goals.
Goals sited off the main pitch.

PLATE 110: If summer play has to be catered for, then mark pitches across the normal winter line of play to remove wear from the renovated goals.

After match repair and renovation, alongside conventional soil-based constructions, are still important to preserve the playing surface through the winter. Odd divot marks should be filled with

191

a mixture of sand, fertiliser, processed seaweed and seed to aid establishment. At the end of the playing season the following procedure is generally adapted:

[a] Produce a level surface, importing additional sand if required.

[b] Incorporate a general slow release fertiliser and a proprietary processed seaweed.

[c] Sow a wear tolerant perennial ryegrass and rake into the surface or even cover with 10 mm of sand.

[d] Roll to produce a firm surface.
Where difficulties are still experienced in retaining a stable surface, e.g. goal mouths, an approved soil can be ameliorated into the sand to help provide a more stable footing.

All the above references to the use of "sand" must relate to the approved material used in the original construction, there can be no compromise as the type of sand used is critical.

BIBLIOGRAPHY

BOOKS & BOOKLETS : GENERAL BACKGROUND

Ambler, C. (1990). *Full Colour Views of the Football League Grounds.* Soccer Book Pub. Ltd., Cleethorpes, 104 pp.

Anon. (1974). *Women's Hockey.* Training and Educational Associates Ltd., London, 68 pp.

Anon. (1990). *Digest of Football Statistics.* Sir Norman Chester Centre for Football Research. The Football Trust, London, 90 pp.

Anon. (undated c. 1935). *Encyclopaedia of Games Sports & Pastimes.* Fleetway House, London, 788 pp.

Arlott, J. (Ed.) (1975). *Oxford Companion to Sports & Games.* Oxford University Press, London, 1143 pp.

Barrett, N.S. (1972). *Purnell's Encyclopaedia of Association Football.* Purnell & Sons Ltd., London, 254 pp.

Boss, D. & Natal, J. (1989). *The Official Guide to American Football.* Hamlyn Pub. Group (Octopus), London, 48 pp.

Brasch, R. (1972). *How Did Sport Begin? A Look into the Origins of Man at Play.* Longman Group Ltd., London, 279 pp.

Brody, M. (1980). *100 Years of Irish Football.* Blackstaff Press, Belfast, Northern Ireland, 187 pp.

Búrca, M. (1980). *The Gaelic Athletic Association : A History.* Cumann Lúthchleas Gael, Dublin, 279 pp.

Butler, B. (1987). *The Football League 1888-1988 : The Official Illustrated History.* Queen Anne Press (Macdonald), London, 352 pp.

Corry, E. (1989). *Catch and Kick : Great moments of Gaelic Football 1880-1990.* Poolbeg Press Ltd., Swords, Republic of Ireland, 341 pp.

Day, H.L.V. (1952). *Rugby Union Football.* Country Books No. 9. Nicholson & Watson Ltd., London, 203 pp.

Disston, H. (1973). *Beginning Polo.* A.S. Barnes & Co. Inc., New Jersey, USA, 200 pp.

Fittis, R.S. (1891). *Sports & Pastimes of Scotland.* Alexander Gardner (reprinted 1975 E.P. Pub., Ltd., Wakefield, Yorkshire), 212 pp.

Frost, T. (1988). *Bradford City : A Complete Record 1903-1988.* Breedon Books Pub. Co. Ltd., Derby, 416 pp.

Gaulton, A.N. (1968). *The Encyclopaedia of Rugby League Football.* Robert Hale Ltd., London, 160 pp.

Gee, H. (1972). *Wembley : Fifty Great Years.* Pelham Books Ltd., London, 176 pp.

Green, G. (1949). *The Official History of the F.A. Cup.* The Naldrett Press, London, 256 pp.

Harvey, C. (Ed.) (1959). *Encyclopaedia of Sport.* Sampson Low, Marston & Co. Ltd., London, 328 pp.

Howell, D. (1977). *Soccer Refereeing.* (Revised Edn., 1st Edn. 1968.) Pelham Books Ltd., London, 159 pp.

Inglis, S. (1983). *The Football Grounds of England and Wales.* Willow Books (Collins), London, 272 pp.

Inglis, S. (1990). *The Football Grounds of Europe.* Willow Books (Collins), London, 288 pp.

Jago, G. (1974). *Football Coaching (for play at all levels).* Stanley Paul & Co. Ltd., London, 128 pp.

Kramer, A. (Ed.) (1979). *Enjoying Track & Field Sports.* Diagram Visual Inf. Ltd. (Paddington Press Ltd.), London, 160 pp.

Lovesey, P. (1979). *The Official Centenary History of the Amateur Athletic Association.* Guinness Superlatives Ltd., Enfield, Middlesex, 223 pp.

Mason, N. (1974). *Football! The Story of all the World's Football Games.* Maurice Temple Smith Ltd., London, 256 pp.

Milford, D.S. (1938). *Hockey.* Modern Sports Series, J.M. Dent & Sons Ltd., London, 216 pp.

Muckle, D.S. & Shepherdson, H. (1975). *Football Fitness & Injuries.* Pelham Books Ltd., London, 142 pp.

Owen, O.L. (1955). *The History of the Rugby Football Union.* Playfair Books Ltd., London, 368 pp.

Parry-Jones, D. (1984). *Taff's Acre : A History & Celebration of Cardiff Arms Park.* Willow Books (Collins), London, 198 pp.

Parry-Jones, D. (1989). *The Rugby Clubs of Wales.* Stanley Paul & Co. Ltd., London, 176 pp.

Pick, J.B. (1952). *The Phoenix Dictionary of Games.* Phoenix House, London, 328 pp.

Reason, J. & Carwyn, J. (1979). *The World of Rugby : A History of Rugby Union Football.* B.B.C. Pubs., London, 299 pp.

Reilly, T., Lees, A., Davids, K. & Murphy, W.J. (Eds.) (1988). *Science and Football.* E. & F.N. Spon Ltd., London, 651 pp.

Signy, D. (1968). *A Pictorial History of Soccer.* Hamlyn Pub. Group Ltd., London, 316 pp.

Thomas, J.B.G. (1962). *Great Rugger Clubs.* Stanley Paul & Co. Ltd., London, 206 pp.

Thomas, K. (1983). *A Guide to American Football.* Orbis Pub. Ltd., London, 128 pp.

Twydell, D. (Ed.) (1993). *Football Grounds.* Aerofilms Guide Dial Press (Ian Allan Pub.), Addlestone, Surrey, 192 pp.

Tyler, M. (1978). *The Story of Football.* Marshall Cavendish Ltd., London, 265 pp.

Various Authoris (1977). *The Hamlyn International Book of Soccer.* Hamlyn Pub. Group Ltd., London, 208 pp.

Various Authors (1981). *Hamlet Sports Special : Soccer.* Hamlyn Pub. Group Ltd., London, 95 pp.

Viney, N. & Grant, N. (1978). *An Illustrated History of Ball Games.* William Heineman Ltd., London, 201 pp.

Waring, E. (1981). *Eddie Waring on Rugby League.* Frederick Muller Ltd., London, 160 pp.

Warters, D. (1979). *Leeds United : The Official History of the Club.* Wensum Books Ltd., Norwich, 109 pp.

Wein, H. (1973). *The Science of Hockey.* Pelham Books Ltd., London, 236 pp.

Williams, J.G.P. & Sperryn, P.N. (Eds.) (1976). *Sports medicine.* (2nd Edn., 1st Edn.1962.) Edward Arnold Pub. Ltd., London, 547 pp.

Wilson, N. (1988). *The Sports Business.* Judy Piatkus Pub. Ltd., London, 186 pp.

Wright, B. (Ed.) (1971). *Rules of the Game.* Stanley Paul & Co. Ltd. (Hutchinson), London, 285 pp.

Wymer, N. (1949). *Sport in England : A History of 2000 Years of Games & Pastimes.* George C. Harrap & Co. Ltd., London, 271 pp.

Young, P.M. (1968). *A History of British Football.* Stanley Paul & Co. Ltd., London, 224 pp.

BOOKS & BOOKLETS : SPORTSFIELD CONSTRUCTION & MAINTENANCE

Adams, W.A. & Gibbs, R.J. (1994). *Natural Turf for Sport and Amenity : Science and Practice.* CAB International, Wallingford, Oxon., 450 pp.

Anon. (1951). *The Soccer Club Groundsman.* The Naldrett Press, London, 108 pp.

Anon. (1966). Playing fields and hard surface areas. *Building Bulletin No. 28.* Dept. of Education & Science, HMSO, London, 84 pp.

Anon. (1980). *Facilities for Athletics (Track & Field).* N.P.F.A. and A.A.A. (2nd Edn., 1st Edn. 1971), 92 pp.

Anon. (1980). *Groundsman's Field Handbook.* Sportsmark Group, Brentford, Middlesex, 32 pp.

Anon. (1983). *Directory of Sports & Amenity Turf Chemicals.* British Agrochemicals Assoc. & The Sports Turf Research Institute, 32 pp.

Anon. (1986). *Nozzle Selection Handbook.* British Crop Protection Council, Farnham, Surrey, 40 pp.

Anon. (1989). *Commission of Enquiry into Playing Surfaces : Final Report.* The Football League, Lytham St Annes, Lancs., 220 pp.

Anon. (1989). *Hand Operated Sprayers Handbook.* British Crop Protection Council, Farnham, Surrey, 44 pp.

Anon. (1993). *Amenity Handbook.* British Agrochemicals Assoc. Ltd., Peterborough, 42 pp.

Anon. (1991). *Boom Sprayers Handbook.* British Crop Protection Council, Farnham, Surrey, 60 pp.

Anon. (1991). *Code of Practice for the Use of Approved Pesticides in Amenity and Industrial Areas.* National Association of Agric. Contractors and National Turfgrass Council, 72 pp.

Anon. (undated). Maintenance equipment for sportsgrounds. *Advisory Leaflet No. 13.* Sports Council for Northern Ireland, Belfast, 5 pp.

Baker, S.W. (1990). *Sands for Sports Turf Construction and Maintenance.* The Sports Turf Research Institute, Bingley, W. Yorks., 58 pp.

Baldwin, N.A. (1990). *Turfgrass Pests and Diseases.* The Sports Turf Research Institute, Bingley, W. Yorks., 49 pp.

Beale, R. (1924). *Lawns for Sports : Their Construction and Upkeep.* Simkin, Marshall, Hamilton, Kent & Co. Ltd., London, 276 pp.

Beale, R. (1931). *The Book of the Lawn : A Complete Guide to the Making and Maintenance of Lawns and Greens for all Purposes.* Cassell & Co. Ltd., London, 151 pp.

Bell, B. & Cousins, S. (1991). *Machinery for Horticulture.* Farming Press Books, Ipswich, Suffolk, 295 pp.

Branagh, A. (undated). Grass playing fields construction and drainage : systems available in Northern Ireland. *Advisory Leaflet No. 16.* Sports Council for Northern Ireland, Belfast, 19 pp.

Branagh, A. (undated). The construction and maintenance of grass playing surfaces for field games. *Advisory Leaflet No. 3.* Sports Council for Northern Ireland, Belfast, 8 pp.

Bures, I.F. (1969). Establishment and maintenance of sporting places under grass cover. *Proc. 1st Czechoslovak Symposium on Sports Turf,* Nymburk, University of Agriculture, Brno, Czechoslovakia, 284 pp..

Castle, D.A., McCunnall, J. & Tring, I.M. (1984). *Field Drainage : Principles and Practice.* B.T. Batsford Ltd., London, 250 pp.

Cave, L.W. (1967). *Cave's Guide to Turf Culture.* Pelham Books Ltd., London, 188 pp.

Chadwick, R.M. (1990). *Spon's Grounds Maintenance Contract Handbook.* E. & F.N. Spon (Chapman & Hall), London, 157 pp.

Chance, M. (1986). Workshop report on maintenance of winter games pitches for voluntary persons. *Workshop Report No. 10.* National Turfgrass Council, Bingley, W. Yorks., 24 pp.

Clamp, H. (1986). *Spon's Landscape Contract Manual.* E. & F.N. Spon, London, 195 pp.

Cobham, R. (1990). *Amenity Landscape Management : A Resources Handbook.* E. & F.N. Spon (Chapman & Hall), London, 458 pp.

Dawson, R.B. (1939). *Practical Lawn Craft.* Crosby Lockwood & Son Ltd., London, 300 pp.

de Thabrew, W.V. (1973). *Lawns Sportsgrounds and Playing Areas : Including Non-Grass Surfaces.* The Thornhill Press, Gloucester, 269 pp.

Downing, M.F. (1977). *Landscape Construction.* E. & F.N. Spon, London, 247 pp.

Escritt, J.R. (1978). *ABC of Turf Culture.* Kaye & Ward Ltd., London, 239 pp.

Faulkner, R.P. (1950). *The Science of Turf Cultivation.* The Technical Press Ltd., London, 64 pp.

Gilbert, D. & Macrory, R. (1989). *Pesticide Related Law.* British Crop Protection Council, Farnham, Surrey, 68 pp.

Gooch, R.B. & Escritt, J.R. (1975). *Sports Ground Construction Specifications.* (2nd Edn., 1st Edn. 1965.) National Playing Fields Association, London, 126 pp.

Greenfield, I. (1962). *Turf Culture.* Leonard Hill (Books) Ltd., London, 364 pp.

Halford, D.G. (1982). *Old Lawnmowers. Shire Album No. 91.* Shire Pubs. Ltd., Aylesbury, Bucks, 32 pp.

Hawker, M.F.J. & Keenlyside, J.F. (1985). *Horticultural Machinery.* (3rd Edn.) Longman Group U.K. Ltd., Harlow, Essex, 180 pp.

Hawthorn, R. (1972). *Association Football Club Groundsman.* The Football Association, London, 97 pp.

Hawthorn, R. (1977). *Dawson's Practical Lawn Craft.* Crosby Lockwood, Staples, London, 313 pp.

Hayes, P. (1984). *Technical Terms in Turf Culture.* The Sports Turf Research Institute, Bingley, W. Yorks., 76 pp.

Hope, F. (1990). *Turf Culture : A Manual for the Groundsman.* (2nd Edn., 1st Edn. Blandford Press 1978). Cassell Pubs. Ltd., London, 293 pp.

Hopper, H.T. (undated, but 1967). *The Provision and Maintenance of Playing Fields and Churchyards.* Trade & Technical Press Ltd., Morden, Surrey, 248 pp.

John, G. & Campbell, K. (Eds.) (1993). *Outdoor Sports : Handbook of Sports & Recreational*

Building Design, Vol. 2, 2nd Edn. The Sports Council Butterworth Architecture, Oxford, 281 pp.

Key, M. (1983). *Sprinkler Irrigation : Equipment & Practice.* B.T. Batsford Ltd., London, 120 pp.

Langdon, D. *et al.* (Eds.) (1991). *Spon's Civil Engineering & Highway Works Price Book.* E. & F.N. Spon, London, 850 pp.

Lawson, D.M. (1991). *Fertilisers for Turf.* The Sports Turf Research Institute, Bingley, W. Yorks., 45 pp.

Lewis, I.G. (1948). *Turf : A Book About Golf Greens, Tennis Courts, Bowling Greens and Playing Pitches etc.* Faber & Faber Ltd., London, 140 pp.

Livesley, MC. (1960). *Field Drainage.* E. & F.N. Spon Ltd., London, 187 pp.

Lovejoy, D. *et al.* (Eds.) (1991). *Spon's Landscape & External Works Price Book.* E. & F.N. Spon, London, 200 pp.

Macdonald, J. (1923). *Lawns, Links & Sportsfields.* Country Life Ltd., London, 77 pp.

Macself, A.J. (1924). *Grass : A New and Thoroughly Practical Book on Grass for Ornamental Lawns and All Purposes of Sports and Games.* Cecil Palmer, London, 204 pp.

Peterson, F. (1973). *Handbook of Lawn Mower Repair.* John Murray, London, 253 pp.

Pettigrew, W.S. (1937). *Municipal Parks : Layout Management and Administration.* Journal of Park Administration Ltd., London, 279 pp.

Rand, T. (1979). *Protection of Football Pitches Against Adverse Weather Conditions.* The Football Association, London, 20 pp.

Sayers, P. (1991). *Grounds Maintenance : A Contractor's Guide to Competitive Tendering.* E. & F.N. Spon (Chapman & Hall), London, 207 pp.

Shildrick, J. (1984). *Turfgrass Manual.* The Sports Turf Research Institute, Bingley, W. Yorks., 60 pp.

Shildrick, J.P. (Ed.) (1984). Sand constructions for sports pitches. *Workshop Report No. 3.* National Turfgrass Council, Bingley, W. Yorks., 39 pp.

Shildrick, J.P. (Ed.) (1985). The mower for the job. *Workshop Report No. 6.* National Turfgrass Council, Bingley, W. Yorks., 60 pp.

Shildrick, J.P. (Ed.) (1985). Growth retardants for amenity grassland. *Workshop Report No. 7.* National Turfgrass Council, Bingley, W. Yorks., 77 pp.

Shildrick, J.P. (Ed.) (1988). The recreational diversification of farmland *Workshop Report No. 13.* National Turfgrass Council, Bingley, W. Yorks., 94 pp.

Shildrick, J.P. (Ed.) (1989). Turf nutrition '88. *Workshop Report No. 15.* National Turfgrass Council, Bingley, W. Yorks., 79 pp.

Shildrick, J.P. (Ed.) (1989). Grass surface standards. *Workshop Report No. 16.* National Turfgrass Council, Bingley, W. Yorks., 73 pp.

Shildrick, J.P. (Ed.) (1990). Pesticide use after COSHH. *Workshop Report No. 18.* National Turfgrass Council, Bingley, W. Yorks., 67 pp.

Shildrick, J.P. (Ed.) (1990). Turf reinforcements. *Workshop Report No. 19.* National Turfgrass Council, Bingley, W. Yorks., 67 pp.

Shildrick, J.P. (Ed.) (1991). Safe disposal of amenity pesticides. *Workshop Report No. 22.* National Turfgrass Council, Bingley, W. Yorks., 86 pp.

Shildrick, J.P. (Ed.) (1992). *Turfgrass Education Update '92 : Your Simple Guide to Career Progression in Sports Turf Management.* National Turfgrass Council, Bingley, W. Yorks., 12 pp.

Shildrick, J.P. & Dye, A.L. (1983). *A Review of Playing Surface Research.* National Turfgrass Council, Bingley, W. Yorks., 28 pp.

Smith, J.D., Jackson, N., & Woolhouse, A.R. (1989). *Fungal Diseases of Turf Grasses.* (3rd Edn.) E. & F.N. Spon, London, 401 pp.

Smith, P.W. (1950). *The Planning Construction and Maintenance of Playing Fields.* Oxford University Press, London, 224 pp.

Stewart, V.I. (1994). *Sports Turf Science Construction & Maintenance.* E. & F.N. Spon, London, 260 pp.

Sutton's of Reading (1948). *Lawns and Sportsgrounds.* (16th Edn.) Sutton & Sons Ltd., Reading, 80 pp.

Sutton, M.A.F. (1962). *Lawns and Sportsgrounds.* (17th Edn.) Sutton & Sons Ltd., Reading, 248 pp.

Symes, B. (1987). *A Research Study and Review of Intensively Managed Amenity Turfgrass in the UK. Special Report No. 2.* National Turfgrass Council, Bingley, W. Yorks., 40 pp.

Weaver, C. & M. (1989). *Ransomes 1789-1989 200 Years of Excellence : A Bicentennial Celebration.* Ransomes Sims & Jeffries PLC, Ipswich, 132 pp.

Webster, F.A.M. (1940). *Sports Grounds and Buildings.* Sir Isaac Pitman & Sons Ltd., London, 305 pp.

Whyte, W.S. (1976). *Basic Metric Surveying.* Butterworth & Co. (Pubs) Ltd., London, 312 pp.

JOURNAL ARTICLES : PITCH CONSTRUCTION : GENERAL

Anon. (1984). Renovation needs more planning (Sheffield Wednesday). *Turf Management* **3**, 6, 9-10.

Anon. (1986). Drainage problems. *Sports Turf Bulletin No. 153*, pp. 2-4. The Sports Turf Research Institute, Bingley, W. Yorks.

Anon. (1986). The value of soil testing. *Sports Turf Bulletin No. 154*, pp. 7-9. The Sports Turf Research Institute, Bingley, W. Yorks.

Anon. (1989). New machines and materials open up new possibilities. *Turf Management Supplement*, February, pp. 17-18.

Anon. (1991). Football : Luton reverts to roots. *The Groundsman* **44**, 7 & 8, 26.

Baker, S.W. (1981). Make the most of the drainage. *Parks Golf Courses & Sportsgrounds* **46**, 6, 25-26.

Baker, S.W. (1982). How to find a permanent solution to your compaction and drainage problems. *Turf Management* **1**, 6, 20-21.

Baker, S.W. (1983). Drainage options for winter pitches. *Parks Golf Courses & Sportsgrounds* **49**, 2, 4-5.

Baker, S.W. (1989). Pitch construction : selecting topsoils for sports turf. *Parks Golf Courses & Sportsgrounds* **54**, 8, 4-6.

Baker, S.W. (1991). Winter pitch drainage : relative effectiveness of different constructions. *Parks Golf Courses & Sportsgrounds* **56**, 6, 34-37.

Baker, S.W., Gibbs, R. & Adams, W. (1992). The playing quality and carrying capacity of natural turf pitches. *Parks Golf Courses and Sportsgrounds* **57**, 4, 3-5.

Baker, S.W., Gibbs, R. & Adams, W. (1992). Cost-effectiveness and life span of different winter games pitches. *Parks Golf Courses & Sportsgrounds* **57**, 5, 11-15.

Baker, S.W., Gibbs, R. & Adams, W. (1992). A national survey of natural turf pitches with improved drainage designs. *Parks Golf Courses & Sportsgrounds* **57**, 6, 7-10.

Cope, F. (1964). The establishment of playing fields using power-station waste-ash. *J. Sports Turf Res. Inst.* **40**, 51-66.

Davidson, G.W. (1977). The economic drainage of sports turf. *Parks Golf Courses & Sportsgrounds* **42**, 10, 30-34.

Dawson, R.B. & Escritt, J.R. (1957). Playing field construction and maintenance. *J. Sports Turf Res. Inst.* **33**, 302-309.

Dury, P. (1986). Technology : sportsground drainage of the future. *Turf Management* **5**, 4, 17-20.

Escritt, J.R. (1982). Overcome compaction by correct drainage. *Turf Management* **1**, 5, 40-41.

Guthrie, A. (1992). Anfield : constructing a pitch fit for champions. *Parks Golf Courses & Sportsgrounds* **57**, 10, 14-16.

Hayes, P. (1987). Research : looking at tomorrow's needs. *Turf Management* **6**, 11, 14-19.

Macadam, G.C. (1981). Constructing a sportsground. *Parks Golf Courses & Sportsgrounds* **4**, 2, 18-20.

Macadam, G.C. (1989). Soccer pitches in Saudi Arabia. *Sports Turf Bulletin No. 164*, pp. 11-12. The Sports Turf Research Institute, Bingley, W. Yorks.

JOURNAL ARTICLES : PITCH DRAINAGE : GENERAL AND PIPE SYSTEMS

Anon. (1984). Drainage options on winter pitches. *Sports Turf Bulletin No. 147*, pp. 7-9. The Sports Turf Research Institute, Bingley, W. Yorks.

Anon. (1985). Turfgrass drainage : big savings claimed for new pipe-laying system. *Parks Golf Courses & Sportsgrounds* **50**, 10, 10-11.

Anon. (1986). Slit drainage of winter pitches. *Sports Turf Bulletin No. 121*, pp. 5-6. The Sports Turf Research Institute, Bingley, W. Yorks.

Bransbury, L. (1985). Large scale drainage systems for sportsfields. *Turf Management* **4**, 9, 55-56.

Cosgrove, C.J. (1956). Southampton Football Club ground. *J. Sports Turf Res. Inst.* **9**, 231-232.

Daniel, W.H. (1969). Vertical drainage for compacted turf areas. *J. Sports Turf Res. Inst.* **45**, 41-47.

Dawson, D.H. (1979). Drainage maintenance. *Parks Golf Courses and Sportsgrounds* **45**, 3, 20-22.

Fry, R. (1988). The brain drain. *The Groundsman Part 1* **41**, 7, 15-16. *Part 2* **41**, 8, 8-9

Hemstock, D. (1991). Drainage : let the drain take the strain. *Turf Management*, December, pp. 12-17.

McAuley, T.A.J. (1979). Reconstruction of four grass pitches. *Parks Golf Courses and Sportsgrounds* **44**, 12, 21.

Pool, S.T. (1992). Football pitch drainage. *Sports Turf Bulletin No. 179*, pp. 8-10. The Sports Turf Research Institute, Bingley, W. Yorks.

Ward, C. (1983). Seventy per cent of Britain's golf courses are affected by waterlogging. *Turf Management* **2**, 4, 22-24.

Ward, C.J. (1983). Drainage of sports turf areas : a survey. *J. Sports Turf Res. Inst.* **59**, 29-45.

Westwood, J.R. (1991). Drainage of soccer and Rugby fields. *Sports Turf Bulletin No. 173*, pp. 5-7. The Sports Turf Research Institute, Bingley, W. Yorks.

Westwood, J.R. (1994). Need for drainage on soccer fields. *Sports Turf Bulletin* **184**, 8-10.

Williams, M. (1991). Drainage : money down the drain. *Turf Management*, December, pp. 10-11.

JOURNAL ARTICLES : SOIL BY-PASS DRAINAGE SYSTEMS (SAND SLITS, FIN DRAINS ETC)

Anon. (1972). Sand slits to improve drainage. *Sports Turf Bulletin No. 98*, pp. 8-9. The Sports Turf Research Institute, Bingley, W. Yorks.

Anon. (1975). Slit drainage. *Sports Turf Bulletin No. 111*, pp. 10-12. The Sports Turf Research Institute, Bingley, W. Yorks.

Anon. (1978). Slit drainage of winter pitches. *Sports Turf Bulletin No. 121*, pp. 5-6 . The Sports Turf Research Institute, Bingley, W. Yorks.

Anon. (1987). Product development : new equipment keeps drainage costs down. *Parks Golf Courses & Sportsgrounds* **52**, 4, 14-18.

Anon. (1988). Millwall : a first class pitch for the First Division. *Turf Management* **7**, 8, 23-26.

Anon. (1991). Innovation : pitch drainage with surgical precision. *Parks Golf Courses & Sportsgrounds* **56**, 12, 12-13.

Baker, S.W. (1982). Principles of slit drainage. *Parks Golf Courses and Sportsgrounds* **47**, 5, 20-26.

Bentley, T. (1979). Sand slitting - an alternative approach. *Parks Golf Courses & Sportsgrounds* **44**, 11, 48.

Canaway, P.M. & Macadam, G.C. (1990). Slit drainage : an update. *Sports Turf Bulletin No. 168*, pp. 8-10. The Sports Turf Research Institute, Bingley, W. Yorks.

Clark, H.E. (1970). Drainage at Twickenham. *J. Sports Turf Res. Inst.* **46**, 14-16.

Clark, H.E. (1982). How to improve bad playing surfaces. *Turf Management* **1**, 1, 13-15.

Davidson, G. (1984). Drainage : contractors must be responsible for the system. *Turf Management* **3**, 2, 30-31.

Guthrie, A. (1992). Cambridge United : emergency drainage restores playability. *Parks Golf Courses & Sportsgrounds* **58**, 2, 13-16.

Harbridge, M. (1984). Maintenance problems of sand slit systems. *Turf Management* **3**, 3, 25-27.

Shelton, D. (1993). Ground improvement : innovative approach to sports drainage. *Parks Golf Courses and Sportsgrounds* **4**, 7-8.

Williams, M. (1992). Drainage equipment : it's draining. *Amenity Management*, February, pp.

26-29.

Willis, D. (1984). The Coleraine experiment in sportsfield drainage. *Turf Management* **3**, 1, 16-19.

JOURNAL ARTICLES : PRUNTY-MULQUEEN SAND CARPET SYSTEM

Anon. (1982). P.M. gets the vote for British sports pitches. *Turf Management* **1**, 1, 17.

Dailey, D. (1988). Sand carpet pitch on trial in Scotland. *Turf Management* **7**, 2, 12-15.

Mulqueen, J. (1983). Sand carpet systems provide the answer to sportsfield designs. *Turf Management* **12**, 12, 18-20.

Swan, H. (1981). Curing the problem. *Parks Golf Courses & Sportsgrounds* **47**, 3, 26.

JOURNAL ARTICLES : ISOLATION SYSTEMS OF PITCH CONSTRUCTION

Anon. (1988). Getting QPR back to natural turf (Cell system). *Turf Management*, September, pp. 21-25.

Anon. (1988). The Vacudrain system. *The Groundsman* **41**, 12, 9.

Connaughton, E. (1987). A prescription for better playability (P.A.T. system). *Parks Golf Courses & Sportsgrounds* **52**, 12, 28-30.

Guthrie, A. (1986). Special project : new pitch construction to control water table. *Parks Golf Courses & Sportsgrounds* **52**, 2, 9-10.

Mills, B. (1988). From Elvington, Yorks., to Loftus Road, W12 (Cell system). *The Groundsman* **41**, 11, 10-11.

Price, G. (1989). Has QPR pitched it right? (Cell System.) *The Groundsman* **42**, 10, 18-19.

JOURNAL ARTICLES : PURE SAND PITCH CONSTRUCTIONS

Anon. (1984). Sand football pitches. *Sports Turf Bulletin No. 147*, pp. 5-7. The Sports Turf Research Institute, Bingley, W. Yorks.

Dury, P. (1985). The use of sand for better surfaces. *Turf Management* **4**, 1, 16-19.

Dury, P. (1986). Getting the best out of winter pitches. *Turf Management* **5**, 8, 27-29.

Everett (1990). Sand constructions for winter pitches. *Sports Turf Bulletin No. 170*, pp. 8-10. The Sports Turf Research Institute, Bingley, W. Yorks.

Pool, S.T. (1993). Sand pitches : construction & maintenance. *Sports Turf Bulletin No. 180*, pp. 8-9. The Sports Turf Research Institute, Bingley, W. Yorks.

JOURNAL ARTICLES : SAND AMELIORATION

Adams, W.A., Stewart, V.I. & Thornton, D.J. (1971). The assessment of sands suitable for use in sportsfields. *J. Sports Turf Res. Inst.* **47**, 77-85.

Adams, W.A. (1982). Soil density and its effect on compaction. *Turf Management* **1**, 6, 18-19.

Anon. (1984). Sands for sports turf construction and maintenance. *Sports Turf Bulletin No. 147*, pp. 3-5. The Sports Turf Research Institute, Bingley, W. Yorks.

Baker, S.W. (1987). Winter games pitches : how sand constructions improve playability. *Parks Golf Courses & Sportsgrounds* **52**, 5, 8-9.

Baker, S.W. (1991). Construction & maintenance : the right sands for winter games pitches. *Parks Golf Courses & Sportsgrounds* **56**, 10, 32-36.

Elliott, J.B. (1971). Preliminary studies on sand amelioration of soil under sports turf used in winter. *J. Sports Turf Res. Inst.* **47**, 66-85.

JOURNAL ARTICLES : FROST PROTECTION & SOIL WARMING

Anon. (1951). Electrical soil warming as an anti-frost measure for sports turf. *J. Sports Turf Res. Inst.* **8**, 27, 25-44.

Anon. (1958). Keeping the frost out of football grounds. *Sports Turf Bulletin No. 40*, pp. 8-9. The Sports Turf Research Institute, Bingley, W. Yorks.

Anon. (1959). Cable laying for soil warming *Sports Turf Bulletin No. 46*, pp. 5-6. The Sports Turf Research Institute, Bingley, W. Yorks.

Anon. (1966). Preventing frozen pitches. *Sports Turf Bulletin No. 72*, pp. 5-8. The Sports Turf Research Institute, Bingley, W. Yorks.

Anon. (1970). New soil heating system (warm air). *Parks Golf Courses & Sportsgrounds* **36**, 10,

878 & 883.

Anon. (1984). Frost protection. *Sports Turf Bulletin No. 144*, pp. 6-8. The Sports Turf Research Institute, Bingley, W. Yorks.

Anon. (1986). How top soccer clubs reduced cancellations. *Parks Golf Courses & Sportsgrounds* **51**, 9, 40.

Anon. (1986). Triumph for underpitch heating (Wirsbro Meltaway System). *Turf Management* **5**, 6, 18-20.

Drury, S. (1993). Warming Wolves (Wolverhampton Wanderers AFC). *Turf Management*, July, pp. 22-23.

Ede, A.N. (1970). Soil heating system using warm air. *J. Sports Turf Res. Inst.* **46**, 76-91.

Escritt, J.R. (1954). Electrical soil warming as an anti-frost measure for sports turf – a further report. *J. Sports Turf Res. Inst.* **8**, 30, 354-364.

Escritt, J.R. (1959). Electrical soil warming as an anti-frost measure for sports turf : a further report. *J. Sports Turf Res. Inst.* **10**, 35, 29-41.

Escritt, J.R. (1982). Deep heat methods are not the answer to winter pitch protection. *Turf Management* **1**, 11, 19-21.

Escritt, J.R. & Fairbairn, C.B. (1961). Pitch protection by air-borne covers. *J. Sports Turf Res. Inst.* **10**, 37, 300-304.

Escritt, J.R. & Fairbairn, C.B. (1961). Winter pitch protection (air house). *The Groundsman* **14**, 11, 12-16.

Langvad, B. (1969). Drainage and soil heating under sports turf (Proc. 4th Int. Congress of Landscape & Sportsground Contractors). *Parks Golf Courses & Sportsgrounds* **34**, 10, 901-906.

Lebeau, J.B. (1967). Soil warming and winter survival of turfgrass. *J. Sports Turf Res. Inst.* **43**, 6-11.

Souter, J. (1987). Turning on the heat. *The Groundsman* **40**, 12, 20-21.

JOURNAL ARTICLES : TURF REINFORCEMENT

Allen, F. (1991). Football : back to grass roots. *Turf Management*, June, pp. 12-15.

Anon. (1987). Reinforcing natural turf. *Turf Management* **6**, 8, 21.

Anon. (1989). Why choose high tech Techturf (Blackburn Rovers). *Turf Management*, November, p. 32.

Anon. (1990). Construction : turf reinforcement increases usage. *Parks Golf Courses & Sportsgrounds* **56**, 2, 10-11.

Canaway, P.M. (1992). Pitch reinforcement : the science behind soil strengthening. *Parks Golf Courses & Sportsgrounds* **58**, 2, 9-12.

Dury, P. (1985). Technology : VHAF for natural and synthetic turf. *Turf Management* **4**, 8, 15-17.

Guthrie, A. (1991). Construction : innovative pitch for Oldham Athletic. *Parks Golf Courses & Sportsgrounds* **56**, 12, 39-41.

JOURNAL ARTICLES : WINTER PITCH MAINTENANCE : GENERAL

Anon. (1982). Maintenance of winter pitches. *Sports Turf Bulletin No. 138*, pp. 5-7. The Sports Turf Research Institute, Bingley, W. Yorks.

Anon. (1982). Warning : dry lining. *Sports Turf Bulletin No. 136*, p. 4. The Sports Turf Research Institute, Bingley, W. Yorks.

Anon. (1983). Problems with dual purpose areas. *Sports Turf Bulletin No. 142*, pp. 9-10. The Sports Turf Research Institute, Bingley, W. Yorks.

Anon. (1986). Autumn & winter maintenance of winter pitches. *Sports Turf Bulletin No. 153*, pp. 10-12. The Sports Turf Research Institute, Bingley, W. Yorks.

Anon. (1986). New sports turf cover system introducced (Parker AWP). *Parks Golf Courses & Sportsgrounds* **51**, 10, 28-29.

Anon. (1986). Spring renovation. *Sports Turf Bulletin No. 153*, pp. 8-10. The Sports Turf Research Institute, Bingley, W. Yorks.

Anon. (1987). Slow release fertilizers. *Sports Turf Bulletin No. 156*, pp. 7-10. The Sports Turf Research Institute, Bingley, W. Yorks.

Anon. (1988). Playing quality for natural turf sports surfaces. *Sports Turf Bulletin No. 160*, pp.

10-12. The Sports Turf Research Institute, Bingley, W. Yorks.

Anon. (1991). Laying it on the line (line markers). *Amenity Management*, December, pp. 17-21.

Anon. (1992). Line marking : top marks. *The Groundsman* **45**, 6, 16-18.

Baker, S.W. (1991). Maintenance : compaction - a problem of wear and tear. *Turf Management*, May, pp. 11-13.

Baker, S.W. (1991). Maintenance : the right steps to take. *Turf Management*, June, pp. 17-21.

Baker, S.W. (1992). Pitch maintenance. Light at the end of the tunnel? *Turf Management*, July, 18-20.

Baker, S.W. (1992). Soil compaction : how to tackle it. *Turf Management*, December, pp. 24-26.

Baker, S.W. (1993). Airing the values of the slit tine. *Horticulture Week***213**, 24, 24-25.

Bell, M. (1985). Research into standards : testing the quality of natural turf. *Parks Golf Courses & Sportsgrounds* **50**, 7, 6-7.

Boocock, D.F. (1982). Repairing the ravages. *Parks Golf Courses & Sportsgrounds* **47**, 6, 14-16.

Canaway, P.M. (1992). Grass mixtures for football and Rugby pitches. *The Groundsman* **45**, 12, 10-11.

Drury, S. (1991). Line markers get you on the right lines. *Turf Management*, May, pp. 21-23.

Escritt, J.R. (1974). Modern techniques in playing field maintenance. *Parks Golf Courses & Sportsgrounds Part 1* **39**, 8, 811-815, *Part 2* **39**, 9, 901-929.

Evans, R.D.C. (1991). Turf maintenance : pitching in for winter. *Amenity Management*, November, pp. 20--25.

Geer, J. (1989). Line marking : white-lining from the grass roots. *Turf Management*, May, pp. 16-21.

Harrison, A. (1984). Pitch renovation : cost effective methods to give rapid recovery. *Turf Management* **3**, 2, 50-51.

Holmes, G. (1985). Correct maintenance : it's a nice pitch – shame about the cost. *Parks Golf Courses & Sportsgrounds* **50**, 8, 28-29.

Kurrein, C. (1991). Sports pitches : pitching in for winter. *Turf Management*, May, pp. 25-27.

Lawson, D.M. (1989). The suitability of slow release fertilizers for turf. *Sports Turf Bulletin No. 167*, pp. 6-8. The Sports Turf Research Institute, Bingley, W. Yorks.

McClements, I. (1993). The playing quality of Rugby and natural turf hockey pitches. *Sports Turf Bulletin No. 180*, pp. 9-11. The Sports Turf Research Institute, Bingley, W. Yorks.

McLauchan, J. (1988). Conditioner that benefits surfaces (Fullasorb). *Turf Management* **7**, 8, 9-13.

Morgan, D.A.V. (1978). Maintenance of Rugby & soccer pitches. *Parks Golf Courses & Sportsgrounds* **43**, 6, 39.

Morgan, D. (1982). A maintenance programme for Rugby & football pitches. *Turf Management* **1**, 1, 26-31.

Morgan, D. (1982). Boundary lines are part of the playing area. *Turf Management* **1**, 3, 40-41.

Morgan, D. (1983). Sportsfield maintenance : some useful hints on how to look after your pitches. *Turf Management* **2**, 22, 32-33.

Newell, A.J. (1991). Choosing grasses for football & Rugby pitches. *Sports Turf Bulletin No. 175*, pp. 11-12. The Sports Turf Research Institute, Bingley, W. Yorks.

Pool, S.D. (1983). Repairing the ravages of winter wear. *Parks Golf Courses & Sportsgrounds* **48**, 8, 26-30.

Prytherch, D. (1985). Vertidraining : Surrey's approach to better sportsfield drainage. *Parks Golf Courses & Sportsgrounds* **50**, 5, 32-33.

Shiels, G. (1983). How to manage the problems caused by waterlogging. *Turf Management* **2**, 1, 18-19.

Shildrick, J.P. (1989). Line marking : procedures for line marking. *Turf Management*, May, p. 15.

Squires, N.R.W. (1991). Winter maintenance of Rugby & soccer pitches. *Sports Turf Bulletin No. 173*, pp. 10-11. The Sports Turf Research Institute, Bingley, W. Yorks.

Thornton, S.L. (1989). Line marking. *Sports Turf Bulletin No. 167*, pp. 8-9. The Sports Turf Research Institute, Bingley, W. Yorks.

Williams, M. (1992). Marking time (line markers). *Turf Management*, July, pp. 13-17.

Williams, M. (1992). Linemarkers : painting pitches. *Amenity Management*, December, pp. 15-17.

Wolftree, F. (1992). Tackling school grounds. *Turf Management* , May, pp. 18-21.

Young, P.L. (1958). Looking after the ground at Wembley. *J. Sports Turf Res. Inst.* **9**, 34, 479-482.

JOURNAL ARTICLES : MAINTENANCE : SOCCER PITCHES

Ainsworth, P. (1992). Ibrox : pitch fit for champions (Glasgow Rangers). *Turf Management*, December, pp. 12-14.

Anon. (1986). How Ipswich (Town AFC) turned mud into a pitch. *Turf Management* **5**, 7, 22-25.

Anon. (1986). Technology : improving soccer goalmouths (Terra-Green). *Turf Management*, June, p. 21.

Anon. (1987). Research update : football pitches. *Sports Turf Bulletin No. 157*, pp. 2-4. The Sports Turf Research Institute, Bingley, W. Yorks.

Baker, S.W. (1993). Perfect pitch. *Amenity Management*, February, p. 19.

Beenstock, S. (1992). Pitch maintenance : fit for the final (Wembley). *Turf Management*, May, pp. 24-27.

Boocock, D.F. (1985). Soccer maintenance : getting the best from the new pitch. *Parks Golf Courses & Sportsgrounds* **50**, 5, 15-18.

Guthrie, A. (1990). Liverpool F.C. : keeping Anfield in first class condition. *Parks Golf Courses & Sportsgrounds* **56**, 11, 11-14.

JOURNAL ARTICLES : MAINTENANCE : RUGBY PITCHES

Beenstock, S. (1992). Rugby Union - land of their fathers (Cardiff Arms Park). *Turf Management*, February, pp. 10-11.

Bird, M. (1989). Building up to the perfect pitch (Cardiff Arms Park). *Turf Management*, April, pp. 32-36.

Fry, R. (1991). Murrayfield has a grand slam finish. *Turf Management*, March, pp. 32-34.

Fry, R. (1991). Murrayfield's winning formula. *The Groundsman* **44**, 5, 16-19.

Mills, B. (1988). Murrayfield. *The Groundsman* **41**, 10, 9-10.

JOURNAL ARTICLES : MAINTENANCE : HOCKEY PITCHES

Anon. (1986). Maintenance of hockey pitches. *Sports Turf Bulletin No. 154*, pp. 10-12. The Sports Turf Research Institute, Bingley, W. Yorks.

Anon. (1993). Maintenance of hockey pitches. *Sports Turf Bulletin* **183**, 8-10. The Sports Turf Research Institute, Bingley, W. Yorks.

Colclough, T.W. (1989). Thatch and the hockey pitch. *Hockey Digest* **16**, 9, 27.

Cole, A.R. (1989). A guide to hockey pitch maintenance. *Hockey Digest* **16**, 10.

Morgan, D. (1982). How to maintain a first-class hockey pitch. *Turf Management* **1**, 2, 44-45.

Spencer, J.H.E. (1993). Hockey : controlling problems on the surface. *Parks Golf Courses & Sportsgrounds* **58**, 10, 3-5.

Thornton, S.L. (1989). An insight into hockey pitch maintenance. *Hockey Field* 77, 2.

Thornton, S.L. (1989). To roll or not to roll. *Hockey Digest* **16**, 8, 17.

Westwood, J.R. (1988). Maintenance of hockey pitches. *Sports Turf Bulletin No. 162*, pp. 8-10. The Sports Turf Research Institute, Bingley, W. Yorks.

JOURNAL ARTICLES : MAINTENANCE : POLO GROUNDS

Allen, F. (1991). Polo : turf fit for a Prince (Guards Club, Windsor). *Turf Management*, September, pp. 20-21.

Anon. (1967). Maintenance of polo grounds. *Sports Turf Bulletin No. 78*, pp. 6-8. The Sports Turf Research Institute, Bingley, W. Yorks.

Beenstock, S. (1992). From parsnips to polo (Cowdray Park). *Turf Management*, May, pp. 11-13.

Foster, J. (1989). Turf management : coping with pirouettes on polo fields. *Turf Management*, September, pp. 17-18.

Spencer, J. (1991). Polo : careful maintenance for historic game. *Parks Golf Courses & Sportsgrounds* 56, 4, 3-5.

Spencer, J.H.E. (1991). Polo fields. *Sports Turf Bulletin No. 172*, pp. 8-10. The Sports Turf Research Institute, Bingley, W. Yorks.

JOURNAL ARTICLES : MAINTENANCE : AMERICAN FOOTBALL

Anon. (1992). American football : touchdown! *Turf Management*, March, pp. 26-27.

Morgan, D. (1986). Development : gridiron football growth. *Turf Management* 5, 4, 48-49.

Stevens, P. (1983). How an American sports stadium plans to make £2 million profit a year (Rose Bowl, California). *Turf Management* 2, 6, 24-26.

JOURNAL ARTICLES : MAINTENANCE : GAELIC GAMES

Anon. (1980). Hurling and Gaelic football. *Sports Turf Bulletin No. 131*, pp. 5-6. The Sports Turf Research Institute, Bingley, W. Yorks.

Brougham, R. (1993). Croke Park Dublin - an emerald green turf of *Poa trivialis*. *NZ Turf Management J.* 7, 4, 24.

SCIENTIFIC RESEARCH PAPERS

Adams, W.A. (1975). Some developments in the selection and maintenance of turfgrasses. *Scientific Horticulture* 26, 22-27.

Adams, W.A. (1976). The effect of five soil fractions on the hydraulic conductivity of sand/soil mixes used for sports turf rootzones. *Razen Turf Gazon* 4, 92-94.

Adams, W.A. (1980). Effects of nitrogen fertilisation and curtting height on the shoot growth, nutrient, removal and turfgrass composition of an initially perennial ryegrass dominant sports turf. *Proc. 3rd Int. Turfgrass Res. Conf.* Ed. J.B. Beard, 343-350 pp.

Adams, W.A. (1981). Soils and plant nutrition for sports turf: perspective and prospects. In *Proc. 4th Int. Turfgrass Res. Conf.*, Guelph, Canada (Ed. R.W. Sheard), pp. 167–179.

Adams, W.A. (1982). How sand affects soil behaviour. *Turf Management* 1 (7), 23-24.

Adams, W.A. (1986). Practical aspects of sports field drainage. *Soil Use & Management* 2, 51–54.

Adams, W.A., Stewart, V.I. & Thornton, D.J. (1971). Construction and drainage of sports fields for winter games in Britain. *Welsh Soils Disc. Group*.

Adams, W.A., Stewart, V.I. & Thornton, D.J. (1971). The assessment of sands suitable for use in sports fields. *J. Sports Turf Res. Inst.* 47, 77-85.

Andrawes, K.Z., McGown A., Hytiris, N., Mercer, F.B. & Sweetland, D.B. (1986). The use of mesh elements to alter the stress-strain behaviour of soils. *Proc. 3rd Int. Conf. on Geotextiles*, Vienna, Austria, pp. 839-844.

Baker, S.W. (1979). Pore size distribution - a factor to be considered in infiltration studies? *J. Hydrology,* 41, 279-290.

Baker, S.W. (1981). The effect of earthworm activity on the drainage characteristics of winter sports pitches. *J. Sports Turf Res. Inst.,* 57, 9-23.

Baker, S.W. (1982). The influence of water temperature on the measurement of infiltration rates for sandy sports turf rootzones. *J. Sports Turf Res. Inst.,* 58, 21-27.

Baker, S.W. (1982). Regional variation of design rainfall rates for slit drainage schemes in Great Britain. *J. Sports Turf Res. Inst.,* 58, 57-63.

Baker, S.W. (1983). Sands for soil amelioration: analysis of the effects of particle size, sorting and shape. *J. Sports Turf Res. Inst.,* 58, 133-145.

Baker, S.W. (1983). Rates of soil replacement by a combined hollow tining and top dressing programme. *J. Sports Turf Res. Inst.,* 58, 146-147.

Baker, S.W. (1984). Long-term effects of three amendment materials on the moisture retention characteristics of a sand-soil mix. *J. Sports Turf Res. Inst.,* 60, 61-65.

Baker, S.W. (1985). Topsoil quality: relation to the performance of sand-soil mixes. *Proc. 5th Int. Turfgrass Res. Conf.* (Ed. F.Lemaire), pp. 401-109, Avignon, France.

Baker, S.W. (1986). Construction, playing quality and usage levels of natural turf football pitches. In *Football. The Club in the Community. Workshop Report. Proc. 17th National Seminar and Exhibition*, Harrogate, 25-27 February 1986. The Sports Council, London, pp.

103-110.

Baker, S.W. (1986). Playing standards for natural turf sports surfaces. In *Proc. 3rd National Turfgrass Conf.*, Nottingham, September 1985 (Ed. J.P. Shildrick), pp. 31-41.

Baker, S.W. (1987). Playing quality of some soccer pitches in Saudi Arabia. *J. Sports Turf Res. Inst.*, **63**, 145-148.

Baker, S.W. (1987). Reinforcement materials for winter games pitches. *Natural Turf Pitches Prototypes Advisory Panel Report No. 2*, 26 pp.

Baker, S.W. (1988). Construction techniques for winter games pitches. In *Science and Football Proc. 1st World Congress of Science and Football,* Liverpool (Ed. T. Reilly *et al.*) pp 399-405..

Baker, S.W. (1988). The effect of rootzone composition on the performance of winter games pitches III. Soil physical properties. *J. Sports Turf Res. Inst.* **64**, 133–143.

Baker, S.W. (1988a). Construction techniques for winter games pitches. In *Science and Football, Proc. 1st World Congress of Science and Football,* Liverpool, England (Ed. T,. Reilly *et al.*), pp. 399–405.

Baker, S.W. (1988b). The effect of rootzone composition on the performance of winter games pitches III. Soil physical properties. *J. Sports Turf Res. Inst.* **64**, 133–143.

Baker, S.W. (1989). A standardised sole for evaluating the traction and sliding resistance properties of artificial turf. *J. Sports Turf Res. Inst.*, **65**, 168-170.

Baker, S.W. (1989). Soil physical conditions of the roozone layer and the performance of winter games' pitches. *Soil Use and Management* **5** (3), 116-122.

Baker, S.W. (1989). The performance of natural turf and artificial turf pitches within the Football League *in* Football League Commission of Enquiry into Playing Surfaces. Final Report pp. 60-107.

Baker, S.W. (1990). Criteria in topsoil selection for sports turf. *Agricultural Engineer* **45** (3), 87-88.

Baker, S.W. (1990). Standards for the playing quality of artificial turf for Association Football. In: *Natural and Artificial Playing Fields : Characteristics and Safety Features ASTM STP 1073.* Eds. R.C. Schmitt, E.F. Hoerner, E.M. Milner and C.A. Morehouse. Amer. Soc. Testing and Materials, Philadelphia, pp. 48-57.

Baker, S.W. (1990). Performance standards for professional soccer on artificial turf surfaces. *J. Sports Turf Res. Inst.* **66**, 42-69.

Baker, S.W. (1990). The effect of reinforcement materials on renovated turf on topsoil and sand rootzones. *J. Sports Turf Res. Inst.* **66**, 70-75.

Baker, S.W. (1990). The use of amendment materials to improve grass establishment on a polypropylene, needle-punched reinforcement. *J. Sports Turf Res. Inst.* **66**, 76-88.

Baker, S.W. (1991). The effect of a polyacrylamide co-polymer on the performance of *Lolium perenne* L. turf grown on a sand rootzone. *J. Sports Turf Res. Inst.* **67**, 66-82.

Baker, S.W. (1991). Temporal variation of selected mechanical properties of natural turf football pitches. *J. Sports Turf Res. Inst.* **67**, 83-92.

Baker, S.W. & Bell, M.J. (1986). The playing characteristics of natural turf and synthetic turf surfaces for Association Football. *J. Sports Turf Res. Inst.*, **62**, 9-35.

Baker, S.W. & Canaway, P.M. (1989). Playing standards for association football fields. In *Proc. 6th International Turfgrass Res. Conf.* (Ed. H. Takatoh) pp. 403-405, Japanese Soc. Turfgrass Science, Tokyo.

Baker, S.W. & Canaway, P.M. (1990). The cost-effectiveness of different construction methods for Association Football pitches. I. Soil physical properties. *J. Sports Turf Res. Inst.* **66**, 8-20.

Baker, S.W. & Canaway, P.M. (1990). The effect of sand top dressing on the performance of winter games pitches of different construction types. I. Soil physical properties and ground cover. *J. Sports Turf Res. Inst.* **66**, 21-27.

Baker, S.W. & Canaway, P.M. (1991). The cost-effectiveness of different construction methods for Association Football pitches. II. Ground cover, playing quality and cost implications. *J. Sports Turf Res. Inst.* **67**, 53-65.

Baker, S.W. & Gibbs, R.J. (1989). Levels of use and the playing quality of winter games pitches of different construction types: case studies at Nottingham and Warrington. *J. Sports Turf Res. Inst.*, **65**, 9-33.

Baker, S.W. & Gibbs, R.J. (1989). Making the most of natural turf pitches. Case studies: II. Playing quality. *Natural Turf Pitches Prototypes Advisory Panel Report No. 4*, 43 pp.

Baker, S.W. & Gibbs, R.J. (1991). Making the most of natural turf pitches. Final results of a case studies approach : II. Playing quality. *Natural Turf Pitch Prototypes Advisory Panel Report No. 7*, 35 pp.

Baker, S.W. & Hacker, J.W. (1988). The use of peat in a Prunty-Mulqueen sand carpet construction: effects of application rate and depth. *J. Sports Turf Res. Inst.,* **64**, 87-98.

Baker, S.W. & Isaac, B.J. (1987). The assessment of soil porosity in sports turf rootzones using measured and calculated values of particle density. *J. Sports Turf Res. Inst.,* **63**, 141-144.

Baker, S.W. & Isaac, S.P. (1987). The effect of rootzone composition on the performance of winter games pitches I. Sward characteristics. *J. Sports Turf Res. Inst.,* **63**, 57-66.

Baker, S.W. & Isaac, S.P. (1987). The effect of rootzone composition on the performance of winter games pitches II. Playing quality. *J. Sports Turf Res. Inst.,* **63**, 67-81.

Baker, S.W., Cole, A.R. & Thornton, S.L. (1988). The effect of reinforcement materials on the performance of turf grown on soil and sand rootzones under simulated football-type wear. *J. Sports Turf Res. Inst.,* **64**, 107-119.

Baker, S.W., Cole, A.R. & Thornton, S.L. (1988). Performance standards and the interpretation of playing quality for soccer in relation to rootzone composition. *J. Sports Turf Res. Inst.,* **64**, 120-132.

Baker, S.W., Gibbs, R.J. & Adams, W.A. (1990). Making the most of natural turf pitches. Final results of a case studies approach : I. Ground cover and botanical analysis. *Natural Turf Pitch Prototypes Advisory Panel, Report No. 6*, The Sports Council, London, 16 pp.

Baker, S.W., Gibbs, R.J. & Adams, W.A. (1991). Making the most of natural turf pitches. Final results of a case studies approach : II. Playing quality. *Natural Turf Pitch Prototypes Advisory Panel, Report No. 7*, 35 pp.

Baker, S.W., Gibbs, R.J. & Adams, W.A. (1992). Case studies of the performance of different designs of winter games pitches. I. Playing quality and usage. *J. Sports Turf Res. Inst.* **68**, 20-32.

Baker, S.W., Gibbs, R.J. & Taylor, R.S. (1991). Particle migration from the sand layer of slit drains into the underlying gravel. *J. Sports Turf Res. Inst.* **67**, 93-104.

Baker, S.W., Isaac, S.P. & Isaac, B.J. (1988). An assessment of five reinforcement materials for sports turf I. Ground cover, drainage and soil compaction. *Z. für Vegetationstechnik* , **11**, 8-11..

Baker, S.W., Isaac, S.P. & Isaac, B.J. (1988). An assessment of five reinforcement materials for sports turf II. Playing quality. *Z. für Vegetationstechnik* **11**, 12–15.

Baldwin, N.A. (1990). Technical note. Post-emergence damping-off of turfgrass seedlings by *Cladochytrium caespitis. J. Sports Turf Res. Inst.* **66**, 170-173.

Bell, M.J. & Holmes, G. (1988a). The playing quality of Association Football pitches. *J. Sports Turf Res. Inst.* **64**, 19-47.

Bell, M.J., Baker, S.W. & Canaway, P.M. (1985). Playing quality of sports surfaces: a review. *J. Sports Turf Res. Inst.,* **61**, 26-45.

Bingaman, D.E. & Kohnke, (1970). Evaluating sands for athletic turf. *Agron. J.* **62**, 464-467.

Bockel, P. (1980). Some physical aspects of sports turfs. *Proc. 3rd Int. Turfgrass Res. Conf.*, Madison, USA. July 1977 (Ed. J.B. Beard), AM Soc. of Agronomy, pp. 437-441.

Boekel, P. & Zuriers, J.S. (1982). Relieving sub-surface compaction in sports turf. *Z. für Vegetationstechnik* **5**, 144-147.

Boggie, R. (1970). Moisture characteristics of some peat-sand mixtures. *Scientific Horticulture* **22**, 87-91.

Boskovic, P. (1972). [The establishment of soccer pitches in Yugoslavia.] *Rasen Turf Gazon* **3** (2), 53-55.

Canaway, P.M. (1976). A differential slip wear machine (D.S.1.) for artificial simulation of turfgrass wear. *J. Sports Turf Res. Inst.* **52**, 92-99.

Canaway, P.M. (1983). The effect of rootzone construction on the wear tolerance and playability of eight turfgrass species subjected to football-type wear. *J. Sports Turf Res. Inst.* **59**, 107-123.

Canaway, P.M. (1984a). The response of *Lolium perenne* (perennial ryegrass) turf grown on sand

and soil to fertiliser nitrogen I. Ground cover response as affected by football type wear. *J. Sports Turf Res. Inst.* **60**, 8-18.

Canaway, P.M. (1984b) The response of *Lolium perenne* turf grown on sand and soil to fertilizer nitrogen II. Above ground biomass, tiller numbers and root biomass. *J. Sports Turf Res. Inst.* **60**, 19-26.

Canaway, P.M. (1984c) The response of *Lolium perenne* turf grown on sand and soil to fertilizer nitrogen III. Aspects of playability - ball bounce resilience and shear strength. *J. Sports Turf Res. Inst.* **62**, 27-36.

Canaway, P.M. (1985). Keynote address. Playing quality, construction and nutrition of sports turf. *Proc. 5th Int. Turfgrass Res. Conf.* (Ed. F. Lemaire), pp. 45-56, INRA Publications, Versailles.

Canaway, P.M. (1985). Playing quality, construction and nutrition of sports turf. In *Proc. 5th Intern. Turfgrass Res. Conf.*, Avignon, France (Ed. F. Lemaire), pp. 45-56, INRA, Paris.

Canaway, P.M. (1985). The response of renovated turf of *Lolium perenne* (perennial ryegrass) to fertiliser nitrogen III. Ball bounce resilience and traction. *J. Sports Turf Res. Inst.* **61**, 104-110.

Canaway, P.M. (1985). Playing quality, construction and nutrition of sports turf. *Proc. 5th Int. Turfgrass Res. Conf.* Avignon (France), pp. 45-56, INRA Publications, Versailles.

Canaway, P.M. (1990). A comparison of different methods of establishment using seed and sod on the cover and playing quality of turf for football. *J. Sports Turf Res. Inst.* **66**, 28-41.

Canaway, P.M. & Baker, S.W. (1988). A question of sport! Sports turf and playing quality. *Physics Bulletin*, **39**, 108-110.

Canaway, P.M. & Bell, M.J. (1986). Technical note: An apparatus for measuring traction and friction on natural and artificial playing surfaces. *J. Sports Turf Res. Inst.* **62**, 211–214.

Canaway, P.M. & Bennett, R.A. (1986). Technical note: the effects of fertilizer nitrogen on the water infiltration rate of a sand rootzone for football. *J. Sports Turf Res. Inst.* **62**, 204–206.

Canaway, P.M. & Hacker, J.W. (1988a). The response of *Lolium perenne* L. grown on a Prunty-Mulqueen sand carpet rootzone to fertiliser nitrogen I. Ground cover response as affected by football-type wear. *J. Sports Turf Res. Inst.* **64**, 63-74.

Canaway, P.M. & Hacker, J.W. (1988b). The response of *Lolium perenne* L. grown on a Prunty Mulqueen sand carpet rootzone to fertiliser nitrogen II. Playing quality. *J. Sports Turf Res. Inst.* **64**, 75-86.

Canaway, P.M., Bell, M.J., Holmes, G. & Baker, S.W. (1990). Standards for the playing quality of natural turf for Association Football. In: *Natural and Artificial Playing Fields : Characteristics and Safety Features.* ASTM STP 1073 (Eds. R.C. Schmidt, E.F. Hoerner, E.M. Milner and C.A. Morehouse), Americal Society for Testing and Materials, Philadelpia, USA, pp. 29-47.

Canaway, P.M., Isaac, S.P. & Bennett, R.A. (1986). The effects of mechanical treatments on treatments on the water infiltration rate of a sand playing surface for association football. *J. Sports Turf Res. Inst.* **62**, 67–73.

Childs, F.D. & Jencks, E.M. (1967). Effect of time and depth of sampling upon soil test results. *Agron. J.* **59**, 537-540

Clegg, B. (1976) An impact device for *in situ* base course evaluation. *Australian Road Res. Bureau Proc.* **8**, 1-6.

Cruse, R.M., Cassel, D.K., Stitt, R.E. & Averette, F.G. (1981). Effect of particle surface roughness on mechanical impedance of coarse-textured soil materials. *Soil Sci. Soc. Amer. J.* **45**, 1210-1214.

Daniel, W.H. (1969). Purr-wick. *Proc. 1st Int. Turfgrass Res. Conf.*, Harrogate, England, July 1969, pp. 323-325.

Daniel, W.H. (1969). Vertical drainage for compacted turf areas. *J. Sports Turf Res. Inst.* **45**, 41-47.

Daniells, I.G. (1977). Drainage of sports turf used in winter : a comparison of some rooting media with and without a gravel drainage layer. *J. Sports Turf Res. Inst.* **53**, 56-72.

Davis, W.B. (1981). Natural versus artificial turf - an economic alternative. *Calif. Turfgrass Culture* **31** (1), 1-4.

Davis, W.B. (1983). Problems and solutions to maintaining sand greens and playing fields. *Calif. Turfgrass Culture* **33**, 1, 2, 3 and 4, 1-2.

Davis, W.B. (1984). Problems and solutions to maintaining sand greens and playing fields. *Sports Turf Review No. 152*, Aug. 84, pp. 86-88 (reprinted from Calif. Turfgrass Culture).

Davis, W.B., Farnham, D.S., Gowans, K.D. (1974). The sand football field. *California Turfgrass Culture* **24**, 3, 17-20.

Dekker, L.W. & van dar Knapp, W.C.A. (1986). [Soil physical measurements in six grass playing fields in the Netherlands. I. Saturated hydraulic conductivity of the top layer.] *Z. für Vegetationstechnik* **9**, 77.

Dekker, L.W. & van dar Knapp, W.C.A. (1986). [Soil physical measurements in six playing fields. II. Bearing capacity of the top layer and playability of the fields.] *Z. für Vegetationstechnik* **9**, 83.

Deller, B. (1985). [Sand as a building material in vegetation technics - physiologically important properties.] *Rasen Turf Gazon* 4 (85), 105-111.

Dierickx, W. (1976). [Drainage of turfed playing fields.] *Revue de l'Agriculture* **29** (3), 607-623.

Escritt, J.R. (1967). Some problems of playing field construction. *Scientific Horticulture* **XIX**, 96-100.

Escritt, J.R. (1970). Construction and maintenance of turfgrass areas in Britain and Western Europe. *Calif. Turfgrass Culture* **20** (2), 9-13.

Gibbs, R.J. & Baker, S.W. (1987). Making the most of natural turf pitches. *Natural Turf Pitches Advisory Panel Information Report No. 1.*, The Sports Council, London, 18 pp.

Gibbs, R.J. & Baker, S.W. (1989). Making the most of natural turf pitches. Case studies: I. Construction, maintenance and usage. *Natural Turf Pitch Prototypes Advisory Panel Report No.3*, The Sports Council, London, 40 pp.

Gibbs, R.J. & Baker, S.W. (1989). Making the most of natural turf pitches. Case studies: III. Soil physical properties. *Natural Turf Pitches Prototypes Advisory Panel Report No. 5*, 30 pp.

Gibbs, R.J. & Baker, S.W. (1989). Soil physical properties of winter games pitches of different construction types: case studies at Nottingham and Warrington. *J. Sports Turf Res. Inst.*, **65**, 34-54.

Gibbs, R.J. & Baker, S.W. (in preparation). Making the most of natural turf pitches. Final results of a case studies approach : III. Maintenance, usage and cost-effectiveness. *Natural Turf Pitch Prototypes Advisory Panel Report No. 8*, ? pp.

Gibbs, R.J. (1988). The influence of winter sports pitch drainage systems on the measurement of water infiltration rate. *J. Sports Turf Res. Inst.* **64**, 99–106.

Gibbs, R.J., Adams, W.A. & Baker, S.W. (1989). Factors affecting the surface stability of a sand rootzine. In *Proc. 6th International Turfgrass Res. Conf.* (Ed. H. Takatoh) pp. 189-191, Japanese Soc. Turfgrass Science, Tokyo.

Gooding, M.J., Baldwin, N.A. & Bennett, J.R. (1989). Post-emergence damping-off in *Poa pratensis* and its relationship with seed weight and seedling establishment. *J. Sports Turf Res. Inst.* **65**, 91-101.

Gooding, M.J., Baldwin, N.A. & Smith, M.A. (1990). Observational note. Red thread on *Poa pratensis* cultivars. *J. Sports Turf Res. Inst.* **66**, 174-176.

Habegger, E. (1981). [Reflections in connection with the layout of turf sports grounds.] *Razen Turf Gazon* 4 (81), 74-89.

Habegger, E. (1985). [Alternative building materials to sand in the construction of turf sportsgrounds.] *Rasen Turf Gazon* 4 (85), 114-120.

Harper, J.C. (undated). Athletic Fields. *Specification Outline, Construction and Maintenance.* Pennsylvania State University, 29 pp.

Hayes, P. (1987). Looking at tomorrow's needs. *Turf Management*, **6**, 11, 14-19.

Holmes, G. & Bell, M.J. (1985). The effect of football type and inflation pressure on rebound resilience. *J. Sports Turf Res. Inst.* **61**, 132-135.

Holmes, G. & Bell, M.J. (1986). A pilot study of the playing quality of football pitches. *J. Sports Turf Res. Inst.* **62**, 74–91.

Holmes, G. & Bell, M.J. (1987). *Standards of Playing Quality for Natural Turf.* Sports Council/STRI Project Report, 59 pp.

Holmes, G. & Bell, M.J. (1987). Variations in the playing quality of different soccer pitch constructions. *Z. für Vegetationstechnik* **10**, 83-88.

Kamp, H.A. (1979). Effect of aeration with slit tines on some soil characteristics of football pitches. *Z. für Vegetationstechnik* **2**, 17-21.

Kamp, H.A. (1979). Einfluss der Aerifizierens mit schlitz messern auf einife Bodeneigenschaften von Rasensportpkizen (effects of aeration with slit tines on some soil characteristics of football pitches). *Zeitschrift für Vegetationstechnik im Landschafts - und sportstättenbau* **2**, 1, 17-21.

Kamp, H.A. (1985). [Dutch experience within a cell system pitch.] *Z. für Vegetationstechnik* **8**, 6-10.

Lawson, D.M. & Baker, S.W. (1987). The nutrient content of sands used for turf culture in the United Kingdom. *J. Sports Turf Res. Inst.*, **63**, 49-56.

Lemaire, F. (1982). Contribution à une meilleure connaissance de la relation fertilisation azotée - aspect esthétique des gazons. (Contribution to a better knowledge of the relationship between nitrogen fertilization and aesthetic quality of turf.) *Agronomie* **2**, 8, 765-772.

Liesecke, H.J. (1980. Bodemphgschalsche untersuchungen an feinsand - und sand-fraktionen sowie Gemischen. *Z. für Veget. im Landschafts - und Sportskättenbau* **3** (1), 1-7.

McGown, A., Andrawes, K.Z., Hytiris, N. & Mercer, F.B. (1985). Soil strengthening using randomly distributed mesh elements. *Proc. 11th Int. Conf. on Soil Mechanics and Foundation Engineering*, San Francisco, August 1985, pp. 1735-1738, A.A. Balkema, Rotterdam, The Netherlands.

Mercer, F.B. (1983). *Strengthening a matrix.* UK Patent, GB, 2 120 475B, London, The Patent Office.

Mercer, F.B., Andrawes, K.Z., McGown, A. & Hytiris, N. (1984). A new method of soil stabilisation. *Proc. Symposium on Polymer Grid Reinforcement in Civil Engineering*, London, March 1984, paper 8.1, 7 Boekel, P. & Zuriers, J.S. (1982). Relieving sub-surface compaction in sports turf. *Z. für Vegetationstechnik* **5**, 144-147.

Moreland, J. (1981). Drainage design to handle intensive football field use. *Weeds, Trees & Turf*, April, pp. 46, 48, 50.

Muller-Beck, K.G. (1977). [Information on sports pitches constructed in different ways. I. Physical soil properties.] *Rasen Grunflachen Begrunungen* **8** (3), 66-74.

Mulqueen, J. (1976). Aspects of construction of sports fields and recreation grounds in Ireland. In: *The Next Decade in Amenity Grassland* (Ed. C.E. Wright), Queen's Univ. Press, Belfast, pp. 40-65.

Murphy, J.P. & Baker, S.W. (1988). A questionnaire survey on winter pitch protection in the Football Leagues of England and Scotland. *J. Sports Turf Res. Inst.*, **64**, 144-149.

National Playing Fields Association (1983). *Technical Publication. Gradients for outdoor sports facilities,* London, 3pp.

Petersen, M. (1974). Construction of sportsgrounds based on physical soil characteristics. *Proc. 2nd Int. Turfgrass Res. Conf.*, Blacksburg, Virginia, USA (Ed. E.C. Roberts), pp. 270-276.

Petersen, M. (1979). [Technical or biologico - technical construction of sports grounds.] *Z. für Vegetationstechnik* **2**, 5-10.

Radford, C., Dury, P.L.K. & Skinner, N. (1985). *The Kirkby Project – a study of outdoor joint use sports facility provision at Kirkby Kingsway Park.* Education Department, Nottinghamshire County Council, 103 pp.

Rogers, J.N. III & Waddington, D.V. (1990a). Effects of management practices on impact absorption and shear resistance in natural turf. In: *Natural and Artificial Playing Fields : Characteristics and Safety Features.* ASTM STP 1073 (Eds. R.C. Schmidt, E.F. Hoerner, E.M. Milner and C.A. Morehouse), Americal Society for Testing and Materials, Philadelpia, USA, pp. 136-146.

Rogers, J.N. III & Waddington, D.V. (1990b). Portable apparatus for assessing impact characteristics of athletic field surfaces. In: *Natural and Artificial Playing Fields : Characteristics and Safety Features.* ASTM STP 1073 (Eds. R.C. Schmidt, E.F. Hoerner, E.M. Milner and C.A. Morehouse), Americal Society for Testing and Materials, Philadelpia, USA, pp. 96-110.

Seager, I. (1984). Fertiliser evaluation for Derbyshire's sports fields. *APFO Journal* **2** (2), 2-4.

Shildrick, J. (1986). Exterior playing surfaces : natural and synthetic. *RIBA London Region Sport & Recreation Supplement 1986*, pp. 59-64.

Skirde, W. (1973). [Soil modification for sports turf playing surfaces.] *Rasen Turf Gazon* **2**, 21-24.

Skirde, W. (1974). Soil modification for athletic fields. *Proc. 2nd Int. Turfgrass Res. Conf.* Blacksburg, Virginia, USA (Ed. E.C. Roberts), pp. 261-269.

Skogley, C.R. (1967). Turfgrass fertilizer research at the Rhode Island Agricultural Experiment Station. *J. Sports Turf Res. Inst.* **43**, 34-39.

Stewart, V.I. & Adams, W.A. (1970). Sports turf, construction and maintenance of soil. *Parks, Golf Courses & Sports Grounds* **35** (9), 794.

Stewart, V.I. (1973). Sports field drainage. *Playing Fields Oct-Dec, 1973* **XXXIV** (4), 70-74.

Thornton, D.J. (1973). A field trial of sports field construction materials extremely high in sand content. *J. Sports Turf Res. Inst.* **49**, 29-44.

Thornton, D.J. (1978). *The construction and drainage of some specified sports field playing surfaces.* PhD Thesis, University College of Wales, Aberystwyth.

Tjalma, F. (1982). Quality analysis as the basis of a management plan for turf sports pitches. *Z. für Vegetationstechnik* **5** (4), 148-150.

Trub, C. (1972). Problems and construction methods relating to sportsgrounds. *Schweserische Gartnerseitung* **75** (32), 402-405.

van Wijk, A.L.M. (1980). Soil water conditions and the playability of grass sports fields. I. Influence of soil physical properties of top layer and subsoil. *Z. für Vegetationstechnik* **3** (1), 7-15.

van Wijk, A.L.M. (1980). Soil water conditions and the playability of grass sports fields. II. Influence of tile drainage and sandy drainage layer. *Z. für Vegetationstechnik* **3** (1), 16-22.

van Wijk, A.L.M. (1981). Use of models in sportsfield construction research. *Rasen Turf Gazon* **4** (12), 89-96.

Ward, C.J. (1983a). Drainage of sports turf areas: results of a questionnaire survey. *J. Sports Turf Res. Inst.* **59**, 29–45.

Ward, C.J. (1983b). Sports turf drainage: a review. *J. Sports Turf Res. Inst.* **59**, 9–28.

Woolhouse, A.R. (1983) An investigation of the effectiveness of IBDU as a slow release source of nitrogen. *J. Sports Turf Res. Inst.* **59**, 93-102.